YOU HAVE A VERY SOFT VOICE, SUSAN

A SHOCKING TRUE STORY OF **INTERNET STALKING**

SUSAN FENSTEN
with BRIAN WHITNEY

WILD BLUE
P R E S S

WildBluePress.com

YOU HAVE A VERY SOFT VOICE SUSAN published by:
WILDBLUE PRESS
P.O. Box 102440
Denver, Colorado 80250

WILDBLUE PRESS is registered at the U.S. Patent and Trademark Offices.

ISBN 978-1-948239-98-1   Trade Paperback
ISBN 978-1-948239-99-8   eBook

Front cover image: Andrii Strakhov
Back cover image: Susan Fensten
Cover design: Tony Judge / www.tonyjudge.com

Interior Formatting by Elijah Toten
www.totencreative.com

YOU HAVE A
VERY SOFT
VOICE, SUSAN

A SHOCKING TRUE STORY OF
INTERNET STALKING

TABLE OF CONTENTS

INTRODUCTION	9
PROLOGUE	11
CHAPTER ONE	15
CHAPTER TWO	19
CHAPTER THREE	32
CHAPTER FOUR	40
CHAPTER FIVE	46
CHAPTER SIX	56
CHAPTER SEVEN	71
CHAPTER EIGHT	87
CHAPTER NINE	98
CHAPTER TEN	103

CHAPTER ELEVEN   107

CHAPTER TWELVE   110

CHAPTER THIRTEEN   119

CHAPTER FOURTEEN   125

CHAPTER FIFTEEN   127

CHAPTER SIXTEEN   132

CHAPTER SEVENTEEN   139

CHAPTER EIGHTEEN   147

CHAPTER NINETEEN   158

CHAPTER TWENTY   172

CHAPTER TWENTY-ONE   180

CHAPTER TWENTY-TWO   187

CHAPTER TWENTY-THREE   195

CHAPTER TWENTY-FOUR   211

CHAPTER TWENTY-FIVE   216

CHAPTER TWENTY-SIX   230

CHAPTER TWENTY-SEVEN   247

CHAPTER TWENTY-EIGHT   254

CHAPTER TWENTY-NINE   259

CHAPTER THIRTY   271

CHAPTER THIRTY-ONE   281

CHAPTER THIRTY-TWO   293

CHAPTER THIRTY-THREE   300

CHAPTER THIRTY-FOUR   316

CHAPTER THIRTY-FIVE   327

CHAPTER THIRTY-SIX   350

CHAPTER THIRTY-SEVEN   374

CHAPTER THIRTY-EIGHT   388

CHAPTER THIRTY-NINE   404

CHAPTER FORTY   420

EPILOGUE   439

ACKNOWLEDGEMENTS   443

INTRODUCTION

I didn't exactly decide to be an author. I never intended to write a book. It was a creative challenge to preserve this multi-layered, complex, and deeply disturbing story. It was also a painful look in the mirror. I don't come from a world of white picket fences or what would be considered a sheltered or conventional family life. My choices in life, like everyone else's, are shaped by responses to our life experiences. I'm not seeking closure. I am simply telling a story from my side of the street.

In the beginning of the writing process, I experienced the expected emotions of anger and shame. There is a tendency when writing about yourself to paint that portrait in the best light. I don't want to do that here. I have done a lot of things that I can explain and some things that I cannot so easily explain. My purpose in writing this book was not out of revenge to say, "Look at the monster" while here I am, the lost lamb.

As the writing progressed, I found it became something that went beyond just the actual people involved, and evolved into a larger story about human psychology as it relates to social dynamics between predator and prey.

This is an abridged reconstruction of real events. This story, in its unedited format, had so many characters, plots, and subplots woven into it, that for the sake of brevity and readability, it was necessary that some of it had to be thinned out. If not, it would be a five hundred page book.

Some individuals' names were changed to protect their privacy.

PROLOGUE

I'VE SEEN WHERE YOU LIVE, I KNOW WHAT YOU EAT

A tremor went down my spine the day I heard that Leonard was planning to sell his ranch-style house in the New Jersey suburbs and move to my neighborhood, Williamsburg, Brooklyn. It was a gray, chilly spring day, fittingly gloomy. The dank weather compounded my mood and lent itself to a scene from a grainy noir movie, dilapidated factories in stages of decomposition everywhere that he could hide, stash a weapon, stash a body. Stash me.

It seemed that Leonard thought a loft might better suit his lifestyle. Leonard, the schizophrenic child math prodigy, who had blossomed into a wealthy swinger, painter, and collector of sexual paraphernalia. This wasn't a good sign since his present residence had apparently been suitably outfitted for his bacchanals for quite some time. He claimed he wanted something bigger, hipper, something located in an area where he wouldn't stand out quite as much from his cookie cutter neighbors in New Jersey. But I knew that wasn't it. His wealth could have easily afforded him lofts in SoHo, Tribeca, or Chelsea—all within striking distance of the downtown dungeons and secret after-hours places. The real attraction for him was his new "cousin Susan." Was he intent on intensifying the deviant nature of his parties with me as his guest of honor?

I'd never met Leonard, but I knew a lot about him. I knew that he had been charged but never convicted of rape and kidnapping. I knew that he had a lavish psychiatric history and that he often went off his meds and had been repeatedly hospitalized. His doctors had decided that he was mentally competent for release. He had been able to keep down his Wall Street job, at least well enough to amass a fortune. Leonard had the knack of appearing so normal at times, so non-descript. If he wanted to, he could look like an ordinary person. He was just an *ordinary* person, one who just happened to be obsessed with me.

I fearfully imagined him dazed, wandering the streets searching for me. The area could readily conceal someone like Leonard by virtue of the eclectic mix of people it attracted. Much to the chagrin of natives and old timers, the "weird folk" had moved in and found that it suited their alternate lifestyles all too well. Williamsburg. It was a forgotten New York neighborhood with exotic, dark alleys; a Mecca for artists, musicians, yuppies, skinheads, and those of the tattooed persuasion. The hulking smokestack of the Domino Sugar factory belched out an aroma of burned brown sugar that draped everything with a sweet, invisible mist. It was a hipster zone, where a chameleon like Leonard could crawl unobtrusively from building to building, from playground to lounge. Leonard, a master of stealth to begin with, might find that Williamsburg rendered his avant-garde lifestyle and morbid moods virtually invisible.

Early spring in New York City can be depressing, and the gloomy weekend served only to fuel my imagination as my mind's eye saw Leonard examining lofts and surveying the neighborhood. He was near, possibly peering through the window from the back seat of a Town Car as it rolled past clothing stores, cafes, delis, a subway stop, the Salvation Army, the Domino sugar factory. He was examining the landscape, beads of water sliding from the glass to the shiny black exterior of the car. These images sliced through my mind like sharp, piercing screams. Had he come to the conclusion that *all* Williamsburg residents were creatures of darkness and decay? Or was it just me? Did he believe that I was a perfect match for the side of his personality never seen by his Wall Street clients? Did he picture me in his harness?

The cold gray rain made me feel only more desolate.

***

It wasn't long after Leonard's trip to Brooklyn that he let his observations be known by updating his Yahoo! profile. It now featured a graphic close-up photo of a vagina tattooed with a fanged red devil, a shiny metal earring piercing the clitoris. He knew I would see it. He knew he had scared me so much I couldn't stop looking. On his new profile, below a list of his favorite torture and rape websites was a taunting poem:

Dear cousin, my cousin, Oh cousin so sweet.

I've seen where you live, I know what you eat.

I want to see your eyes when we first meet.

He was getting closer, I could feel it. He was emerging from my email inbox, coming out into the real world, my world. He was going to get a closer look at me, see me on the street, go by my house, and run a finger along the gate. And I had nowhere to go.

CHAPTER ONE

INFORMATION NOT RELEASED
TO THE PUBLIC

Murderers are not monsters, they're men.
And that's the most frightening thing about them.
—Alice Sebold

After an hour of questioning and getting nowhere, one of the detectives pulled out a photograph. He looked at it, placed it on the table, and with his index finger, slid it toward me across the metal desk. My heart constricted like a convulsion of sharp pins. Fearing it might be a crime scene photo I braced myself. But then I recognized it immediately, it was a simple color photo of Jennifer Whipkey in life, one of two images that I had seen in internet news reports about her murder. Her beaming face seemed to hover ghostlike above the cold steel desk, lying in front of me, looking at me. A presence that was chillingly real. Her cheerful expression was frozen in time. The atmosphere in the blue lit room felt like a morgue. A mere one hundred pounds, she perished under a frenzy of sixty-three stab wounds.

Feeling helpless, I thought of her young child, motherless, like my nephew when my sister died. Death and sorrow—my uninvited twin companions, the feeling was always the same—my soul touching the third rail. I wondered what the detectives thought of me. They seemed like any other overworked cops following up on leads and hitting dead ends three years and counting. Could they really hold suspicions that I was connected to murder? Or were they hoping for just a shred of detail that could point them in the right direction and spring the case back to life? I told them that I felt horrible about her death, about the nature of this extremely violent crime, and how terrifying it must have been for her. That I had heartfelt sympathy for what her family was going through. I knew all about how the violent death of a young woman decimates the surviving family. My words felt futile. I wished that there something I could do to help them, but I knew nothing.

The meeting was long and unsettling. It was obvious they really wanted to solve this case which almost seemed personal for them. They had to answer to her family and her community. Their labor, frustration, and emotion were coming through in their questions about my life, my social life, how I came to know about Jennifer Whipkey's murder. The killing wasn't highly publicized outside of the small New Jersey Township of West Deptford. They wanted to know why I had information about a crime that wasn't made public. Of course it would draw the immediate attention of homicide detectives; that was completely understandable. But I was far removed from the terrifying deed and had only been pulled in by a net of lies as complex as a spider's web.

When it concluded, I thanked Special Agent Waller. I had the feeling I would be seeing him again very soon.

I was escorted to the elevator by another FBI official. I passed once again through multiple security checkpoints, each time fishing out ID from my wallet. All the while I reflected back in hopes of finding some sense in it all, while at the same point realizing that there are some things in this world that will never make any sense, things that you are forced to accept. Like actions with no reason or purpose, minds without conscience. In the thick glass that seemed to be everywhere, I caught a glimpse of my transparent reflection. It was still me, at least I looked the same, which surprised me as my life had been bluntly interrupted and thrown around like rag doll. I waved 'thanks' to the last security guard who buzzed me out and pushed through the revolving door. Out into the financial district, the city sunlight and street noise brought me back to normalcy. My town, New York City; ever moving along, never stopping, and reverberating in a million directions. It reinvigorated me.

It was a relief to re-join the ordinary world. I had emerged from the underworld, an 'other' realm, an unpretty world where bodies washed of their evidence are posed in caked puddles of blood. A world of chaos and order where square-shouldered law enforcement personnel dutifully knocked on doors, chased down witnesses, and presented evidence to prosecutors. Most of the time they wrapped up their cases, but tragically sometimes not, moving on to the next one in a ceaseless cycle of reward and frustration. I was left with the indelible knowledge that there were butcherers traveling the highways and lurking in back yards never to be found. Maybe even in my own backyard.

At the core of this saga is the reason I was here in the first place. This very strange thing that I had encountered had affected me in ways I could not have imagined. It had been almost two years since this all began in 2003, like a carnival of cracked mirrors with a quicksand floor with phantoms reflected in the distorted glass. I had to shake off these images and get back to my desk at Rizzoli International Publications just a few stops away at 22nd Street and Park Avenue South. I had missed enough time already.

My life started out unsheltered, I was spared little in the bad old days of New York, but it was now all about books and publishers, authors, tours, media lists, and high expectations. A book publicist is essentially a salesman, a pitchman with an idea clutching a roster of ambitious authors and anxious editors. It's at times a waltz on a high wire, at others glamorous, yet bone-grinding hard work. I hopped on the uptown subway immersed in a reel of thoughts of how I came to be exhaustively questioned by two New Jersey Homicide Detectives at One Federal Plaza, FBI Headquarters in New York City.

How did I get here? How did an otherwise normal everyday New Yorker who did not operate in the world of crime, wind up at FBI headquarters in downtown Manhattan now being vigorously interrogated about an unsolved brutal murder?

CHAPTER TWO

INTO THE WORLD

*There is always one moment in childhood when
the door opens and lets in the future.*
—Graham Greene

In the cab, my sister wouldn't even look at my mother. She stared straight ahead in a fury on the way home from the hospital. It was just hours after I was born. Upon news of my arrival, my father almost fainted because he had another daughter. Less than a day old and already my reception into the world was fractured. My father and mother met in a Greenwich Village café. He was twenty-four and an aspiring actor; she was nineteen and had moved to New York to study fashion illustration at Parson's School of Design. My father, John Fensten, studied at the Actor's Studio with Lee and Susan Strasberg (Susan, my namesake, visited mom in the hospital when I was born). He landed a role on *Playhouse 90*, the acclaimed ninety-minute live TV series that ran from the late fifties to the early sixties. One would think that such a couple, blessed with talent and connections, could look forward to a happy life together. After my parents married in 1961, however, things unraveled almost immediately. The years that followed would be tough—at times grueling—for my mother and father and their children, my sister Ilia and me.

Still, I love to think about the early years of my childhood even though they don't represent an idyllic time of innocence or white picket fences. My parents lived on the Upper West Side when I was born in July of 1962, but by the time I was two, we lived on the Lower East Side, moving from apartment to apartment just one step ahead of the rent collector. My father began to disappear for weeks at a time, occasionally landing in Bellevue Hospital. We had no clue as to his whereabouts during these disappearances. He was generally unemployed except for a brief stint as an insurance clerk, and my mother worked as a waitress, standing on her feet eight hours a day for thirty-five bucks a week.

Despite the hardships, there were good times. Desperation had an air of excitement and surviving in the streets of Manhattan conferred unspoken badges of honor on Ilia and me. Life in Fun City, New York's nickname before it became known as the Big Apple, was gritty and hard. Films like *Midnight Cowboy*, *Taxi Driver*, and *Mean Streets* could have been documentaries about life in my neighborhoods. My mother had come from an upper-middle class home in New England and didn't find living in survival mode so enchanting, but my sister and I loved every minute of it. Uptown or downtown, there was always adrenaline in the streets—junkies, gang fights, or a naked woman walking down Lexington Avenue—the island was ours. Life was raw, never dull. Our apartment on St. Mark's Place in the East Village was burglarized nine times. Our missing things were found in the junkie's apartment upstairs but the detective investigating the crime wouldn't make an arrest unless my mother agreed to sleep with him. She didn't and we moved out soon after.

Things weren't much different when we moved uptown to Spanish Harlem in 1967. It was the summer of the race riots. Bottles and metal garbage cans rained down from rooftops within days of moving in. Upon the discovery of a woman upstairs in the hallway who had been stabbed, my mother quickly ushered us into our apartment door. There were used syringes and burned spoons of heroin addicts outside of our apartment door on the way to school in the mornings. Fires routinely flared up across the street when junkies shot up in dark rooms of abandoned apartment buildings, the matches used to cook heroin igniting the filthy mattresses they slept on. We could feel the intense heat on our faces while leaning out the apartment window, lurid yellow flames lighting up the night as they licked the brick and mortar.

While waiting to be buzzed into our building one night, Ilia and I were held up at knifepoint by a teenager who threatened to cut our tongues out. The thief got all of twelve dollars by shoving his hand in Ilia's pocket. It was a good trade. He got the cash and we kept our tongues, although Ilia, normally full of swagger and attitude—"Ya gotta get tough, Susie!"—cried like a baby when we got upstairs. I, on the other hand, was fascinated. I wasn't scared. It was neat and fast, over in a few seconds. His hand movements were light and quick, and he knew exactly which pocket to grab. Despite the threat, I knew we weren't going to get hurt. He wanted fast money for drugs and got it. It was part of the city's pulse which we lived every day—a pulse I had mastered. Our neighborhood was all color, life, movement. Small repair shops, corner groceries, sirens, brawling—I drank it all in.

***

My mother, Nancy, was strong, talented, beautiful, and fiercely optimistic. She had movie-star good looks. A tussle of blonde hair, lipstick, a cigarette, black miniskirt and boots —that was my mother. Endlessly resourceful and creative, she made our dresses and clothes, knitted sweaters, hats, and mittens, and even made our stuffed toys and animals using scraps of material and patterns that she drew herself. She held us together, literally and figuratively, collecting soda bottles to get the five-cent return in order to pay for the subway to work every day. Each morning she grabbed that long train ride from the East Village to the World's Fair in Queens to sling hot dogs and beer to the crowds in the sweltering New York City summer heat.

She continued waiting tables until she got her start in animation, hand-inking and painting animators' drawings onto cels for TV commercials at Stars and Stripes Studios. She went on to work for Academy Award-winning Hubley Studios, helping create both short and full-length features for PBS. She also worked on such classics as *Schoolhouse Rock*, and while at Cel-Art Studios she did the inking and painting for classic television commercials for Hawaiian Punch, Hostess Cakes, and Cheerios. Much later, in the 1990s, she worked on MTV's animated series, *Beavis and Butthead* as well as the 1996 full-length feature *Beavis and Butthead Do America*. In a very real sense, cartoons saved us. We always got a thrill watching my mother's handiwork on the old black-and-white television, the one with the bent coat hanger for an antenna in our railroad apartment uptown.

***

My mother said few good things about my father. When I asked her why he would turn up in Bellevue, she had no specific answer. No diagnosis was ever made clear, but on those occasions he was administered medication that just put him to sleep. He was a loner who didn't talk much. Like most very young kids, I accepted what I saw without much questioning.

My father and his younger brother Larry were nine months apart. Their twenty-two-year-old mother promptly left them right after Larry was born. Her name was Violet, and my father had little to say about her except that "she was a dancer—burlesque." No reason was given as to why she'd left, a familiar parallel to my father's own vanishing acts.

Dad and Larry came to the city in the late nineteen fifties, both joined the Army as soon as they were old enough to enlist. In later years, my father told me that he and Larry just kicked around a bit before they enlisted with the service. According to my father, he and Larry hustled in Times Square. I pictured them as loners at night leaning against a building, one leg bent, boot heel against the façade as they made eye contact with strangers, lit by the blinking lights from seedy theater marquees. Was it true? Was my father a midnight cowboy like Joe Buck, hustling for some change and a place to stay? Whatever he did, it all played into what I saw in my earliest years: a man of mystery and eccentricity who suffered from some unknown emotional turmoil.

When I was four, my mother had had enough of my father's instability and mysterious disappearances, so we moved out. Dad came uptown just once the following year to visit briefly. And then the urban high plains drifter dropped out of sight for another seven years.

***

Despite our mutual love affair with the mean streets of Manhattan, Ilia and I were very different from each another. Even with blonde hair and blue eyes, I resembled my father. I looked Jewish. Ilia had brown wavy hair, hazel eyes, fair skin, and my mother's Irish features. Our differences, however, went far beyond superficial appearances. Ilia liked danger—the road. I liked art and books. Always defiant, by 1974, Ilia had become a genuine hell raiser. At nearly thirteen, she ran away with her eighteen-year-old Puerto Rican boyfriend, José, staying in Detroit with him for a year and a half, living among gypsies. My mother, who hired a private investigator to find her, was upset, to say the least, but she wanted Ilia to make the decision to return to New York on her own.

When she came home, it wasn't long until Ilia hit the road again, sixteen years old and hitchhiking to California with a friend who had a pair of dice tattooed on her neck. Ilia began using other drugs, but not the soft stuff—not marijuana or even LSD. She scored some prescriptions for Methadone and Dilaudid and ended up occasionally using heroin.

When Ilia was eighteen, she showed me a shiny silver .22 caliber pistol while we stood in an alley on Bond Street. I had never seen, much less handled, a gun before. She suggested I get one for myself.

"What do I need a gun for?" I asked.

"For protection, Susie."

I just laughed. "Protection from what? I don't need any protection, Ilia."

"All right then," Ilia said, "but don't tell Ma."

***

John Fensten had emotional issues, to say the least. He was a spectral presence in my life. I had not seen my father in seven years when I spotted him at a bus stop in 1974, the hot air blowing across Queens Boulevard like a desert wind from a mirage.

That afternoon I intended to go to the movies to see *Gone with the Wind*. My mother and I were living in Sunnyside, then. My sister had just run away from home. I had no friends, and no other way to occupy my time. I had gone to the movies alone pretty often when we lived in Manhattan and no one had ever been bothered by my age there. So I was brought up short when the woman at the ticket office refused the dollar I slid under her glass.

"How old are you?" she asked.

"Twelve."

"Sorry, but kids are not allowed without parents," she said, firmly.

"But I'm not a kid," I told her. She wasn't persuaded. It was as I was walking away that I saw him.

I recognized him instantly even though the last time I'd seen him, I was five years old. He had taken me to the Central Park Zoo that day, given me a sweater, and taken a few pictures of me. It was an awkward memory, but it was also a clear one, and he hadn't aged a bit. My father was unmistakable, a striking man, with wide-set eyes and good looks that put him somewhere between Gregory Peck and Tony Perkins. He was as thin as ever, his lean frame hung inside his slightly wrinkled clothing.

So I walked right over to this man waiting for a bus, and he stared at me blankly.

"Hi. I'm Susan. I'm your kid," I said.

He was surprised. He even looked a little shaken. I'm sure the last thing he ever expected was to have his second child waltz up out of the blue the way I had. He did manage to ask me how I was and how my mother and sister were. I told him they were okay.

There was nothing else to say after that. His bus hadn't arrived yet, but I said goodbye and continued on my way. The encounter was short. There were no hugs, tears, blubbering 'I miss yous,' nor searching for pens to scribble down addresses or phone numbers to stay in contact. No promises of getting together. It was awkward, and I'm not sure which of us had the greater share of that.

Later, though, I was glad that I took advantage of that chance to force my existence on him. I wouldn't see him again until I was twenty-one.

At nineteen, I moved out of my mother's house. I worked in a clothing shop on Astor Place in the East Village for about a year. One hot summer afternoon, I ran into my father outside a deli on Second Avenue while I was on a lunch break. After nearly a decade, he was still unmistakable. He was sitting on a moped on the sidewalk. I walked up and introduced myself, again. That was the beginning of a futile attempt to interact with him. After this I saw my father a lot more, usually on First or Second Avenue or at Veselka's Diner, where he would be sitting alone at the counter, having his usual hamburger and a cup of coffee or buying lottery tickets. He never had a telephone, so I either knocked on his door on East 5th Street or left a note stuck to his mailbox. There were many days when I knocked or rang his bell and got no answer that I knew that he was home and had ignored me. He wanted to be left alone; I was fine with it. At times it was almost a relief to not have to see him.

***

I realized that I had to do something other than work in retail, so I decided to go to college. I took classes in film and art at Hunter College but I was miserable. The school seemed impenetrably cliquish and institutional. After one pointless semester, I took the advice of my art teacher, left Hunter, and enrolled at the Art Students League on 57th Street. I studied anatomy, painting, and drawing for two years at night while working full-time at a photography studio across the street. During this time, getting to know my father proved difficult. He was still a quiet man who kept to himself, and our conversations were brief and awkward. It seemed as if he was impatient with me, as if everything I said was wrong.

He worked as a bike messenger and took pictures—he was a dedicated photographer and a master printer—but that was the extent of his existence from what I could tell. His dingy studio apartment was the perfect dark room—brown walls, brown rug, brown table, brown coffee, and brown roaches. The place reeked of cats. He was a minimalist in every respect and seemed to have no aspiration but to be left alone, take photographs, and collect cameras.

My frustrating relationship with him, where even a simple conversation was awkward and painful, stood in contrast to his relationship to Ilia. She and my father understood each other in some way that still defies description. As a child, she was his preferred photographic subject. They were accessible to each other on some level that I couldn't understand.

But that connection was wrought with decay.

For a while, Ilia was living at the Hell's Angels clubhouse on East 3rd Street. At one point she was thrown out, so she stayed with my father in his small, dark studio a couple of blocks away. She told me that one day she was in the bathroom and my father came in with his genitals out. Alarmed and upset, she went back to the clubhouse and told a few Angels what had happened. They all headed to my father's building on East 5th Street and pounded on the door threatening to beat him up. He didn't open the door and they left. She told me about it and warned me that I should never be alone around him, ever. I was devastated. I wept for her and for me, because I had being trying to build a relationship with him.

When I asked him about it he said that he did it because she smelled like heroin and didn't want her around getting high. His answer was confusing and strange. A lot of things he said didn't make sense to me.

The times he was the easiest to be around were when he was talking about cameras and dark room technique, types of printing paper and exposure times. He liked to give me cameras, lenses, and all kinds of accoutrement. He made it something in common between us, even if it was only one thing. I set out across the city like my father—with a camera. The seedy allure of the Lower East Side and Times Square drew me often. It was the early 1980s, pre-Guiliani era New York City. I was twenty-one years old, fearless and wanting to capture the dirt and the grit before it was gone. Like my father, I wandered alone with my thirty-five millimeter.

But I was not to be spared. One summer morning in 1986, when I was twenty-three years old, I walked over the Williamsburg Bridge to the East Village. It was early and warm, the streets mostly desolate except for one lone figure, my father, who sat on his moped. I walked up to say hello and he asked me what I was doing. Telling him I was just out for a walk, he eyed me over and said that all the boys must be after me. A smile streaked across his face as he raised both hands making a double grabbing gesture at my chest level. I stood there frozen trying not to show any facial expression. Part of me tried to brush it off as another example of his disordered behavior, but I was sickened. Feeling degraded and aching with nausea, I told him I had to leave and walked away. His actions had crushed me, causing me to feel like trash, like an object used for sex and not a human being or even his own daughter.

There was another time, when I was thirty years old, during a visit with him. We had lunch at Velselka's Diner on East 9th Street and then walked around the neighborhood. As usual, it was awkward. He had one of his cameras with him and asked to take a picture of me, which had never happened before. Stopping outside one of the small storefronts on East 6th Street, he asked me to turn around, facing the store, instead of facing forward toward him. He directed me to hold on to the gates with my hands up and to spread my legs apart like I was about to be frisked. He clicked off a few shots. It happened so fast. Why didn't he want a picture of my face? I knew something was wrong. And now he had pictures of me this way. I was too afraid to ask him or say anything. Remaining mute seemed safer than opening up a pandora's box of pain and disappointment. AfterI got home, it slowly began to sink in even deeper.

After years of trying to break through his barriers of silence or short, staccato sentences, I realized we would never really connect with each other in the way that I needed and yearned for. We drifted even farther apart, although I would occasionally see him in Manhattan as he glided by on his bike.

Right before Christmas in 2000, I received a letter from my father's next door neighbor informing me that my father was ill with lung cancer. He was in a VA hospital in Manhattan, about to be transferred to the Fort Hamilton VA in Brooklyn. The doctor said that my father wouldn't last five days, so he was sent to a nursing home in Cobble Hill instead, where he lingered for five months.

I visited him every weekend, cashing his Social Security checks and paying his rent and electric bills. I brought coffee and sandwiches as we sat in silence most of the time in the midst of the noisy ward. As the days turned into weeks and months, my father occasionally looked at me and made a brief conversation.

"Do you have a boyfriend?" he asked.

"No, not right now."

"I can't believe you don't have someone," he said.

Small words of kindness. A few syllables. And yet they touched me. Now, at the end of his life, he was giving me a compliment.

Another time he said that I had a gold light around me when I was very young. I wished he could have told me at the time. It's what children want—and *need*—to hear.

I'd had a short ghost story about a noisy poltergeist published by Warner Books in 1992 in an anthology of true tales of the supernatural.

"You're going to be the next Eugene O'Neill," he remarked.

I wasn't familiar with O Neill's work or with his tragic and difficult life, but I had heard of the writer's name. It was a generous thing to say because he rarely said anything, much less offered compliments.

When the weather grew warmer, I would push him outside in his wheelchair. I could tell that he was starting to slip away. One day, in the midst of the silence, he said, "Your patience is beautiful."

Those simple words again. I had never received a compliment like that. I was escaping an abusive boyfriend, and these gentle silent sittings in the spring air with my dying father were a welcome relief from the fear that raged in my personal life.

He died in May of 2001. I was sad, although the grief didn't approach the searing pain I experienced after my sister's death. It was almost as if my father was simply gone again. My mother, who couldn't understand why I had invested time in pursuing my father in the East Village or attending to him in his final days, commented that his death was "a nothing end to a nothing life." But I was his daughter so, to me, it seemed as if my mother had essentially said that I, too, was a nobody—as the daughter of nothing.

But my father wasn't just a nobody. He was a man with definite artistic talent, and many creative people live inside a world they choose not to share. My father was a puzzle that I had never quite figured out. I remained curious about his life and about his side of the family.

CHAPTER THREE

BOBBY

Of two close friends, one is always the slave of the other.
—Mikhail Lermentov, *A Hero of Our Time*, 1840

I met Bobby Ironside in Williamsburg, Brooklyn, in 1986. A lot of new people were moving into the neighborhood because of the cheap rent and large spaces. I discerned rather quickly that Bobby, like many of my friends, was gay when he knocked on my door and introduced himself. He lived with a roommate, a straight man named Mark, in the upstairs loft. Bobby was witty; a natural raconteur who held forth with great theatricality at parties, relating marvelous stories and outrageous anecdotes. He told me that he worked as a model, although I was skeptical of his veracity on this point, especially since he seemed to have a great deal of time on his hands. More to the point, he just didn't *look* like a model. I figured he was living in New York "on a dream" like a thousand painters, writers, and musicians.

We spent a lot of time together watching old horror movies, talking, or just hanging out. We discovered our mutual love of campy horror and true crime. Our favorite film was *The Honeymoon Killers*, a 1969 cult classic about a pair of deadly con artists roaming the country taking advantage of vulnerable rich lonely hearts and sometimes murdering them. We would watch it over and over in Bobby's apartment, reciting the dialogue on cue as we knew it by heart. I was twenty-four and in some ways the artist stereotype, painting while I worked at whatever job that could hold body and soul together. Like with many of my gay friends, I felt comfortable with him. I felt safe. We rapidly became good friends; he often spoke of how close we were. We were born a day apart in the same city, and he often likened our relationship to that of brother and sister.

As much as I liked him, it quickly became obvious that Bobby had feet of clay. He was a gossip, and a busybody. But what are good friends if not people that can accept each other's failings and idiosyncrasies? Despite his frailties, Bobby Ironside was first and foremost a fun and engaging man, a good listener in whom I could confide and discuss anything, from my innermost thoughts to how my day had gone, to the rash of shark attacks being reported in the news every week.

It wasn't long before I came to know more about Bobby's unconventional life. We were friends, but there zones in his sphere that were dark and secretive. During our movie afternoons and nights, I had noticed the eyehooks screwed into the exposed beams in the ceiling as well as the mysterious men that came and went. Bobby gradually drifted into the expanding world of S&M, which was very popular in New York City and elsewhere in the late eighties. By 1990, I was married and my life had changed. Bobby had moved away and we drifted apart.

***

For a while in the mid-nineteen eighties, Ilia was stripping and hustling champagne at the Metropole Go-Go in Times Square to get by, and ended up out in Brooklyn with a big black dog and a Harley Davidson chopper that had been taken apart in her living room.

In 1986 she got pregnant by a Vietnam vet named Augie, who was sixteen years her senior. My mother wasn't pleased, but I was thrilled. I thought her having a baby would give her something to live for and thereby straighten out her life. For the first time in many years, Ilia and I became sisters again. She stopped cold using drugs during her pregnancy. After a long period of alienation, we spoke often, and our differences seemed almost nonexistent. A few months later, she gave birth to a beautiful baby boy and named him Anthony.

But Ilia and Augie fought often, and Ilia started using again.

On May 23, 1987, after an argument with Augie, Ilia went into the bedroom, wrote a suicide note and shot herself in the head in front of Anthony's crib.

I'd arrived home late that evening, and found a message from a former roommate pinned to my front door. I had just moved out, and the note said my sister had been calling all day. I didn't have a phone in my South 2nd Street apartment yet, so I went downstairs to an auto repair shop and used a pay phone on the sidewalk to call Ilia's house. A police officer answered and told me I had to contact a Brooklyn detective since a crime had been committed. A crime? My first reaction was that Augie had beaten up Ilia and that she was in the hospital. I desperately hoped that it wasn't anything worse. But the word crime was vague and ominous. When I called the detective, he said point-blank, "Your sister is dead. You need to come down to the morgue and identify the body." Everything began to spin around me, and I felt nauseous and frozen with shock.

I ran up to Bobby's apartment across the street to use his phone to call my mother. He was having a party when I knocked. He led me into a back room, handed me the phone, and closed the door. The music and laughter murmured in the background as I dialed. The phone rang a couple of times as I wondered how I was going to say what I needed to say. She picked up.

"Hello?" she answered.

"Ma. Are you sitting down?"

"Yes. Why Susan?" she asked.

"Ilia is dead."

She screamed and dropped the phone. Still in shock, I then took a taxi over the Williamsburg Bridge to tell my father the news.

That night, I was too terrified to go to bed. Sleep was too close to death. The following day, my mother and her husband drove down from upstate to pick me up to go to the morgue. I was bowed by grief, and my mother's screams echoed down the hall when she saw my sister behind the glass as they pulled back the curtain, saying what words alone could not express.

Shaking her head, a social worker read the suicide note Ilia had written, but she said we weren't allowed to read it because it was addressed to one of her friends, not us.

This was the most agonizing time of my life, and I felt a crushing, unbearable loneliness. The pain was shattering. I missed my sister, who had once been my companion on the mean streets of the Lower East Side and Spanish Harlem, the sister who had ironically said, "Come on, Susie! Ya gotta get tough."

***

The last time I saw my Uncle Larry was in the hallway of my father's building. Once very handsome, he'd been a junkie for decades and was beaten down by years of heroin. He was missing a few teeth, but I could nevertheless see his good looks hiding beneath a dope-ravaged face. A building super, he lived in a rent-free basement apartment on East 6th Street, around the block from my father's place. By the middle of 1987, Larry fell apart completely. He tried to hang himself from a pipe in his apartment, but the pipe broke, and Larry injured his neck. Regaining his composure somewhat, he staggered around the corner to my father's apartment, wearing nothing from the waist down but a pair of shoes.

"You're going to live, and I'm going to die," Larry announced in my father's hallway. "I'm going up to 125th Street and Lexington for an Irish potato." The "Irish potato" was probably an obscure slang for heroin. Though I had never heard it before, knowing Larry, I understood what it meant. It was the last thing he would ever say to my father.

There was some confusion as the ambulance rushed Uncle Larry away, and it took my father a couple of weeks to locate his brother at St. Vincent's Hospital. My father said that Larry was in terrible condition and that the hospital pressured him into signing a DNR—Do Not Resuscitate—order because the hospital didn't have room for old junkies. Accordingly, he signed it, Larry was taken off life support and died.

***

The next years of my life were comprised of scenes both serious and light, routine and dramatic. I was married to an artist in 1989. The marriage ended amicably after three years. I continued to paint, pursuing various relationships, some of which were abusive, as pages slowly disappeared from the kitchen calendar.

I found my accidental career while working for a temp agency. In 1989, I was given an assignment in the publicity department at Doubleday. There was no turning back after becoming immersed in the world of books, a universe of words and printed pages that conveyed an infinite number of ideas. My creative bent had found legitimacy in the world of publishing filled with literary, artistic people. At times, I worked among many luminaries such as Jackie Onassis and her former White House social secretary Nancy Tuckerman in the Doubleday editorial department, and science fiction writer Isaac Asimov was in the reception area every Wednesday, waiting to speak with his editor. This was heady wine for a young woman, but I relished every moment of working at a major publishing house, totally embracing a culture that spoke to the world through the titles it announced on its list each year. In the capacity of publicist, I would go on to work for Vintage, Pantheon, Rizzoli, and Oxford University Press. I wasn't an author, but my skills helped the creative labors of others to compete in the literary marketplace.

I loved it.

***

During the summer of 2001, when the biggest national scare was shark fins slicing through the waves before aluminum fins savagely cut into the Twin Towers, Bobby Ironside emailed me out of the blue. It had been ten years since we parted ways. He asked if I remembered him, which, of course, I did. He said he'd Googled me and found my email address at Oxford University Press, where I was the paperbacks publicist. Other friends from my past had located me the same way, so I wasn't entirely surprised when Bobby's message showed up in my inbox.

The internet was still relatively new to me in 2001, and I enjoyed the immediacy and limitlessness of it, chatting or corresponding with virtually anyone in the world. The internet seemed to be a world with endless horizons. Paradoxically, it also offered intimacy. The fact that Bobby had been able to track me down was proof of what a great tool the World Wide Web was becoming.

I replied to Bobby's email without hesitation, and we caught up quickly. He said he had moved to Washington, DC, a few years earlier after living in West Palm Beach, Florida. Our bond was rekindled, even though our friendship was nothing more than disembodied communication traveling along the information superhighway. Although we lived in two different cities, we stayed in touch on a daily basis thanks to email.

It was clear that Bobby had grown during the years. He seemed fairly grounded now and said that he had attended a spiritual retreat while in Florida. In the vernacular of therapy, he claimed to have done a lot of "personal work" on himself. His communication exhibited a lighter, sunnier disposition. Perhaps getting older naturally softens one's edges.

Soon after that, the attacks on the Pentagon and the World Trade Center—buildings located in cities where we both lived—drew us close again. In just a few hours on September 11, the world became strange, frightening, and unpredictable, a world where trust could be assaulted in new and unforeseen ways. Fear was palpable, visceral. Anything familiar, therefore, was welcome, and Bobby and I found solace in one another.

He soon became a regular in my daily routine. He was happy that we were friends again. There was always a funny email message or maybe some gossip about a notorious friend. Within a couple of months I took off for DC to spend the weekend at Bobby's place. It was nice to see him in a different backdrop, out of the underside of NYC. His studio apartment was small but bright, a phalanx of white file cabinets sat across from the windows. After a long walk around the sights in the nation's capital, we went back to Bobby's apartment and he began to talk about his collection of letters from incarcerated serial killers. I had read many true crime books and it piqued my curiosity. He dipped into the ocean of files and placed in my hand a wrinkled sheet of lined paper. Across it marched words written in almost childlike letters in pencil that spoke about lying in wait in a van while sizing up potential victims.

I thought about all the times that I could have been unknowingly 'sized up' for prey and just how real all of this was. Being a true crime book reader was one thing, but holding a handwritten letter by a caged monster is another. It gave me a shiver and I handed it back feeling like I touched something evil, a mental stroll into in a criminal mind. I understood Bobby's interest, but this was a bridge too far for me.

CHAPTER FOUR

HE'S A LITTLE MYSTERIOUS

Never lose a healthy curiosity.
—Albert Einstein

I had survived all of that. I was all right. I felt lucky to be a loner by disposition, happy to be independent – or at least, that's what I told myself.

A couple of summers into the rekindling of Bobby's friendship, little cracks began to emerge in his new persona. His snippy comments and sometimes intrusive messages to a mutual friend of mind on AOL Instant Message about their personal living situation that he and I had discussed in confidence pushed me away. I took a time-out from him. He could be trying and demanding.

I was living alone in a ground floor, railroad tenement apartment on North 7th Street off the corner of Kent Avenue. It was a quiet area along the East River. Three blocks from the L train, one stop from Manhattan. For years, I thought of that apartment as a country house with a backyard oasis and the intoxicating smell of baked bread from Moishe's Bakery on the corner, a quiet little hamlet where Polish women swept leaves off their stoops and the stores on Bedford Avenue closed at 11 p.m.

The apartment had cracked, linoleum kitchen floor tiles, and a BEWARE OF DOG sign stuck in the loose old front windows that hung in their casings like dying teeth. People often took pictures of those windows because they were so decrepit-looking. Traces of old staples and tape glue covered the sills, from the sheets of clear plastic I used to insulate from the icy draft off the river, evidence of winters that came and went. But it had high ceilings and came with a small private backyard, the first in my life. It was home.

I treasured the space and found it peaceful. The only sound at night was gunfire on the waterfront. The cracking gunshots never worried me. It reminded me there was still something kind of wild and free about New York. I loved the isolation and the desolation of the place.

The lifelong curiosity about my father's family seemed to find an outlet when I began dipping my toe into the internet in the early 2000s. I wanted to know what I was made up of. I found myself searching for my grandfather's name on the Ellis Island website. But thousands of Feinsteins had immigrated to America. I didn't find anything that led me directly to a Morris Feinstein, who I knew had been born in the late 1880s on the Lower East Side to Jewish immigrants.

A quick search led me to *Genealogy.com.*

Genealogy.com by today's standards, was pretty primitive. You simply looked up the message board that pertained to the last name you were looking for, and then you post a query asking any question you like. Strangers would then chime in, and some of them were more helpful than others.

It was the last week of October 2003. Sitting at the table that night, I toyed with the idea of posting a message before I did it. I knew it was a long shot. With so many Feinsteins in New York, it was overwhelming. But I couldn't help but think it was worth trying. Not expecting much to come of it I wrote:

> *My father's father was Morris Feinstein. From what little I know, he was born either on the Lower East Side of Manhattan or in Brooklyn around the turn of the century. His family, I was told, originally came from Austria, but I can't be sure.*
>
> *He had 2 or 3 daughters, remarried and had two sons. Larry and Kenneth. Any information would be greatly appreciated. Thanking you, Susan Fensten*

If you had asked me then, that day, what I expected to happen, I'm sure I would have said, nothing much. In fact I didn't think about the post for long, I forgot it entirely over the next few days, assuming nobody would even answer.

That week I was pretty busy at the office. I was working as a book publicist at Oxford University Press and I loved it. At the time it felt like a small independent house. It had a quiet intensity, a place that made its bread and butter on reference titles. It didn't *look* glamorous, as maybe Random House or Doubleday – generally untrod by celebrities or glitterati, the offices stood in an atmosphere of 'library as church.' A house of worship for word and meaning, history and place, for teaching and learning. It was filled with old academic reference books and bibles. I liked working with people who knew things the world needed to know. In the aftermath of the attacks of September 11, our authors were very much in demand.

My job left me so tired in the evenings that I'd come home and collapse. Most nights were spent curled up with the pitbull-German shepherd mix I'd scooped up off Classon Avenue in Bedford-Stuyvesant one freezing January day, taking into my car one of the best friends I'd ever know. I named him Mini Me.

November 1, on one of those nights I spent sitting at the computer on my kitchen table, the L train rumbling under my floors, and Mini Me curled up at my feet, I got a reply.

Hi, My mother's father was named Morris Feinstein, born in NYC 1902. Mom died 5 yrs ago and didn't talk much about her siblings or past, but we know my grandfather Morris's father is supposed to be from Austria.

Karen Gardiner

Karen reached out to me through the board's direct message system to explain more. She had found me almost by accident, she said. She was on the site looking up her husband's family history when, as an afterthought, she searched her mother's last name. Her mother's name was Lania Fensten. When she saw my post, she said she just about fell out of her chair.

I just about fell out of my chair too. Did I really have a distant living relative? Somehow, I had never imagined I would make contact with a real person, much less the enthusiastic correspondent that Karen proved to be. We began to email back and forth.

I learned that Karen lived in Massachusetts, had two daughters, and that her husband owned a toy company. Karen also told me she had a sister named Sharon, who was a widow, also had two daughters, and lived in the same house where they'd grown up. There was a brother, too, named

Leonard, who Karen described as successful on Wall Street, good-looking, and somewhat oddly, a "little mysterious."

For a couple of months, Karen did not tell her husband or sister about me, or about having found me online. She told me she was reticent because she'd once made a pen pal in a recipe club, and then he'd demanded money. I'd read stories like that in the news, so I accepted her explanation. Though I didn't like the idea of being kept a secret, I wanted to signal my respect for Karen's privacy.

As we wrote back and forth, I began to get attached to the idea that there was an entire branch of the Fensten family, with sisters, a brother, and children, all ready for me to join. I couldn't help but wonder what they were like and, more importantly, if they would like me. I suspected they'd find me something of an oddball. I hadn't lived a conventional life. I was forty-one, divorced, and had no children. Karen and her siblings lived in the suburbs, kept ordinary corporate jobs.

I got even more apprehensive about that when Karen emailed me photos. One was a formal family portrait in black and white. To another person it might have seemed an ordinary picture. But it grabbed me, because I didn't personally know anyone who had these kinds of photos taken of themselves. This family seemed so ... together, compared to the people I knew. Seven adults and four small children standing in a close, happy huddle in a big group smile. There were four men in tweed jackets and suits standing with one younger woman in the middle. Two more women buttoned and shoed in conservative clothing were seated—each with a baby on their laps and each a toddler at their knees.

The people in this photograph gave the impression of having completely planned and organized lives. Even the room they were in conspired to make them seem terribly normal. There were glass doors on the bookcases. There was a stylized swan figure sitting on the fireplace mantle. I had never, ever lived in a room like this.

Because Karen didn't point herself out or anyone else, I looked at everyone closely trying to figure out who was who. I wasn't sure who was Hal or who was Karen or Sharon, but of the three men, it was clear which one was Leonard. We had the same smile.

Maybe it was his off-kilter personality I was picking up on, I thought later. In passing, Karen mentioned that Leonard had emotional issues. Probably this should have repelled me, but it didn't. In fact it was the opposite. I knew what it was like to have family members that couldn't quite seem to adjust to the normal world. My father, my sister, even myself, we didn't fit. I began to tell Karen little bits about them. I sensed she and her family might understand that too.

CHAPTER FIVE

It takes your enemy and your friend, working together, to hurt you to the heart; the one to slander you and the other to get the news to you.
—Mark Twain

After a brief pause in the email exchange, Karen told me that she'd finally informed Leonard and Sharon all about me. She reported that they were quite happy to hear they had a distant cousin nearby. According to Karen, they especially loved the 1940s photo I'd sent in which my father and Uncle Larry, just kids, were in a boat on a lake in upstate New York, a flag with forty-eight stars flying behind them. Seated in the bow was a smiling young woman with her arm caressing a small dog. In all the years I'd had the photograph, I hadn't devoted a single thought as to whom the young lady might be. Karen, however, knew exactly who it was: her mother. This news hit me like a tidal wave, but it made sense. The woman in the picture seemed about the right age to be my father's older half-sister, and she also bore a strong resemblance to Morris. The photo also apparently had a profound impact on Karen and her family since their mother—the woman in the boat—had died only five years earlier. Karen said that Leonard actually wept upon seeing it.

The holidays were around the corner and I received a Christmas card in the mail from Bobby. The snowy crystals on the envelope melted my heart a little. It was a signal that he was sorry and wanted to mend fences. I was in such an upbeat mood with my new-found family, I thought it would be okay to forgive and share the good news with him. After a phone call, we were fast friends again and Bobby had some news, he had found his own birth mother. So, in a sense, we were both connecting with lost family.

I was known to Karen's larger family now and given that Leonard lived in New Jersey and worked in Manhattan, I thought I might hear from him relatively soon, but he made no attempt to get in touch. It had been firmly established that we were related, and I felt more than a little rejected when it became obvious that Leonard, for the time being at least, wasn't interested in meeting me.

At the time, I was seeing a younger man, Nolan, who wondered why I was so upset. Nolan, a tall, blond student in his twenties, was athletic and interested in baseball, golf, surfing, and film. Being involved with a younger man may raise eyebrows, but Nolan wasn't going to hurt me, bust up my apartment, or choke me into an airless scream such as in the abusive relationships that I had recently had. He was a quiet man who hadn't expressed much interest in my intense focus on finding and communicating with lost Fensten relatives. He apparently just didn't "get it," but I nevertheless felt overlooked by Leonard. I had begun telling Bobby about my new relatives and he, on the other hand, completely understood my disappointment and told me to be patient.

I searched my mind for a reason that might explain Leonard's aloofness and thought about Karen's statement that her brother was "a little mysterious." I had come from a long line of loners, so it wasn't implausible that such a trait would manifest itself in someone from my father's side of the family. Some people just want to be left alone. I still wasn't going to ask Karen to explain the reference, but the term "mysterious" began to seem more than an apt description of her brother.

When Karen asked if Leonard had gotten in touch with me yet, I said no. I urged her to give her brother time and not make an issue of it. Ironically, Karen wrote not long after, informing me that Leonard wished to know if it was all right for her to give him my email address. Touched by the almost old-fashioned formality of Leonard's request, I said "yes" and couldn't wait to hear from him. Karen issued the caveat that I shouldn't worry if he cried when I met him, saying that he was a bit emotional. I reasoned that it was understandable if he were overwhelmed since he'd just seen a picture of his mother as a child, a mother who had passed away just a few years earlier. Indeed, I wondered if I might cry, too.

On the other hand, there was always the possibility that we would meet and have nothing to say to each other. We might sit across a table, total strangers with a little genetic material in common, nothing more. It would be like sitting down with my silent, stoic father. The meeting might well turn out to be awkward and uncomfortable—a situation I hated under any circumstance—but I was willing to take the risk. I was curious, but more importantly, I hoped deep down for a connection with someone who would not only accept me but also fully understand me in a way that only family can. He might even turn out be fun and have interesting friends.

Right before New Year's Eve, Leonard sent me an email, welcoming me to the family. He matched my sentiments exactly when he wrote that he was overjoyed to simply know I was "out there." He gave me his AOL screen name, LNachman1 so that we could chat online. In turn, I gave him my AOL IM name, GirlFensten (which was what my original birth certificate read since I wasn't named immediately). He asked if I would be interested in having lunch with him soon, and I immediately replied that I would love nothing better.

***

I excitedly told Bobby that I had finally heard from Leonard, and we both added him to our IM buddy lists. Time passed, but Leonard and I didn't chat. Bobby and I communicated via AOL's Instant Messenger on most nights, so Leonard should have seen that I was readily available. He didn't make contact, nor did he send another email. I wrote him a second time but received no reply. I was very disappointed again, having allowed my hopes to rise at the prospect of getting to know someone who sounded like a friendly person and who also was a part of my family.

The strangest aspect of Leonard's silence was that Bobby and I could see LNachman1 sign on and off repeatedly over the course of an evening, staying online for only a few seconds at a time. I myself was too shy to initiate conversation since Leonard hadn't responded to my second email. Bobby and I agreed that my cousin's erratic, rapid fire use of AOL's IM was strange, to say the least. This was the second time Leonard was ignoring me.

Exactly what did "mysterious" mean?

***

A few weeks later, I learned that Karen assumed Leonard and I had already met and were becoming friendly since she'd heard that her brother and I had exchanged instant messages. Karen expressed surprise when I told her that I hadn't even received an email reply from Leonard much less an IM. Karen surmised that Sharon may have already said something negative to their brother about me.

A bizarre twist in our communication ensued when Karen tried to get more photographs from Sharon, pictures that she wanted me to see. She claimed that Sharon had some photos of my father as a child stored in a box in her garage. I anxiously awaited their arrival in my inbox since they would constitute further proof that we were related. Why else would the Nachman family possess photographs of my father? When Karen wrote back, she said that although the file size was quite large, she'd managed to attach them to her email. Upon opening the attachment, however, I saw no pictures. The screen was blank. Not being email-savvy, I printed the entire email to see if there was anything I might have missed. I had, but not photos.

After a single blank page slid from the printer, the machine produced a lengthy email discussion between the two sisters. It was like gazing at a transcript, and what I saw was disturbing. Sharon's tone toward Karen was mean-spirited and gave me some insight into the dynamics of their relationship. Even worse, Sharon had made a decidedly pointed comment about a photo I'd sent to Karen of me standing near the East River. Sharon said that my dogs were "awesome," which was fitting since I "lived in a slum." She went on to say that she had a bad feeling about me since I was so impatient to see the photos in her garage. Sharon admonished Karen, reminding her of the unpleasant experience with the online recipe club and asking if I had asked for money yet. Sharon seemed convinced I was a con artist.

I was more hurt than shocked, feeling as if Sharon had landed a sharp blow to my stomach. We hadn't written to each other, and the woman didn't even know me. I'd never mentioned a single word about money to Karen, and I hoped that she would be able to explain to her sister the sincerity of my intentions. This was about genealogy, about meeting family, nothing more. This first taste of Sharon's acerbic nature was unpleasant . . . and it wouldn't be the last.

When I broke down and cried after reading the printout, Nolan's reaction was again one of mild bewilderment as to why I should be upset, this time at a silly email printout from people I'd never even met. What I needed, however, was moral support. I had put my trust and hopes into establishing a relationship with my new relatives, but from the beginning, Sharon Barnes seemed rude and abusive for no reason at all.

***

I got the support I craved from Bobby who assured me that Sharon was probably a bit crazy. Bobby and I examined her emails carefully and could find no sensible reason for Sharon's paranoid reactions. We also analyzed the photo I'd sent to Karen in order to figure out why Sharon believed I lived in a slum. Looking at the photo more objectively, we conjectured that someone from the suburbs might interpret the scene differently. There I was, standing on the Brooklyn waterfront on a hot day in a gray tank top, khaki cargo pants rolled up over desert boots while holding the leash for two huge dogs panting like circus animals—one was Mini Me and the other, Cody, my Malamute who died in early 2003. The New York City skyline loomed in the distance. It wasn't exactly a picture of femininity, and we joked about a beer bottle on the ground nearby that I hadn't noticed before. My choice of pictures could have been better thought out, and given the Nachman family portrait, maybe a picture of me in a dress would have elicited a different reaction. Bobby and I nonetheless decided that there wasn't anything that unusual about the picture, certainly nothing to draw forth such venom from the seemingly irrational Sharon Barnes.

I wrote to Karen, apologizing for any trouble I'd caused while also explaining that I'd read the attachment by mistake. I acknowledged that we were virtual strangers, but that my feelings had been hurt since my quest to learn about my father's family had been quite sincere. I also mentioned that Williamsburg was a chic up-and-coming area in the process of being scooped up by developers. It wasn't a slum by any stretch of the imagination. Additionally, I reminded Karen that I'd never written anything suspicious or probing in my emails. But I had misjudged Karen as well. She promptly forwarded my heartfelt response straight to the jaws of the beast—Sharon—in what could only be interpreted as a move representing quintessential family loyalty. Sharon was quick to seize the moment for more harsh invective.

> Dear Susan Fensten, or whatever you call your-self,
>
> This is Sharon, Karen Gardiner's sister. What business is it of yours what I say or do concerning my family? You have some nerve reading person-al stuff between my sister and me. The polite thing

to do would have been to see it wasn't for you and delete it, but I guess you don't know manners.

You can stop bothering my family too. My brother said you wrote him a few times and asked to go to lunch. He has been through enough in his life and does not need to know your type. You send my sister photographs of a little girl sitting in a dress looking pretty and cared for and then one of yourself now looking nothing like that pretty child.

My sister is very trusting and has a big heart and people like you always try to take advantage of her. Whatever you are trying to do it won't work. Now you bother to tell her you are hurt. That's your own fault for not minding your own business.

Sharon

No manners? I had never been so insulted. Additionally, having lunch had been Leonard's idea, not mine. Was this tantamount to a game of kindergarten "telephone," in which information becomes distorted as it gets passed along? I had no way of knowing. I showed it to my friend Bill at work who had been following this little saga with me, and he reiterated that Sharon Barnes had to be more than just a *little* crazy. I wrote back, copying Karen and Leonard to show them that I didn't intend to take any nonsense and that I didn't deserve any of this.

Madame-

Spare me your vitriol. People search for relatives all the time, read up on it sometime. There is no evil plot.

Your nasty comments were in an email addressed to me. I printed it and saw it by accident.

Your brother wrote to me asking to meet, not the other way around.

Unlike you, I understand that adults can handle their own affairs.

I leave you to shadow-box with your own paranoia.

Susan

Leonard's reply was terse: "Not interested. Leave me alone." As for Karen, she surprisingly took Sharon's side, telling me she was surprised at how mean I was and that this "was no way to come into a family." She nonetheless wished me luck on my job search and expressed regret at not being to "help me at this time." This latter detail was extremely puzzling since I hadn't even hinted that I might be seeking any financial assistance from her family. Once again, the Nachmans were hearing an online "money pitch," although it was certainly only in their heads, not in the emails.

I couldn't decide which hurt more: Karen siding with her sister or Leonard's outright dismissal of me. But Karen was apparently the peacemaker of the clan, and she soon suggested I apologize to Sharon. I wasn't in an apologetic mood—quite the contrary—but in the interest of the greater good, I offered the proverbial olive branch. I gave the very naive Karen my mailing address and phone number in order to show that I had nothing to hide. In retrospect, I may have been the naive one by sharing such personal information so freely.

Although Karen had already sent word to her family that "Susan was sorry," Sharon fired back threatening to report me to the police, advising me how to dress more appropriately, and affirming her suspicions about my money-grubbing intentions. The email ended with directions on where I could put my olive branch.

I'd had enough. I wrote to Karen, telling her that I found her sister's emails dark, and discomfortingly juvenile, and that while I had initially been willing to devote energy to my new family members, the process had proved entirely too draining. I requested that she not forward my final message to Sharon and, wishing her luck, informed her that future emails from her family would be deleted.

By the end of January, I got news that I would be laid off with thirty other staff members. Sales were down after September 11 due to federal budget cuts to libraries, which was nothing short of an economic disaster for an academic press. Oxford offered me a severance package, which I accepted, and when I'd collected my thoughts, I decided that a little time off might give me time to think things over. A change would do me good.

While gathering my personal things on the last day of work, I noticed a copy of *Schizophrenia: A Very Short Introduction,* one of several reference books I'd accumulated over the years. I put it into my box. My gut instinct told me I would need it.

CHAPTER SIX

GREYSTONE

As an experience, madness is terrific . . . and in its lava
I still find most of the things I write about.
—Virginia Woolf

I was happy to be rid of the dysfunctional Nachmans. I had to concentrate on finding a new job, but otherwise things were thankfully quiet. The peace lasted only a short time.

At night, Bobby and I chatted as usual via IM, we had become fixated on the dynamics within Karen's family. Abruptly, Leonard once again started signing on and off as LNachman1, remaining online for only a few seconds. His rapid appearances coincided with numerous porn and email notifications pumping into my inbox suggesting I had subscribed to escort services, live webcam sex,— every kind of gay and straight porn one could imagine. The logical conclusion was that Leonard was responsible since it happened whenever his screen name briefly appeared.

Is he dangerous? I wondered about the Wall Street entrepreneur who had recently welcomed me to the family and invited me to lunch. I was scared and repulsed, and the repulsion was intensified by the fact that the cyber filth was ostensibly coming from my cousin. If he was indeed responsible, Leonard suddenly seemed more than just a little mysterious. The actions of the perpetrator, whoever he or she was, were depraved. Pains settled in my chest and stomach, the kind caused by basic, elemental fear.

Ten to twelve emails arrived each time LNachman1 appeared online and were addressed to a multitude of names, including my own, someone called Sondra, or just "Shit." I forwarded the cyber garbage to Bobby in real time since we were online watching this happen. We agreed that Leonard wasn't joking around, simultaneously displaying both anger and sexual attraction toward me. Leonard had a bizarre fixation on me. This realization made my stomach churn even more. Bobby and I were both disgusted.

Bobby explained what IP addresses were and showed me how to look them up using sites which could narrow the IP's point of origin to country, server, or both. After a few searches, AOL came up as the originator every time, but they had millions of users. It would be an impossible task to zero in on one person. While we suspected Leonard was responsible because he was on AOL and his online appearances coincided with the "porn dumps," I would also get the same filth at other times of the day. What we did have, however, was a place to direct a complaint. We lodged a complaint with AOL, although I heard nothing back. The "mysterious" Leonard was also a prime suspect for the simple reason that I didn't know anyone else on the web. Now I was receiving X- rated material daily.

A few weeks after my message to Karen telling her I wasn't interested in further contact, she emailed me out of the blue. Sounding as nice as ever, she said she was coming to New York City with her husband for the toy fair at the Jacob Javits Center and wanted to have lunch with me. I hesitantly said yes and picked a restaurant where we could meet. I wasn't going to tell her that I had reasons to believe her brother was sending me dirty and hostile messages for the past month.

Meanwhile, porn continued to dispense into my mailbox that was increasing in volume and depravity as LNachman1 continued to make his nightly on-off appearances. I made a second complaint to AOL, attaching dozens of the harassing emails and demanding appropriate action even though I wasn't going to hold my breath for an answer.

I received an email from Karen the day before her scheduled arrival in the city. One of her daughters had the flu, so she'd canceled the trip. I was both relieved and annoyed because I'd spent time mentally preparing myself to confront someone whose brother and sister seemed quite disturbed. I'd gathered up my courage, and now Karen wasn't coming. Perhaps I shouldn't have been surprised.

***

Leonard wrote to me. The title of the email was "GirlFensten"; the message simply said, "You like to complain. *I bet I can make you moan too.*"

I felt violated and horrified. This was confirmation that Leonard, my cousin, was attempting to play some very nasty sexual games with me. Did he have no boundaries? Did he think this was funny? Worse yet, did he expect a response? What had I gotten myself into? Leonard Nachman was apparently obsessed with me—Leonard, who was "a bit mysterious" and "a little emotional." Fear sank from my brain to the pit of my stomach. Yes, Leonard was "out there" all right—*it's good to know you're out there*, we'd both thought—and he had me fixed squarely in his sights.

My complaint to AOL had obviously worked, hence the brief, menacing message. The ISP probably received thousands of complaints a day, so I hadn't anticipated a response directly from them. I forwarded the message to Bobby for inspection and comment, prompting him to call me on the phone so we could discuss this frightening turn of events. Bobby suggested that I should reply with humor or insults, but that was risky. They might irritate Leonard even more and let him know that he'd gotten to me. I decided to ignore it.

Near midnight, Leonard sent the "make you moan" email again. He was rubbing it in my face. My knees felt weak and my heart clenched. He was no longer sending his trashy email anonymously, no longer hiding. Bobby and I were still online when the second mail arrived, and again he called me right away. I was so glad that he'd come back into my life. We'd once again been able to talk about anything, and I needed someone familiar to speak with, someone that I could talk to about anything, no matter how dark and odd.

Bobby and I talked it over. He was worried about me, and after a brief discussion, we decided I should send another complaint to AOL, this time with Leonard's email attached. I copied Leonard with no comment included in the message. I would continue to be hands-on and show him I meant business.

Shortly after, I received a nightmarish reply that took me farther into the depths of Leonard's disturbed mind. A long, disjointed group of old emails had been pasted together. Most were not in chronological order.

THIS GIRL IS BOTHERING ME. SHE STARTS OUT NICE AND GETS MAD IF I DONT PAY HER OFF. PLEASE MAKE HER STOP BOTHERING

ME. READ HER E-MAILS TO SEE HOW SHE IS A CON ARTIST. MY SISTER HAS POLICE REPORT ON HER PROSTITUTION. ALIAS SUSAN FENSTEN, SFENSTEN@nyc.rr.com, publishingnyc@yahoo.com . I WILL NOT PAY HER MORE MONEY. I DO NOT WANT SEX WITH THIS PERSON. I WANT TO BE LEFT ALONE.

LEN NACHMAN

Date: Thu, 15 Jan 2004 13:20:07 -0800 (PST)

From: "Leonard Nachman" <leonard_nachman@yahoo.com>

Subject: Re: re;

To: SFENSTEN@nyc.rr.com

CC: s_barnesny@yahoo.com

Not interested.

Leave me alone.

SFENSTEN@nyc.rr.com wrote:

madame-

Spare me your vitriol. People search for relatives all the time, read up on it sometime. There is no evil plot.

Your nasty comments were in an email addressed to me. I printed it

and saw it by accident.

Your brother wrote to me asking to meet, not the other way around.

Unlike you, I understand that adults can handle their own affairs.

I leave you to shadow-box with your own paranoia.

Susan

Date: Fri, 16 Jan 2004 11:24:45 -0800 (PST)

From: "Sharon Barnes" <S_barnesny@yahoo.com>

Subject: Re: feinstein/34 Submitted for Review

You're wrong. It was not only through email outside of your service. She is also writing to other people and she's not who she says she is. I have some of the letters still.

She wants money and passes herself off as different peoples long lost relative.

I can handle an ISP complaint, the reason I wrote you was because she is using your Website as a hunting ground for her financial gain. Does this not concern you?

Or do I need to bring the law into this?

<rootsweb.com> wrote:

Sharon,

If you feel this individual has been inappropriate, nasty, etc. you should

contact your ISP and report her. Unfortunately, since these exchanges were

conducted via private email (GenForum was not used), Genealogy.com is unable to intervene. But I will keep my eye out for further posts from her. Thank you for reporting this.

--

RootsWeb Staff, supporting GenForum

rootsweb.com

On 1/16/04 8:33 AM, "kgardiner001@yahoo.com" wrote:

URL: http://genforum.genealogy.com/feinstein/ messages/34.html

>

> Author: 228158235 - Susan Fensten

> Message:

> ----

> --

>Thank you, Susan

> ----

>

> Problem Description:

> ----

> --

> Description From: Sharon Barnes

> This girl must be some kind of con artist. Ever since coming in

> contact with her she has caused nothing but trouble for our family.

> My sister received a disgusting letter from her just yesterday,

> and my brother, her supposed cousin, has felt inappropriate sexual

> advances from her. The pictures she sends out don't match up with

> her story, and we generally have a bad feeling about her. Already

> I've told her personal things about myself and our family and now

> I don't know what she is going to do with it all.

> We are frightened. The experience using this service has been

> devastating to my family. Is there any way to get rid of this con

> artist please?

_____

Date: Tue, 30 Dec 2003 13:39:06 -0800 (PST)

From: "susan" <publishingnyc@yahoo.com>

Subject: Re: Hello Cousin

To: "Leonard Nachman" <leonard_nachman@yahoo.com>

Dear Cousin Len-

It's so nice to hear from you. Let's get together sometime soon. I work on 34th and Madison, but we can meet almost anytime downtown. I am open to suggestions. Just drop me a note anytime you like.

All my best,

Susan

I told you she was bad news. When I went to pick Jolie up from Karen's the other day I found a 718 number in the kitchen drawer. It has to be the monster. Who else does she know in 718 Brooklyn? I bet she made plans to see her when she was going to the toy fair. If she trys anything else let me know right away, and keep fending off her advances. You know she's after one thing and one thing only. This is another ad from the same person. I know it's her.

lookingforpussyanddick (82) - NY female, age: 41, seeking Kinky Women|seeking Kinky Men|seeking Kinky Couples|seeking Kinky Lesbian Couples|-seeking Kinky Group Sex (3 or more)|seeking Kinky Swingers|

[GirlFensten| United States, Brooklyn, NY]

Leonard Nachman <leonard_nachman@yahoo. com> wrote:

I think she is complaining about me to aol for some reason.

Bobby and I were startled. Reading this twisted collection of emails was like "looking through the glass darkly." They represented an unwell mind focused intensely on me. Or should I say "minds?" Was Sharon complicit with Leonard? Judging from one of the later emails in the string, Sharon had found my number in Karen's kitchen drawer. Still convinced that I was out to get money, she'd urged Leonard to keep "fending off" my advances and had added a listing near the very end soliciting any form of deviant or group sex, telling her brother that she was certain that I had placed the ad. Someone had obviously added my AOL name as a perverted joke.

Even more twisted, Sharon had even filed a police report in Massachusetts, accusing me of prostitution. She'd also complained to *Genealogy.com*, asserting that I'd made unwanted sexual advances to her brother in addition to passing myself off as a long lost relative to other families on the site. These were random emails from myself and Leonard patched together like a crazy quilt. The bizarre content of the entire collection made it clear that the accusations, as bad as they were, were not the most troubling aspect of the email chain. Leonard, possibly with the help of Sharon, was playing some pretty serious head games, ones designed to terrify me and they had succeeded.

I forwarded the messages to Bobby for analysis and feedback. We were poring over every word and detail on the telephone at 12:30 a.m. when two sharp beeps—the first low and the next a little higher—told me I had an incoming call.

My heart skipped a beat. No one called me at this hour.

Beep—*beep*! There it was again. I nearly jumped out of my seat. There was no ID for the incoming call. It was anonymous. Bobby and I both suspected it might be Sharon since she had found my number in Karen's kitchen drawer.

The caller ID beeped a third time. My hands were shaking. Bobby and I decided it was better not to take the call. The phone beeped a few more times as my hands continued to tremble, my mouth dry with fear.

And then silence.

The Nachmans, who were appearing more deranged by the day, had my name, address, and phone number, and there was nothing I could do about it.

***

Two days later, Karen emailed me that Leonard was upset, and she had no idea why. She said that she hoped Leonard hadn't done anything to hurt me—not exactly the most reassuring part of her letter—adding that whenever anything happened in her family, she was always the last to know. Bobby and I realized that Karen had not been totally forthcoming about her brother, who was apparently capable of causing serious mental anguish in others. I decided to give her a full account of what Leonard had been doing. If her own family wasn't going to put her in the loop, *I* would. It was *my* safety at stake, not hers. In my reply, therefore, I informed Karen of the email string from Leonard that included the insulting verbiage and accusations from Sharon. I also forwarded the email in which Leonard said he could make me moan and said that I was getting anonymous calls at night.

***

Going online was like walking into a fright house, but not the one at the theme park, where alarming images last only a few minutes. No, this one was like the dark house at the end of a block, the one that kids are warned to stay away from.

The following day I, received an email titled "Bigmouth" from *GirlFucksten@yahoo.com*, a play on my IM name. The message within was brief: "Nice face. You're a star baby!" Below the message was a link. I had no desire to see where it led. It might contain sexual filth, or more threats from Sharon. I sent it straight to Bobby, who agreed that it might be better if I didn't look at it. He later told me that the link led to a page where my face had been photo-shopped onto the body of porn actresses. I also forwarded this to Karen—I wasn't letting up, no matter how much it might disturb her delicate constitution or cause dissension within her family—and added that I'd had enough and was changing my email address.

After a week of blessed cyber-silence, Hal wrote me to say that Karen was in the hospital. He claimed that his wife wanted me to know she was okay and that she was truly sorry I had become involved in her family's trouble. Curiously, Hal didn't tell me why his wife had been hospitalized, although he did mention that Karen was remaining there an extra day or two in order to rest since she'd been overwhelmed when she'd learned about Leonard's deeds. Hal himself apologized for any distress I'd endured and assured me that Leonard had been dealt with. I appreciated the notification, although I would like to have known what "dealt with" really meant. The Nachman trust factor had been eroded. Dealt with? It was a vague term that only served to worsen my fears.

This was the bottom line: Karen was in the hospital for unspecified reasons, Leonard had been "dealt with," and Sharon, wherever she might be, was on the warpath. Bobby and I were amazed that a few innocent emails about family history could have generated such chaos within a family. I thanked Hal for his update but told him plainly that I needed to be sure Leonard wasn't going to bother me again and that, quite frankly, he had scared the wits out of me. Hal said he understood my concerns and that Leonard had been sent back to a psychiatric facility in New Jersey: Greystone, where "they knew him well."

Where they knew him well. Hal's reassurance was a double-edged sword. Intended or not, Hal's message cemented my fear that Leonard was far more ill than I had been led to believe.

I Googled "Greystone" and what I found was chilling. Greystone Park was a massive, Victorian-style psychiatric facility, one that looked like it came straight out of a Gothic movie or a nightmare. Originally built for upper-class society, it was now in a near state of dilapidation, with long, dark rows of broken windows, halls, and eerie shadows. The brooding and forgotten buildings of the complex were strangled by overgrown weeds. It seemed to have a life of its own, a life harboring the memories of thousands of tortured minds. This was where Leonard Nachman was being "dealt with."

Bobby and I scoured the internet to find out more about what looked to be a madhouse straight out of a horror novel. What we learned was disconcerting. Even though Greystone looked as if it was condemned and slated for demolition, it was nevertheless a functioning hospital that had a reputation for treating high-risk sex offenders. What kind of effective treatment could my cousin possibly receive in such a deplorable psychiatric hospital? We were speechless and aghast.

The paramount thought in my mind was *how can this be happening to me?* Oddly, I felt partly responsible. I wasn't culpable for Leonard's medical history, of course, but none of this melodrama would be playing out if I hadn't started looking up my father's family on a genealogy website. But ultimately, I knew that I couldn't be held responsible for the Nachman family pathology. Karen should have leveled with me early on. I had trusted her with my family's history. Given my own background, if she been more forthright, I might have understood her explanations, but the cloak-and-dagger routine was now wearing on my nerves. The sooty little tribe of Fenstens may have been troubled. The Nachmans were in a league of their own.

As if things weren't bad enough, Karen and Hal told me that all the unsavory activity surrounding Leonard and the family drama surrounding it had taken its toll on Sharon's fiancé, Tom Shoef, who had postponed their wedding. Karen admitted it wasn't my fault but implied that everything that had gone wrong pointed to my sudden appearance in their lives. Karen claimed that the postponement had cost Sharon thousands of dollars in wedding expenses and travel deposits, not to mention the ultimate cost: the loss of a husband as well as a father for her two little girls. Was this *my* doing? Hardly.

Sharon lost no time in emailing me, spewing forth her usual threats and condemnations. I was a home wrecker who had destroyed her future. "I hope you die in a burning hell," she said. "You don't know who you're dealing with." I didn't reply. What would have been the point?

The phone calls began again. Anonymous callers hung up quickly. I was inside a horror paperback, only this was all too real. I couldn't just close the cover and walk away. The Nachmans had written me into the narrative, and they weren't about to let go of their protagonist.

Hal and I began to be in touch more often. He seemed to be the voice of reason in a chaotic situation. He told me that Leonard was bouncing off the walls in Greystone even though he was being administered three times his usual amount of antipsychotic medication. A nurse informed Hal that Leonard was painting a picture of a woman and that it was turning out well.

Somehow, I knew it was a picture of me.

CHAPTER SEVEN

SMILE AND SHOW HIM YOU ARE FRIENDLY TOO

The family—that dear octopus from whose tentacles we never quite escape.
—Dodie Smith

If I had been written into the Nachman family saga, then I deemed it crucial to gather material. While I knew little about them, they seemed to know almost everything about me.

It's not difficult to find out information about people on the internet—even conviction records are public and accessible if one knows where to look. Dig deeper, and a surprising amount of data is available. Bobby and I, now working together like detectives, found that there were many people named Karen Gardiner and Sharon Barnes living in Massachusetts. In West Milford, New Jersey, however, there was only one Leonard Nachman. Bobby checked out Leonard's Yahoo profile, which revealed that he was divorced and indeed worked in finance. Bobby then located Leonard's home address and phone number in New Jersey and found that his ex-wife, Marcia Nachman, resided in Manhattan. Next, we did a search on registered sex offenders in West Milford. The results turned up one hit, and although the name of the offender was not accessible, it wasn't difficult for me to imagine that Leonard Nachman was the human face behind the statistic.

Karen had never revealed the town in which she or Sharon lived. At first, I thought she was merely being careful, and I chided myself for not being more careful myself, given that Leonard was a sexual deviant and return guest at Greystone Psychiatric Hospital. In mid-March, Karen finally opened up a bit more about Leonard's background, but the email did nothing to pacify my concerns.

> Susan, how do I begin to tell you how sorry I am you had to see this ugly side to our family? What can I say or do to make this up to you? I knew there was something wrong when Len didn't return my calls or e-mails. He has a history of disappearing when things go bad. Then when you sent me those disgusting letters I wanted to die. I wanted to go off somewhere and die of shame. I wish I had been more forthcoming regarding Len's problems, but he's a good person underneath it all, so is Sharon. She means well but her actions don't always show it.
>
> I read the things she said about you and almost didn't recognize my own sister. Being a widow has only hardened her. My family is ruined Susan, and I am still in physical pain. I had an accident in the kitchen last week carrying a pot of boiling water from the stove to the sink. My nerves were frayed and Sharon was over screaming at me. What else is new, LOL. I don't know what happened but I went blank and dropped the pot of water, making third degree burns on my ankles and calves. I didn't feel anything, I just went blank.
>
> I'm ok now and taking antibiotics, but I had to get some rest and let the doctors treat my burns. It

was a stupid thing to do but it has all been too much for me and I lost it. I felt sorry about not getting back to you. And to be honest I didn't even know what to say to you. I hope you don't mind that I asked Hal to write you and tell you I was ok and would get back to you eventually, LOL. Better late than never.

I don't know what I would do without my husband Susan. He has been my pillar of strength and has put up with what no one should have to with my family. Lenny is in a hospital in New Jersey where they know him and understand his problems. He is getting counseling and medications to help him with these breakdowns. My brother was diagnosed as a kid with schizophrenia, with antisocial something disorder. My mother had it too. When he takes his medicine he is very sweet and nice to be around, but he doesn't remember to take it sometimes and gets into the bad personalities. My mother was the same way. He isn't really dangerous or anything like that. Ok, he got involved in that Burr thing, but that was almost 20 years ago. They were just friends and Len was in the wrong place at the wrong time. I know my brother and he wouldn't knowingly hurt anyone. And in the Belarus mess there was no conviction but they did take his computer and stuff. So Hal had to bail him out again, but he got everything back when it was over. We are praying for him that he gets better. No one should have to suffer the way he does. Right now I have to take care of myself and my children. Susan is there any way you can forgive the things you've seen? I wanted to reach out to you so many times but didn't know how. It was so nice getting e-mails from you and getting to know you and then it was like everything changed. I still don't know what happened. I'm going to lay down now because I have a headache and I have been taking Tylenol. Thank you for the nice things you said in your note to Hal. I love you my cousin and am so ashamed about what you were put through.

Please forgive my family and me.

Love, Karen

The "Burr thing"? The "Belarus mess"? What was Karen talking about? She'd casually dropped these alarming phrases into her email as if she was intentionally leaking information although these references nevertheless indicated that Leonard had been in some kind of serious trouble. It seemed contradictory that he wasn't considered dangerous but was nevertheless capable of assuming "bad personalities." The whole letter did not portend well for what I might face in the future, and I had a sinking feeling that the whole mess might be the kind of family problem that could linger indefinitely. From the standpoint of my own emotional stability, I saw no end in sight.

My ever-present partner in DC was quick to suggest that we try to uncover the Burr and Belarus mysteries. What we found was disconcerting. Bobby's search skills were far more advanced than mine, and he tracked down the offender page for a convict named Lou Burr on the New Jersey Department of Corrections website. Burr had been convicted of kidnapping, rape, and weapons possession in 1986. He had forced an under-aged girl off the street at knifepoint and sexually assaulted her. He'd served thirteen years, had been paroled, and then sent back to prison in 1999 for a parole violation. Burr's profile and the details of his crime were also on the website of New Jersey's registered sex offenders. His alias was Lou, and his New Jersey Department of Corrections photograph showed a disturbing, dead-eyed predator staring from the screen. He was currently free and categorized as a Tier 2 moderate offender. The designation meant that he was assessed as a possible recidivist and a threat to public safety. As with all convicted sex offenders, he was required to notify law enforcement and other organizations within the community—prosecutors, courts, schools, religious and youth organizations—of his presence. What had Leonard been involved in twenty years earlier?

Next, we searched the term "Belarus" and discovered news links to stories of child sex trafficking. A CNN story from a few weeks earlier reported a federal bust involving dozens of people in a New Jersey child pornography sting. Had Leonard been involved in this, too? If so, he might have been engaged in nefarious activities for almost half his life.

I wrote to Karen, reminding her of my own family history, and told her plainly now that I might have been in a better position to understand some of Leonard's problems if only she had been honest with me from the outset. Her brother had severe psychiatric problems, and I confessed that I was more than a little worried since Leonard lived relatively close to Brooklyn and was sexually fixated on me. In what was becoming a pattern, Karen wrote back with even more horrifying details.

March 15, 2004

Dear Susan,

Thank you for your long and thoughtful letter. You ask a lot of questions in it and I will try to answer them all in this letter. There is something I never mentioned to you, and I feel terrible having to tell you like this. Susan there was another one of us. Another sister named Sondra, she died when we were children growing up.

When Lenny was in second grade my mother caught him playing with matches behind the house. All boys do it so no one was concerned. That same summer part of our house caught fire and burned down, killing my baby sister. She was in an upstairs bedroom over the garage. The fire department and police figured it started in the garage near some gasoline rags and lawnmower, a spark from a bad wire. But they also talked to Lenny a lot that summer. I think they thought he had something to do with our sister's death. Nothing was proven and he was a few blocks away playing when they found him. My mother went into a deep depression after that and was different towards Len. I think she always blamed him for that fire and Sondra's death.

We didn't talk about it much and nothing really bad happened until a few years later when he was 12. The man next door caught him looking in their window one night while his daughter got undressed. She was my age in my grade. It might have been being scared at being caught but Len overreacted and did violence against him. When our neighbor confronted him about looking in the window Len picked up a shovel from the front porch and hit him in the head with it. Thank God the man lived and only needed a few days in the hospital, but Lenny got sent to a psychiatric hospital by the juvenile court up here in MA for 3 months before he could come back home. Then he never was right in the head we thought because he came back different. My sister swore she saw him kill a stray dog in an empty lot and my father had enough to worry about with my mother's condition not getting any better. Dad's brother had a house in New Jersey where he and my aunt ran a business. Their son had been having problems of his own and they put him in a psychiatric hospital which helped him a lot. So my parents decided to put Lenny in there too. He spent one whole year in there. Susan, I don't know what happened to him there but he was not the same person I knew when he came out. Whatever good that was left inside him was buried and it took years to see him smile again and start to act happy. To this day he still has involuntary movements and tremors. Susan he had shock treatments, a few series. By the time he got out he was ok but I remember visiting him at that big place and he didn't seem to know who I was or where he was. After he got out he was ok and getting back in the swing of things calling friends and getting invited places, and seemed almost normal again. He caught up in school quickly and was popular with some of the older boys for doing their homework and helping them with math problems. He was taking money for his work and I think that is where he got his head for business. For another few years everything was ok except for mom. She was starting to see people in her room, flames in the window and blaming all of us for hiding things on her. She would also carry and hug an old doll of Sharon's and pretend it was Sondra. She was also very mean to Len. It was very sad for us to see her like that losing her mind. I feel like crying now just thinking about it. Mental illness is a terrible thing Susan right up there with cancer and all these other diseases.

Then when Len was in his early twenties he got involved in a terrible thing just by being in the wrong place at the wrong time. He decided to go to school in New Jersey and had been staying with my uncle and aunt until he met Lou. They met at college and ended up becoming roommates in an apartment off campus. Susan, what happened to him should not happen to anyone. From what I understand he was at home studying for his classes when Lou came home with another man named McCottry and a girl. You know how young people are, one thing lead to another. There was drink and music and the girl was apparently already drunk when she got there. By the end of the night or morning she ran out into the street without her clothes on and flagged down a car. At the hospital she said her injuries and marks were from a sex assault, but Len thinks she was so drunk she hurt herself bumping into things and falling down on her way out. She also claimed that they made her drink and take pills. Ok the girl cried rape and Lou's semen was the only one that they could tell. He got arrested and charged with a crime but Len was able to finish school and keep his life thank God. He said the stuff was consensual between the woman and the two others but Len never ever touched her. He kept studying and then went to bed. He was asleep when the police woke him up and arrested Burr and the other man. We were worried for a long time that he would get in trouble for that but they couldn't prove anything. It was a drunk's word against his.

About a year later he started working on Wall Street in where he met Marcia. They got married that spring and things seemed to be ok except for the death of their first and only child. The baby died from what we think was SIDS. It ruined their marriage and Len's mental state even more. Then a few years later she called up one night crying saying that Lenny had hurt her or something. My father got involved and supposedly there was more to the story I still don't know, but he put Len back in the hospital for another few months. When he got out that time he had to take injectable longer lasting drugs to keep him stable. Marcia divorced him and he's been alone ever since as far as I know. Then there was a long period where I didn't hear from him and none of us could get a hold of him. I found out later that he immersed himself in his work and because of that he made a small fortune. He's always been very smart Susan, but this other thing kept him from being a real person I'm afraid. About a year ago we got a call from the police in his jurisdiction telling us he'd been found outside some family's home wandering around. He wasn't taking his medication and was lost. He was confused as far as wearing women's clothing he must have thought was his own. He had stolen them from another person's clothesline. Sharon flew to NJ to take care of him and got his doctors to give him an easier pill to take. He seemed to be doing good on the new medicine, and was staying in touch more. He even expressed an interest in dating again which I thought would never happen. After that Hal had to fly down again to help him with some problem with the Jewish life organization. He was blamed for something he didn't do and got out of it. Then at the beginning of this year he got into some trouble with a credit card scam where his name showed up on some illegal sex webpage or something. He was innocent, but they took his computer and stuff to see if he was doing anything wrong. He got all of it back a few weeks later and wasn't convicted. Hal got him a great lawyer and they are still going through some court stuff over it all. I thought everything was going to be ok, until he started on you.

I understand completely how you feel about wishing I had told you more about Len, but I didn't want to scare you away and also thought my brother was doing ok. He's a very gentle person normally and is very bright to be around. He just has this dark side that comes out now and then because either his medicine isn't right or he doesn't take it. I thought maybe if you two started talking or being friends living so close to each other it would be a good thing. Unfortunately something set him off again and he took his anger out on you. Sharon thinks you provoked him somehow with your E-mails and instant messengers. It's not your fault, because you didn't know he was a little ill, but I told her that you showed me what you sent him and it was all very normal. He was the one who asked for your E-mail and if you remember I even asked you first if it was ok and you said yes it was.

Hal has been busy repairing this damage to our family. He's spoken to doctors and temple officials that Len knows and even police getting that stupid prostitution report thrown out. My sister must have made a mistake or found someone else that resembled you who was doing that. She was only trying to protect us and especially Lenny, but I wish she hadn't gone this far because I think she did more damage than good. That's what we were fighting about when I dropped the pot of water on myself. She had found your phone number here last month and went ballistic. I promised her I wasn't going to meet you when I came to NY and she thought we weren't in touch anymore. When she found your phone number she flipped out on me. That night I yelled back at her and told her she was wrong for everything she did and now Susan I will tell you what really happened. She slapped me in the face just as I was moving the pasta to the sink I didn't see it coming. So not only do I have burns on my legs but a black eye, LOL but it's almost gone now. I was so stunned by the hit that I froze and just went blank. I didn't tell Hal about her hitting me, just our family doctor who knows her. She's my sister and I'm sure you and your sister used to fight too. Her over protectiveness has been very smothering even though she means well. I don't think she liked how I told her it was wrong all the things she wrote to you and said. I was mortified and so was Hal. But nothing could prepare me for what you sent me Susan. I have never seen that kind of stuff before and never want to again. I wanted to die when I read what he had said to you. It was like the floor opened up beneath me and I was falling. I knew we had to do something so I told my husband and he contacted some people we know near Len and then flew there himself to make sure everything went ok. My sister tried to stop it all by saying he would be locked up for too long, and that's kind of what I wanted to talk to you about. Susan! He is due to be discharged sometime next month, maybe sooner.

Hal or my sister will fly down to help settle him back into his house. Hal bought some new timers and alarm clocks to set around the place to keep him taking his medicine when no one is around. I was told yesterday that he is doing very well and is acting like his old self again. He is taking a combination of chlorpromazine and something else called thioridazine. I wrote it down after talking to his nurse. My only concern aside from Len's well-being is that he doesn't start to bother you again. You have been very kind throughout this entire thing and I don't want you to be hurt anymore. Susan if he tries to contact you with an E-mail please use discretion. He is probably feeling sorry for what he did and might want or need to express that. Also if for any reason he shows up at your house or something please, please don't call the police or report him. We have worked so hard as a family through the years to keep Len out of legal trouble. One more thing would just be enough to have him sent away for a very long time I'm afraid. And he's really a good man.

You said you are a strong person and can handle the truth and most things, and I commend you.

But please use discretion if he does attempt to see you. Remember we are talking about a human being here. I know this sounds really bad, LOL, and I'm not trying to sound that way but I want to be truthful. Len has been known to arrive unexpectedly on more than one occasion. I can't tell you how startled we were one Passover a few years ago when we were eating our dinner, all family and friends when Lenny appeared in the dining room window. He had driven up without telling any of us and brought presents for everyone. And then when Sharon's husband died he didn't come up for the burial but a week later she had a special service for him at the cemetery and Len appeared there also standing back a few hundred feet watching. He called from NJ the next day and said he was sorry he couldn't make it, but we all saw him standing there. I think the death was too much for him and he couldn't handle it so he stayed back and pretended he didn't come. LOL. So you see he has his own way of doing things, but he is very gentle and kind too. Did you know he is involved with unfortunate children and with the Jewish Federation for Kids and Teens? He also is part of the NYU Jewish Life program. He has given so much money away to Israeli projects too Susan, this man has a heart of gold. If you see him just be nice to him. Smile and show him you are friendly too.

He responds to that I've found. Also please don't act nervous or afraid because that would hurt his feelings and then he gets mad. Just be yourself and talk to him calmly. You will see he is really a good person. You will know how to handle him after your father and his problems. I'm sure you learned how to talk and act around a sick person who loves you. Schizophrenia is a terrible thing and I know you must have suffered terribly with your father's illness. My mother was bad at the end of her life, she was tied down most of the day and only let up for bathroom needs and to eat. Her mind and violent behavior were too much for four big hospital aids once. She was a gentle woman who was small in size but could pack a mean wallop when she wanted to, LOL. Lenny is not really violent. It was just that one time back home with our neighbor and everything else was just circumstantial or blamed on him because my brother is different or was in the wrong place at the wrong time. If anything bad happens or you don't feel comfortable with his visit or anything he does instead of calling the police, please call Gracie Square Hospital in New York City at 212-988-4400 and ask for the attending psychiatrist, they know him there. Let them know where you are and they will send a car around to get him.

Thank you for understanding dear cousin, your letter really means a lot to me. I just wish there was some way to turn back time and erase all this bad stuff that happened. I hope you will feel better about things in time. I am still worn out from everything but getting around a lot better with these burns. My doctor said that if I keep using this salve they gave me I might not have too much scarring. I hope not because summer is right around the corner and I like to go to the pool. Maybe you can come up and stay with us this summer for a week and really get to know us the right way? Think about it please and say yes. I hope I answered your concerns and explained Len to you. I'm sorry I didn't tell you about our sister, but to be honest it is very painful to talk about and I didn't want you to judge my brother unfairly.

Please let me know how you feel about all of this because I want you to be comfortable with everything.

Love, Karen

She signed off with a rose emoticon after her name. The letter hit me like a massive charge of electricity. More than ever, I felt like a catalyst for something dark and foul that had been simmering within the Nachmans for years. I felt saddled with this baffling and dangerous family and wanted to disappear, but things had progressed too far. Extricating myself was going to take time. Karen had originally portrayed Leonard as a troubled youth who was basically a good person. Now he was described as an innocent bystander to vicious crimes who has a penchant for violence. Additionally, the sweet, down-to-earth Karen seemed as if she had no sympathy for the poor girl who'd been attacked by Lou Burr. Karen was trivializing a very serious matter and minimizing her brother's involvement in the despicable affair. He had been arrested for rape.

The letter itself was long, rambling, and at times contradictory in tone, but it contained a great deal of material that only served to heighten my fear. I was connected with a family that was complex and dysfunctional in the extreme—and quite possibly dangerous. Had Leonard started a fire when he was young, killing his little sister? Had he driven his already sick mother into madness? The idea was very troubling and indicated that he might have a genetic predisposition toward cruelty and aberrant behavior. Leonard had also spied on a young girl, hit her father with a shovel, and been hospitalized as a child. Not exactly a great resume. And yet, according to Karen, he was really a good man whom I should be kind to if he materialized at my home in Brooklyn in much the same fashion that he had appeared at his family's window on Passover.

I was supposed to simply smile and show that I was friendly, even though Karen wasn't ruling out that something bad might happen, requiring that I call Gracie Square Hospital, which would dispatch a car to retrieve her brother. As with Greystone, Gracie Square also seemed familiar with Leonard's condition. He wasn't the only person I needed to be concerned about, however. Sharon, enraged that Karen had my phone number, had slapped her sister, causing severe burns and a subsequent hospitalization. Would she be hunting me down as well?

New York was a big city, and as a native, I was aware that some of the most prominent people—celebrities, legislators, and entrepreneurs—led secret lives, the macabre nature of which might occasionally surface in the media or tabloids. It had been my misfortune to find a cousin whose Wall Street career masked what seemed to be a psychopathic personality. Nothing, however, could have prepared me for this deepening nightmare.

I showed the latest email to Nolan, who had little to say except that it was awful and that I should never have gotten involved with the Nachmans to begin with. He was concerned, but he didn't represent a groundswell of support. He wanted me to be done with it all, or at the very least to not have to hear about it anymore. But as someone who had been abandoned by those in my family that I needed, I felt it hard to do the same to those in my family who might need me, no matter how crazy they might seem.

Bobby was far more amenable. We talked over the latest "information dump" from Karen, discussing what might have happened the night Lou Burr brought home a girl who may or may not have been drinking prior to what she herself clearly described as a rape. Bobby also quickly located

McCottry's offender profile on the NJDC Website. McCottry had more than one alias, some having varied spellings of his last name, two of which began with the name Felix. Bobby was of the opinion that McCottry was scarier looking than Burr, although it was hard for me to imagine one as worse than the other. Both had been convicted of rape in New Jersey around the same time, and the basic facts of their cases matched. Like Burr, McCottry had served his time and been released. He, too, was "out there."

Considering Leonard's troubled past, it was conceivable that he might well have fallen in with bad company of the worst sort, but one question remained in the forefront of my mind: Was he still in contact with Burr and McCottry? If he was, I might be in grave danger. As Karen had said, Leonard was being discharged the following month. Or sooner.

CHAPTER EIGHT

RELEASED

Sweet is revenge—especially to women.
—Lord Byron, *Don Juan*

Unsettled by the details of Leonard's history, I received an email from Karen on March 18 informing me that her sister would be coming to New York with some friends to see a Broadway play over the weekend. Sharon supposedly needed a diversion to get her mind off Tom Shoef's decision to postpone their wedding. Sharon was beside herself, and because she blamed me for Tom's decision rather than Leonard, Karen believed she might attempt to see me or at least drive by my apartment building. Karen reassured me that Sharon was inherently a good person who had experienced a lot of grief in her life that had taken its toll over the years, especially after losing her husband in "that accident."

The last thing I needed was a renegade group of wrathful suburban housewives in a minivan slamming the pedal all the way to New York City, headed straight for my front door. I felt like a sitting duck.

Karen had further distressing information. Leonard was going to be discharged from Greystone in a few days, with the ever-dependable Hal picking him up. She mentioned that her brother might eventually want to visit me in Brooklyn and reminded me to call Gracie Square Hospital in Manhattan rather than 911 in the event of trouble. The only good news was that Karen believed that Leonard and I were not IMing each other, although she had been "led to believe otherwise."

The thought of the possibility of Leonard's sharp, unannounced knocks on my window made me shudder. I lived on a quiet street along the East river, where there were few pedestrians. I was vulnerable. Acting natural or unafraid seemed impossible if I finally came face to face with the man who'd become sexually obsessed with me, someone who consorted with violent convicted felons.

Distressing messages continued to arrive. Lydia Shoef, Tom's sister, sent me an email with "Troublemaker" typed in the subject line.

> You don't know me but I heard all about you. You must be a very sad person to do the things you did. You hurt people and don't know how to mind your own business. I hope you get everything you deserve.
>
> Lydia

The madness of the Nachmans was spreading, now spilling over to other families. It didn't make any difference in the long run, as yet another person I'd never met was wishing me harm. Angry, I fired back an email to Ms. Shoef and told her quite tersely that those who are not qualified should refrain from comment. She was a peripheral character at best in the Nachmans' tawdry soap opera, and I wasn't interested in her uninformed opinion.

I forwarded Lydia's comments to Karen, hoping that she might stem the tide of bad feelings toward me and prevent more barbed emails from pouring into my inbox. I explained in no uncertain terms that things were already out of control and that I didn't want Sharon or her friends bothering me at home. Unwanted visits were an intrusion on my privacy. While I couldn't restrict access to my street—people were free to come and go as they pleased on "the free roads of America"—I made it clear that Sharon would be foolish if she ever "tried to pull something."

Her response was laced with innocence and contradiction, caution and conviviality. She said that I shouldn't be worried, that Sharon was friendly once people got to know her. Besides, I was getting myself worked up for nothing since the roads were indeed free and people were entitled to a little sightseeing. This kind of mixed sentiment was becoming her signature reply. In this case, reassurance tinged with a few words implied criticism.

The next paragraph was also an exercise in mixed messages. Karen said that if anything *did* happen and Sharon caused trouble, I should act naturally and ignore her, which is how Karen said she herself managed conflict with her sister. She ended by naively saying that she hoped I wouldn't let all the commotion prevent Nolan and me from spending time with them in Massachusetts during the summer. Somehow, I think Nolan would have been less than thrilled at this notion.

Karen was becoming as enigmatic as her unstable brother and sister. She seemed to be walking a tightrope, trying to be the peacemaker as she tried to mollify me while explaining—even defending—their erratic behavior. The idea that either Leonard or Sharon might suddenly confront me in Williamsburg with their tripwire personalities instilled nothing less than dread in the marrow of my bones. I became suspicious and insecure. I began to alter my appearance each time I went out, changing my hairstyle or wearing sunglasses with wide-brimmed hat. On the streets, I observed every person, vehicle, and license plate. I even bought a black studded leather dog collar for Mini Me to make him look tougher. It was a bit theatrical, but I felt outnumbered, unsafe and exposed.

***

Leonard was released from the grim confines of Greystone on March 23. He was to be loosely supervised by another outpatient named Ray Hooch. Hooch was to look in on Leonard from time to time, but otherwise my cousin would be on his own. Hal and Sharon helped their brother get settled into his New Jersey home, with Hal placing alarm clocks around the house to remind Leonard to take his medication. A few alarm clocks and a fellow graduate of Greystone hardly constituted legitimate supervision of my cousin or a guarantee of my safety.

The following day, Sharon emailed me through a domain at Hebrew College in Massachusetts to boast of her trip to Brooklyn to spy on me. She did so in her usual less-than-charming manner.

Susan B. Fuckstein,

I saw where you live on N. 7th St. and you deserve to live in a place like that you filthy whore. People know you in your neighborhood too, at the stores and pet place. One dog in the picture is dead now and you were married to a man in the neighbor-hood once. What happened Susan, did he find out about you too? It's amazing how people like to talk and give out information.

Yesterday my brother got out of the hospital where he spent 3 weeks thanks to you and your bullshit lies. If you only knew what you were playing with when you toyed with his feelings. He's a very sick man and hates you with all his heart for what you did to this family. I hope he comes at you with a vengeance and if he does I will laugh and have a party.

You were told to keep your mouth shut but had to complain and show everyone all your stupid e-mails. My brother and sister ended up in the hospital over your dirty lies and interference. When I mention your name to my brother he just cries and I bet you like that don't you? Ruining a good family all for your own sick gain gets you off. I hope you pay for your fat mouth and lies. I had you pegged from the beginning "Miss Oxford University Press".

What you did to me and my family is unforgivable and disgusting. I have children to raise who are now without a father thanks to you and your interference. I hope your lies and conniving ways will come back to bite you in the ass.

Even if it's the last thing my brother does and has to spend the rest of his life locked away some-place, I pray to God that he takes care of you, you and your "younger" boyfriend. Who is he your pimp? Does he supply you with crack too? Your ugly soul should burn in hell with your nutcase sister and schizoid father. You're all shit and de-serve to live forever in pain. When I told you to go away and leave my family alone you should have listened. And go ahead and report me. At this point it doesn't matter anymore.

Have a nice day.

It was apparent now that Sharon was indeed as cracked as her brother. I considered her to be as dangerous, possibly even more so when it came to my well-being. Hate and venom flowed red hot from every word. Of more immediate concern was the fact that Sharon and her crew had indeed cruised down my street and scoped out my building. I wondered when they had come and how long they'd lingered outside. I also wondered if she'd spoken with my neighbors. She'd obviously made some contact since she knew that the dog in the photo I'd sent to Karen had died.

***

In the following days, Karen wrote that Leonard was doing well. He was already back at work and feeling good. She also validated my earlier intuition about Leonard's artwork executed behind the walls of Greystone, saying that her brother had painted my portrait. It was to be a gift of apology, a fact that brought Karen to tears since it indicated that Leonard was "back to his old self again." Her chief concern was that Sharon might "upset the applecart." This vague reference did nothing to bolster confidence that I might be able to safely step off the emotional roller coaster that sped through madness, childhood trauma, sexual obsession, and family jealousies.

In an email a few hours later, Karen added what she considered an important postscript: Hal had reminded her that Leonard wanted the painting to be a surprise. I should therefore express a suitable measure of grateful astonishment when he gave it to me in person.

Bobby's reaction mirrored my own. We shuddered as we imagined what the painting might look like since neither Hal nor Karen had mentioned its style. The gift was a portrait painted by a sexually obsessed madman biding his time inside the thick walls of Greystone Psychiatric Hospital. Frightening, hideous images flooded our imaginations. The art of the insane conjured up depictions of crude brushstrokes, twisted perspectives, misshapen eyes, and an exaggerated sexuality. The painting might be an unsettling combination of Picasso's severe cubist portraits and Edvard Munch's "The Scream." Most important to Leonard, he wanted to give me the gift in person so he could see the look on my face. I desired no such meeting, but Karen was of the opinion that I should "give the guy a break" because "he obviously thinks a lot about you."

I felt like an emotional hostage, with equal parts of guilt and terror running along my frayed nerves. With trepidation, wrongly hoping that I could fix all of this, I wrote to Leonard, wishing him well and expressing the hope that he was comfortable. In reality, I felt I was inside a monster's cage, a hummingbird hovering over the mouth of a beast. Despite my attempt to weigh every word, and forgetting Karen's plea to keep secret my knowledge of Leonard's painting, I committed the unpardonable crime of thanking him for the portrait.

As I sat at my computer the following morning, feeling the heart palpitations I'd recently developed, I realized I'd lost weight too. My hands trembled so much that I could hardly guide my mouse as I stared at the glow of the monitor, noting that new messages awaited opening. Taking a deep breath to steady my wits and my hand, I clicked on the first email. It was from Karen. My slip about the painting had precipitated a huge fight since Leonard was distraught that his surprise had been ruined. The argument escalated when Sharon, realizing the significance of the subject of the painting (i.e. Leonard's continuing mental involvement with the home wrecker), kicked a hole in the canvas causing Leonard to storm out of the house.

In the aftermath of the argument, Leonard went missing. My hands began shaking again as I read in horror Karen's hypothesis that her brother, disappointed and anguished, might be headed toward the bus station with no specific destination—or worse, on his way to see me. She asked me if I had seen him. It was a foolish question since I would have contacted Karen or Hal immediately if Leonard's perturbed visage had appeared in my window. But where *was* Leonard? Was he stumbling through the streets? Had he hailed a cab outside of Penn Station? Was he in New Jersey? Manhattan? Heading over the Williamsburg Bridge to Brooklyn? My breathing was tight and shallow as I realized that all I knew for sure was that he was "out there" somewhere, and that he was thinking of me.

The other emails remained unread. Until now, each new note had transmitted additional pain, shock, and fear. In a panic, I called Bobby, my lifeline. He said I should have no hesitation in calling the police if Leonard showed up, and I was in full agreement. I answered Karen, telling her that I hadn't seen her brother and hoped that he wouldn't try to visit me.

Over the next few days I sat nervously in my apartment with the curtains drawn until Karen notified me that Leonard was back home. He'd gone to Ray Hooch's place to get away from Sharon after the blowup about the painting.

Hal warned me not to get involved any further with Leonard given his frightening background and lifestyle. According to Hal, the contents of his brother-in-law's home were bizarre, and the activities Leonard and his friends engaged in were exceedingly degenerate. Leonard threw a lot of sex parties, and pictures of nude women, some painted by Leonard himself, hung on every wall in the house. The chandelier in the foyer was festooned with bras, and another room was equipped with a sexual harness. Hal said that the couches and wood paneling were covered in so much slime and bodily fluids that, on occasion, the home's interior had to be literally hosed down.

Unfortunately, that didn't mean Leonard wasn't going to contact *me*, yet another indication of how difficult it was going to be to sever myself completely from the Nachmans. His emails were much different from the first two he'd sent back in December. They were almost childlike, although their peculiar style wasn't simply a matter of odd typos, spacing, and misspellings. Rather, it was the way he expressed himself: short, direct sentences, most of them run together without punctuation, although I attributed the errors of style to his medication. At first, the content of his letters was normal and somewhat apologetic in tone. In what was probably an attempt to find common ground, he frequently reminded me that he was artistic. But this innocent banter didn't last long. His emails became personal, unctuous, and distasteful. It didn't seem as if Hal's alarm clocks were operating.

Subject: Re: try LNachman1 on aol message

Susan,

you have to talk to me. Don't go away now cousins I want to see you. I can bring you everything you could ever want if you want anything. or you can come to my house and my friend will drive. What will it be pretty lady do you want to have a close dinner under the stars or do you like the firplace crackling by youre head? You will live in the luxurious area and wear what you please or buy what you want and never worry about money. Do you like champane my pretty one. you can have everything. When will it be? I can get you tonight when will you be home from your mother's house? or you can come to my by cab and I will take care of it no sweat. you mean so much to me sweet Susan I am so happy to know you. See you soon my cousin. be home tonight.

your best cousin,

LenDogLenny

LenDogLenny. His meek tone had been rapidly replaced with an inappropriate familiarity. He was Lenny, that old "dog," that scoundrel, that good-time party animal and misunderstood financier who just wanted to be friends. Needless to say, I didn't want to meet his buddies or chauffeurs, drink champagne in his home, or have a crackling fireplace near my head, nor did I want to be called "pretty lady" by my cousin. There was also something in between the lines, a subliminal message of sorts, indicating that he wasn't going to take no for an answer. When he said, "What will it be," it was as if at least one of the options presented would be acted on, whether I liked it or not. And then there was his closing sentence, an imperative: "be home tonight."

He gave me his IM handle again—as if I could have forgotten it—inviting me to chat again. Paradoxically doing exactly what Karen had urged me to do all along, I was smiling and being friendly, albeit in a virtual way, lest something bad happen that would send him packing to either Gracie Square or Greystone. The IMs quickly degraded to sexually suggestive notes containing soft-core porn of naked women as well as amateurish drawings of torsos and topless girls he had sketched himself. I was afraid that ceasing communication with him abruptly might provoke further instability in his personality (and by extension, conflict with Sharon), so I played for time, thanking him for sharing his artwork but admitting that most of it was a little too racy for my taste. I apologized for not being online as much and told him that I wasn't going to be at my computer very often in the coming weeks because I needed to visit my mother in upstate New York. Excuses aside, I needed to find a job. If I channeled my energies and stayed offline, maybe this would be my opportunity to back out of the whole thing.

I knew, of course, that this would be impossible. Leonard was more interested in me than ever. He'd even offered to pay my cab fare to his home in New Jersey, the one that had to be hosed down.

***

On March 30, I came home and my PC had gone offline while I was out. When I managed to get back online later, I found an email from Sharon sent from yet another email address. Her message claimed she could get into my system any time she wanted. She'd typed a long string of numbers and letters into the email—a password—as evidence of her ability to access my computer and online accounts. My internet provider had also sent me notification that I'd requested a new password, which I hadn't.

But I wasn't the only target anymore. Nolan began to get hang-up calls on his cell phone.

CHAPTER NINE

A TRIP TO THE 19TH PRECINCT

Cops are like a doctor that gives you
aspirin for a brain tumor.
—Raymond Chandler, *The Long Goodbye*, 1953

April began to unfold and things were no better. News from Hal that Leonard was real estate window shopping in my Brooklyn neighborhood spiked the level of concern that had become an endless siren of warning in my thoughts. At a distance, even from across two rivers and an island, I could barely handle this motley tribe of relatives, but this was a new factor to grasp, enough that I decided it was time to make a report to law enforcement. Before I headed to the police station, I checked my mail and found a note from Hal. His words were perhaps the most chilling he had sent thus far. He suspected that Leonard may have been involved in the murder of Jennifer Whipkey in May of 2002 in West Deptford, New Jersey. The killer was never found, but Hal was certain that Leonard dated Whipkey shortly before she was murdered. It appeared that Leonard was quite smitten with Whipkey, who worked in the pizza parlor where they'd met. Leonard talked excitedly about Jennifer to Hal and Karen, but after only dating her briefly, he abruptly ceased speaking about her. When Hal had read the newspaper reports on the murder, he realized that Leonard, or one of his friends, might have been responsible for the crime. Hal was painfully aware of his brother-in-law's shaky mental state, and even though he said Leonard had been questioned by the police and cleared of any involvement, he felt it his duty to share his suspicions with me.

This latest news was alarming in the extreme—I felt as if a needle of ice had been shoved down my spine—but it was good to know that someone was running point for me in this genealogical fiasco.

I rang Bobby at once. We Googled the young woman's name, and the search results listed several sites devoted to unsolved murder cases. Jennifer Whipkey was a slender five-foot-four, with blonde hair and blue eyes—just like me. I took a deep breath. I was getting ahead of myself. Leonard had been investigated and cleared.

Together, we read the facts of the case. According to witnesses, Jennifer was in a nightclub on a Saturday night when she began to argue with her date, who left the club shortly thereafter. She appeared upset but continued dancing and drinking until the club closed at 3 a.m. Jennifer told people that a friend would pick her up, although no one knew whom she was alluding to. She was last seen making phone calls from the parking lot and talking to a group of men. It was thought she had left with an unknown person driving a gray Chevy Corsica with a dented door.

When her body was located, it was discovered she'd been strangled and stabbed multiple times. The killer—or killers—had murdered her elsewhere before placing her body in a wooded area bordering a busy road behind a motel in West Deptford. She was still wearing her jeans and red shirt, but her shoes were on the wrong feet.

Even if Leonard himself hadn't been personally involved, had this been the work of Robert McCottry or Lou Burr? Had this been another instance of the two felons approaching a young female who'd been drinking, only this time things had gone a little too far? I was allowing myself to engage in unwarranted speculation again, but certain facts were indisputable: the crime had occurred in New Jersey; Leonard, a former friend of McCottry and Burr, had dated Whipkey; and Leonard now had a definite sexual fixation on someone with a startling resemblance to the murdered girl. If Hal was concerned, then so was I.

Literally quaking with fear, I printed out Hal's email and took it with me to the 90th Precinct in Brooklyn. My complaint revolved around twenty-first century technology, and yet the precinct headquarters was a stereotypical police station, a stone edifice with two globed lights on either side of heavy doors with glazed panels of thick glass.

Inside, there were several people waiting to speak with officers, so I anxiously awaited my turn. My heart pounded as my sweaty hands tightly gripped the bundle of emails and lurid pictures. I tried to remain calm, but it was difficult, having just learned that Leonard might have been involved in murder. An older cop—someone who hadn't seen squad car duty in a while—performed a legal triage, speaking quickly with those in the corridor in order to prioritize their problems. Some people were there because of a broken windshield, a stolen bike, or a noisy neighbor. When the officer looked at me in a kind, sympathetic manner, I asked if I could speak to him privately since I didn't want to belt out the ugly details of the emails I'd received. Heads would surely turn, and each word I spoke would hang in the air as people tuned into my recitation of the crazy guy who threw sex parties and emailed nude pictures to his female cousin. Thankfully, the officer ushered me into a side room, where I explained that I wanted to file a sexual harassment complaint against my cousin who had been charged with rape when he was younger. I was careful to say "charged" rather than "convicted," nor did I mention anything about Leonard's possible connection with the Whipkey case since he had come up clean, according to Hal. I found myself oddly trying to diffuse and obfuscate. Inexplicable to all reason, but I didn't need to open a can of worms that would send Karen into apoplexy or Sharon on her own murderous rampage. I just wanted to make a report and have something be on record. The policeman looked at me gravely and said, "Okay. Wait right here. I'll have someone speak with you in just a moment."

I collapsed into a chair, the printouts on my lap. A few minutes later, a female officer sat across the desk, looking intently into my eyes. The petite Hispanic cop took out a complaint form and listened carefully to my tale of the long lost cousin who'd spent time in Greystone and sent me highly suggestive emails. I explained that he was charged with a sexual crime in the past and that, obviously obsessed with me as evidenced by the pictures and letters, he was thinking of moving to my neighborhood soon. I was embarrassed to be nervously regurgitating this information to a stranger, but I was grateful to be speaking to a police woman. She flipped through my stack of emails and photos, commenting that she wasn't sure whether or not they qualified as obscene by established legal standards. She said she'd have to show them to the other cops and solicit their opinions. I could imagine snickering as the male officers paged through the graphic pictures and invitations from LNachman1. Would they peg me as just another weird artist from Williamsburg who'd hooked up with a guy who liked things on the kinky side?

I waited in the small room, as seemingly every police officer in the 90th eyeballed the pictures. The process seemed to take forever, and I grew more ashamed with each passing second. The female officer finally returned, stating that the pictures were dirty but didn't exceed the guidelines for obscenity, which required graphic images of sexual encounters or erections. Full frontal nudity was considered to be art by many standards, a view I was already quite familiar with. Another impediment to pursuing the matter aggressively was that Leonard had never actually been convicted of rape, and also he lived out of state. If he lived in New York, she said, they might have been able to pick him up for questioning and put him 'on notice.' That having been said, the sympathetic officer took a report of my complaint anyway, as I provided her with Leonard's name, address, and description. I reviewed the complaint form and signed it. After giving me a copy, she told me that since Leonard was a relative, the case might be kicked into domestic court, which offered more options in terms of seeking protection. She was going the extra mile for me and promised there would be follow-up from an officer who handled domestic violence cases. She looked at me with understanding eyes as I thanked her and departed. I knew she would have done more if she could have.

It was dark by the time I left the station and headed home.

CHAPTER TEN

LEONA

The wish to hurt, the momentary intoxication with
pain, is the loophole through which the pervert
climbs into the minds of ordinary men.
—Jacob Bronowski, *The Face of Violence*

The walk back to my apartment along Kent Avenue was lonely and cold. Once home from the police station and still feeling shaky, I looked at the copy of my complaint. There was a sinking realization that there was no turning back. Leonard and I were intertwined and I didn't feel empowered by seeking the aid of law enforcement. Quite to the contrary, it felt that things were going to get worse before they got better. The copy of the complaint folded in my hands wasn't necessarily the arbiter between life and death—or what stood in between, such as rape or torture. My trip to the station was precautionary in nature so that I could point to something tangible in case I looked up one day to see Leonard, unannounced, standing on my stoop, ready to throw me into the back of a black Town Car. Showing up quietly was his modus operandi, and there was a low expectation that domestic court could give me a hearing. Meanwhile, I wasn't going to tell Hal or Karen about my visit to the police. Karen was nervous and lackadaisical, and it wasn't safe to send an email with such information to one of the Gardiners' computers. I still didn't know where in Massachusetts they lived, although they knew my location with the precision of a surveillance satellite. I would take care of myself—but quietly.

When I called Bobby to update him on my visit to the 90th, I heard James, Bobby's boyfriend, talking in the background. He sounded apprehensive, worried about my safety. They were, for all intents and purposes, my two gay grandmothers, fretting and nervous. I gave them a quick rundown of the legal guidelines limiting what the police could do, but Bobby assured me that whatever constraints might currently be in place, I'd done the right thing by contacting the authorities.

Almost in the same breath, Bobby told me I might want to brace myself since Leonard's Yahoo profile had once again been updated. Holding the telephone, I nervously reached for my computer mouse and clicked on the bookmarked profile page. On the other end of the line, I heard Bobby shriek, "It's a woman!" His voice faded as the page loaded and I viewed Leonard Nachman as Leona for the first time, all other sight and sound falling away from my consciousness. The new persona before me was not simply a man dressed in women's clothing, but a full-blown fetishist encased in black hosiery from head to toe. He wore spiked heels and a wide, leather strict-looking belt on the outside of his nylon body suit. The most disturbing aspect of the image was the suffocating hose pulled tightly over his head, enhanced by two gold hooped earrings worn over the black mesh. It was a picture of breathless confinement—a kind of macabre jubilance. His distorted lips were smeared with cheap red lipstick as a result of the black nylon rubbing tightly against his face as he puckered for the camera. He seemed exultant as he posed, the shades drawn behind him while he writhed on a sofa for an unseen audience. It was a theater of degradation and domination, but Leonard was reveling in his alter ego. Leona, like a black flower, was proudly on display.

On display . . .

About a year ago we got a call from the police in his jurisdiction telling us he'd been found outside some family's home wandering around. He wasn't taking his medication and was lost. He was confused as far as wearing women's clothing he must have thought was his own.

He was confused? I thought of how Karen had gradually revealed Leonard's history in her correspondence. Exactly how far down the rabbit hole could Leonard descend when he wasn't taking his medication? What imaginary worlds did he inhabit in Greystone or in a New Jersey house that needed to be hosed down? What inner world would he inhabit if he moved to Williamsburg, where he could shun the light in a secluded loft in which sound itself might be muted, where Leona could writhe in perverted pleasure and where no alarm clocks would interrupt his erotic pursuits.

Leonard's features were ghoulish beneath the semi-sheer black facemask, but I nevertheless saw a resemblance to my father. It was profoundly disturbing to see this similarity of features in such a context, for the photos spoke in malevolent whispers—promises of pain and violence. A wave of nausea swallowed me.

On the computer screen, Leona was enclosed in nylon, a willing prisoner of her own twisted desires. I, on the other hand, was sealed in a cold, paralyzing panic. Bobby kept talking, his voice my connection to sanity and logic.

Together, we tried to make sense of Leonard's bizarre world. His physique was strong and muscular, but it was suspended between male and female, strung between human and trans-human. His Leona manifestation was saturated with a menacing carnal power. Something in Leona's costume spoke of a violent, dominating mother, someone who herself was immersed in austere cruelty—even madness.

CHAPTER ELEVEN

I'M GOING TO GET YOU

No passion so effectually robs the mind of all
its powers of acting and reasoning as fear.
—Edmund Burke, *On the Sublime and Beautiful*

Nolan began receiving threatening calls on his cell phone almost every day, usually arriving in the early afternoon. The caller ID always read "anonymous" or "unavailable." A voice would hiss, "Watch out" or "I'm going to get you" in a hushed whisper that could not be identified as either male or female, the line going dead immediately after the murmured threats. I didn't understand how this was possible. I had never given Nolan's number to anyone. Even Bobby, who almost always offered a theory for everything that was happening to me, was at a loss as to how or why Nolan was receiving the calls. My nightmare was increasingly expanding, spilling out of control into his life. I felt awful and responsible. As if somehow, my own flawed and inherent wickedness attracted this and now it was attaching itself to someone pure. The calls would arrive while he was in class, and even if he didn't answer, the brief forewarnings would roll into his voicemail. They affected his concentration and his grades to the point where he considered dropping out of film school until things blew over. If I wasn't at home when he called or if I didn't return his call right away, he became increasingly upset, fearing I might be in danger. He was becoming a nervous wreck too, and the stress began taking its toll on our relationship, causing us to spend less time together.

My mind was growing fuzzy, and I wasn't eating or sleeping regularly. Still unemployed, a voluntary prisoner of my apartment for most of the day, I didn't paint, read, listen to music, or smile. I'd lost interest in living life since my energy was constantly devoted to anticipating what was around the next corner. Thank God for Bobby. He and I boundlessly processed the hundreds of emails I'd received, talking about Karen, Sharon, Leonard, and Hal, analyzing the behavior of each. We did further research on Lou Burr and Robert McCottry, trying to find out as much as possible about the cast of characters in the play in which I'd been cast without ever auditioning.

Thankfully Hal had convinced Leonard to buy a loft in New Jersey instead of Williamsburg. This was welcome news, of course, but given the hang-up calls, I decided to make a clean break with the Nachman clan regardless of where Leonard had found new digs for his sex parties. I vowed never to open their emails again, much less reply. I placed a block on anonymous calls because I'd been getting hang-ups as well. Simply changing my email address wouldn't offer enough security, so I decided to cancel my Time Warner account, and signed up for a Verizon DSL line. Additionally, I decided to let my *publishingnyc@yahoo* address expire, by leaving it inactive and let the creepy missives pile up until they bounced back as undeliverable. It was time to pull up stakes and get the hell out of Dodge. With any luck, Leonard and Sharon would be left wondering what happened to me. They'd go back to torturing each other as if they were trapped in the endlessly looping circles of hell in Dante's *Inferno*, small battles burning incessantly all around them.

I swore that I would never use my real name in an email address again. This was going to be a clean break.

Or so I thought.

CHAPTER TWELVE

IT'S NOT OVER

Nobody ever forgets where he buried a hatchet.
—Frank McKinney Hubbard

Six weeks passed without any contact from Karen, Leonard, or Sharon. I cherished the peace, slowly returning to my routines, vowing never to become involved with the Nachmans again. There would be no more gut punches every time I sat down to read my email, no more anguish every time Leonard or Sharon decided to turn the screw and ratchet up their dysfunctional family horror show.

Six weeks, however, wasn't enough time for my mind to erase the images of Leona enveloped in black nylon. Things were back to normal and I was able to function again, but fear lingered, as if the fetishes of Leonard or the accusations of Sharon were persistent afterimages from a bright camera flash. The two siblings were now flickers, yet the cries of their deranged behavior still echoed in my mind, demanding to be heard.

Occasionally, I removed the anonymous call block so some of my friends who might have had a privacy setting could get through. Sooner or later I would have to start answering the phone on a regular basis again if I was going to get back to normal. I couldn't continue to be held captive by the ringing of a phone or the memories, however uncomfortable, of sordid pictures and mordant emails.

The phone rang on a warm mid-May evening, and the caller ID read "anonymous." Should I pick up? Was it time to take another step toward normalcy? Did I need to exorcise the ghosts? Between rings, I wondered if I was going to be afraid for the rest of my life.

Sooner or later, I would have to start answering the phone . . .

If it was Sharon or Leonard, I'd just hang up.

I tentatively picked up the receiver and said, "Hello."

A deep voice responded. "Susan?"

I didn't recognize the voice and asked who it was.

"It's Amit."

I breathed a tentative sigh of relief. Amit was a pen pal, an Israeli soldier calling from Jerusalem. We'd met in a chat room devoted to mid-east politics and had started a long-distance email friendship. We discussed politics as well as our jobs, dogs, and friends. We'd never spoken before, and I wondered how he'd obtained my number. I suddenly became suspicious as to whether I was really talking to Amit since I'd never heard his voice. For reasons unknown, he too seemed to be a bit reticent about speaking over and above his greeting. Since both of us were clearly uncertain to whom we were really speaking, we asked each other a few preliminary questions, the answers to which only the other would know. All bets were off when it came to the level of deception involving the Nachman family, but the caller's Israeli accent was so heavy and authentic, I was convinced it was Amit. When we were finally convinced that it was safe to speak, Amit asked me why I'd been absent for a while, and then seemingly only to reappear in order to send him a picture of a man masturbating in a dress.

My heart sank like a dropping elevator. They'd even gotten to my friend on the other side of the world.

I didn't want to overwhelm Amit with all the ugly details, so I gave him a thumbnail sketch of the problems I'd had with Leonard and Sharon: one was a crazy distant relative who sent me porn, the other a witch who thought I was out to bankrupt her family. I added that I'd ditched my old email address and dropped out of view on the web.

His reaction thrust me back into the Nachman inferno. When he'd noticed that my old email address was no longer functional he became concerned. Amit tried several combinations of my first and last name at Yahoo and by pure luck had gotten a response from *susanfensten@yahoo.com*. There was only one problem with my friend's explanation: I hadn't created this address, although anyone was likely to accept it at face value as a legitimate address. First name, last name, domain—it was a no-brainer. Amit therefore began a correspondence with someone he thought was me but soon began to worry when the nature of the emails grew disturbing. He received porn, plus my narrative voice within the messages was out of character. He feared for my personal safety and decided to call.

I asked him to forward the disturbing emails if he still had them on his PC. He agreed, with the stipulation that there were some he couldn't, in good conscience, send because they were simply too filthy. Informing him that I might need to involve the authorities, I convinced him to send even the most obscene email messages. After we ended the call, Amit forwarded me the emails that he had received.

The exchange started out normally.

Amit. M <Amitm@hotmail.com> wrote:

i hope u get this email. tell me why u dont answer me.

love, Amit

It was a simple request to learn why I had dropped out of sight. The fraudster's reply was straightforward, calculated to pull Amit in by degrees.

Hi Amit, I just got your e-mail thank you, how are you doing? I have been so busy lately. What is new with you my dear friend? Where are you and how do I reach you?

Love, Susan

Seeing my name hijacked brought it all back again, although I shouldn't have been surprised considering who I believed the hijacker to be. I had no doubt Leonard was behind this latest attempt to invade my life. Amit replied that he'd recently finished rehab for his left hand and ankle after being injured. He was currently working in the army's computer department until he could be redeployed. He said he was getting stronger and concluded his email by saying "thanx for the painting. I don't know who it is but it's a very good pic."

It was a filthy tide returning. Leonard had sent Amit several images, among them were pornographic photographs and crude drawings. Instinctively, I could see where the correspondence was headed as I continued to read Amit's forwarded emails. The reply made from the bogus Susan Fensten account wasted little time in injecting a sexual component to the exchange.

Hi Amit, I'm sorry I was out of touch but a lot has been going on in my life. I am sorry about your hand and wish I was there to help you. You are so kind and sweet.

I think about you all the time and cry when I think of you in harm's way. I miss you Amit and hope we can be together soon. Life is lonely for me. Send me some pictures if you can. That painting is of me so I hope you like it.

sexy dreams, Susan

My relationship with Amit had always been platonic, and yet Leonard had signed off with "sexy dreams" and told him that the person in the painting was me. I'd previously sent pictures of myself to Amit, but people can look very different in paintings (or even pictures, depending on the pose). In a very diplomatic reply, Amit said, "u don't pose for her/him do u?" The painting was apparently a bit on the erotic side. Leonard was not likely to let a question like Amit's go unanswered.

Well good luck with everything Amit, let me know how it works out.

Yes I pose for my cousin to be honest. I hope this does not shock you.

I can make any pose you want and he will draw it for you. Let me know what you want to see next. Also I want some sexy ones of you too. Send me something soon!

I would love to have you in my bed. When will it be dear Amit? I am feeling very

sexxxy lately.

Leonard had gone from being coy to aggressive. He was also offering to send lurid shots. More emails were sent from the Susan Fensten account, one of which veered into the ever-present subject of cross-dressing.

He likes to wear my clothes or some other woman's and trys to be very sexxxy. What do you think of his pictures?

This was Leonard's way of saying that "Leona is alive and well, thank you very much, and you can expect to see more of him, oh cousin so sweet." The calculated way in which Leonard, master puppeteer, was pulling Amit's strings and mine didn't bode well. The ghostly images of Leona's poses were becoming sharper again, more vivid. The stone pit returned to my stomach.

Amit finally got annoyed and grew more emphatic in protesting the receipt of any kind of graphic pictures.

Amit. M <Amitm@hotmail.com> wrote:

dear susan,

im not into men. i would apritiate if i didnt get pics of a guy jacking off.

is this really susan? uv been acting weird.

be well naf

At least my friend had begun to suspect that I wasn't the real author of the emails. The next message provided the answer as to how Amit had obtained my phone number.

Sorry Amit. I dont mean to offend you. I hope you like these pix better my friend.

Why not call me sometime you cheap Jew. 718-XXX-XXXX

Make it collect. I can afford it being an American.

I would never have directed an ethnic slur, or anything else such as implying by being American I was in some sort of a superior position to him. It obviously served as further proof that the author of the messages wasn't me. For a time, Amit quit responding. Realizing that my pen pal wasn't going to play his game, Leonard came out of hiding in a manner that not only upset Amit but also telegraphed a message to me: "It's not over."

> o naff, when you talk to dear cousin Susan you can let her know that I will get her this summer. her and her young boyfriend will pay. i follow him too. its not over. she can hide her E-mail but i still know her addy 62 n.7 st. 1L bklyn ny 11211 718-XXX-XXXX as a matter o fact i just saw the pretty girl last week walking on the street but she did not c me in my disguise LOL

> we know she switch to verizon again an it is only a matter of time till i get in.

> i hope you like these pix and that this never happens to u sweet dear Amit

> keep ur head on straight! LOL

> lenster

Leonard had been following me. My clean break had been an illusion. I also had suspicions that Sharon was involved and had maybe put Leonard up to writing the emails. I thought back to the previous week. Close to home, I'd seen a man dressed as half-man, half-woman and wearing heavy make-up. Had it been Leonard? I couldn't be sure, but if it *had* been him, then my earlier concerns about him cruising my neighborhood hadn't been paranoid imaginings.

All of my renewed sense of safety was gone. This was a new level of depravity and evil, even for Leonard. Two days later, Amit received another email, this one from Leona, with implied threats directed at Nolan.

Dear sweet Amit,

What you must think of me.

I am really a very nice person once you get to know me.

I cum to Israel sometimes and would love to meet you my dear.

My cousin and her young man friend have been very, very naughty.

I had him followed and know where he lives too.

Here are some things to look at so you may think of me before we meet.

http://profiles.yahoo.com/leonakink

http://www.geocities.com/leonakink/index.html

I will wear what you want me to and please you like no other woman can.

You may cum to my pictures my sweet Israeli soldier.

But don't lose your head, I want you in one piece. LOL.

Kisses,

Leona

Nolan was being followed, indicating that the situation had progressed far beyond annoying phone calls while he attended class. As for the website pictures provided by Leona, they were pure porn: Leona head-to-toe in nylon while posing and masturbating.

Going to the police with this wasn't an option since these emails had been addressed to Amit, not me. Besides, the last visit to the police had been a formality that had resulted in an officer sending me a pamphlet about domestic abuse. That had been the "follow-up" I was promised.

Hal seemed to be my best bet. He had experience dealing with Leonard, and if anything happened to Nolan or me, Hal and Karen would have been made aware of Leonard's latest misadventures.

Hopefully, another trip to Greystone could be arranged.

CHAPTER THIRTEEN

TRUCE AND A SHIFT IN ALLIANCES

*There is an unseemly exposure of the
mind, as well as of the body.*
—William Hazlitt, *Sketches and Essays*

I took a deep breath and emailed Hal, informing him that Leonard—and quite possibly Sharon—was up to his old tricks again. I related my conversation with Amit and described the emails brimming with filth and horror that Amit had forwarded to me. To ensure that Hal would be convinced that Leonard and Sharon were behind the harassment of Amit, I explained that the emails had been sent from *LeonaKink@yahoo.com*, which was obviously more of Leonard's handiwork. I also mentioned that Nolan had been under surveillance and that I'd filed a police report accusing Leonard of sexual harassment. Hal responded immediately, saying as always that he would take care of matters. He wasn't specific as to what steps he'd take, but I'd always been able to trust him in the past and at least I knew he was on my side. I would now have to wait to see what he would do to curtail his renegade in-laws.

I didn't have to wait long. A few days later, Hal told me that he'd confronted Leonard, this time offering details and forwarding me Leonard's lengthy reply.

In it, he hit some truth saying that I was too timid and scared to write him—which was absolutely true. He went on to chide me about my "rudeness" and the way I just "shut off my emails and disappeared without saying anything." Of course, he knew that I had reported him to AOL and didn't think that it was any "big fucking deal" over some naked pictures. He suggested that perhaps I was the crazy person and he made it a point to know everything about me. He was hurt because I didn't want a gift from "my mental cousin." He said that I made a "grown man cry" and "brought him to his knees to feel unloved and hated like a mental nuisance." Signing off he asked that I never bother him again, yet said that I could email him if I wanted to.

Leonard spoke of how I'd called the hospital, which was true. But the only people who knew I had done this were Bobby and myself. A few months earlier, Bobby and I thought that it was a good idea to Greystone to find out his status and express concerns over his condition, despite knowing that patients' records are always confidential. Unsurprisingly, the staff member I reached supplied no information. I didn't think that he would find out. I felt exposed again, as if Leonard or Sharon had a wealth of information about me, down to the calls I made or the places I frequented.

I wasn't sure I had the power to deal with this any longer. I felt weary and worn down, resigned that this may never end. Maybe I should have written to Leonard, who was, after all, someone with a disease as common and real as diabetes or arthritis. I wondered if I could I have stemmed his tide of hateful emails by responding to him directly and stating that, while I acknowledged his good intentions, I was his cousin, someone who was not interested in any kind of romantic or sexual relationship with him. The more

I reflected on what Hal had told me of Leonard's history, the more sympathy I had for the man, an occasional resident of Greystone and someone who had grown up with a mentally ill mother. Hal didn't approve of Leonard's actions either, but at least he attempted to help his brother-in-law as best he could. Hal's unwavering concern for Leonard's well-being made me realize that there must be something redeeming about Leonard. Perhaps I should have tried to understand Leonard's point of view months earlier in order to keep him at bay. Leonard had even left the door open at the end of his letter, inviting me to write him if I felt so inclined.

Bobby disagreed with this approach, believing that I should fire back with another email salvo in my defense, matching Leonard's anger word for word. Bobby didn't appreciate the cruelty the Nachmans had displayed toward me over the months, and he felt I should maintain a posture of toughness rather than lower my guard. He didn't want to see me traumatized any more than I already was.

I appreciated Bobby's ongoing concern and feelings of protection over me. I couldn't have survived emotionally thus far without him, but I felt an angry response was likely to enflame the situation even more. I simply wasn't going to beat Leonard and Sharon at their own game; I simply wasn't crazy enough. I would therefore have to try to make peace with Leonard, so, in a last ditch effort, I set my anger aside and emailed him, apologizing for any problems I may have inadvertently caused and suggesting that we should go our separate ways in peace. I extended the olive branch by validating his emotions to the extent I was able to do so.

I had no idea what kind of response I might receive after intentionally contacting a man I regarded as a monster. Would he once again try to lure me into his cage, or would I succeed in spreading a balm over his fractured ego? To my great relief, Leonard seemed to be touched by my email. He said he was sorry and embarrassed. As for Hal and Karen, they were thrilled that I had managed to defuse a potentially volatile situation with kindness and understanding. In the passages of Leonard's reply, however, were eye-opening revelations that explained much of the horror to which I'd been subjected.

I breathed a deep sigh a relief. His answer was friendly, with a straightforward explanation for his behavior. There was no porn, no attachment, no web link. I felt like I had won Leonard over, but his letter confirmed my suspicions about Sharon: she had been manipulating Leonard by sending him emails that were allegedly from me to her which claimed I was sexually attracted to him. Naturally, he was confused by the advances in them. He cut and pasted one in his reply as proof.

Subject: Re: Your sexxxy brother

know it's wrong to have these thoughts about your brother but I am a woman with feelings to share. He is so handsome >and sexy and I bet he makes loads of money with his work. I know that if he felt the same way we could > really make a go of things. Am I so wrong to feel this way? I can't stop thinking about what it would be like to be in his arms. >I have to stop myself some nights from<

It all made sense now. The bogus email from Sharon not only declared that I thought Leonard was handsome and sexy, but it also mentioned that I was aware of his wealth. Even more outrageous was the claim that I was hoping to "make a go of things," a statement that was unbelievable for so many reasons: he was my cousin; I'd never met him; and our tenuous relationship consisted of a one-sided exchange of cyber porn. Leonard finished his email on an optimistic and happy note, promising not to think of me in sexual terms any longer.

Sharon, puppeteer extraordinaire, had been impersonating me, not only to Amit, but in emails to Leonard that dated back to January. Though Leonard had his own creepy modus operandi, he was direct about what he wanted. Sharon, on the other hand, seemed capable of far more complex forms of deceptions. It became a maze of mimicry to sort out. She had cruelly manipulated her unstable brother in an attempt to show him that I was a con artist using sex to get his money, but Leonard, sexually confused on so many different levels, had been convinced of only one thing: I was coming on to him.

I welcomed Leonard's reply, although I was far from giddy. While genuinely feeling sorry for him, I'd had a singular motivation in my approach: to stay on his good side so that I could deal with him. Nothing changed the fact that Leonard and Sharon had been seething in a cauldron of ceaseless family drama for most of their lives, with Sharon miles in the lead.

I told Nolan that we could both breathe easier now. His reaction consisted of relief mixed with irritation. Why was I still bothering with this family? Hadn't I walked away once before? Why did I continue to reply to all of the crazy emails, regardless of what explanation was proffered by Leonard? I understood his sentiments, but I truly felt I'd done what I needed to do. I reasoned that keeping an eye on them would keep me from being blindsided because clearly I wasn't able to shake them.

It was that simple. Everyone had been controlled by Sharon, including me, as she flew low under the radar. The whole debacle was starting to make sense, albeit in a creepy, convoluted way, especially if viewed from the perspective of someone living within a nightmare.

I was vindicated. The truth was out, Leonard was sorry, and Hal and Karen thought I was a saint. Perhaps I could now deal with all of them—at a distance.

Of course, there was always Sharon to worry about.

CHAPTER FOURTEEN

BACK TO WORK

The devil finds work for idle hands to do.
—Proverbs, early 17th century.

Summertime was approaching, and with no immediate danger on the horizon, I was focused enough to land an interview for a freelance publicity spot at Rizzoli International Publications. My unemployment checks were about to end and hope of a job was a welcome break from the cycle of doom and gloom that had been permeating my thinking. Rizzoli published big, beautiful books on art, architecture, photography, food, travel, and leisure. I thought it would be an enjoyable, creative job, something different from the academic (though beloved) halls at Oxford University Press. I needed to reclaim my life by getting out in the world again and mixing with regular people. I'd been trapped in a Hitchcock film, only the characters had been real, and even now I wasn't sure if the last reel was done spinning through the projector.

I was nervous about my upcoming interview, but it went well. Over the weekend, I would have to compose a press release as a writing sample before a final decision would be made, but I was enthusiastic and excited. The only thing I'd written for the previous five months was stomach-churning emails. I was out of practice but nevertheless optimistic about my chances with Rizzoli. I avoided checking my email all weekend in order to concentrate, and the decision to stay away from the internet proved to be a good one. I got the job and would start immediately. This was a professional resuscitation after so many dark months, and I wasn't going to share such good news with Karen, Hal, or Leonard. The position with Rizzoli represented a new start in more ways than one, and the Nachmans, with their various and sundry intrigues, weren't going to be privy to where I worked.

When I checked my email on Monday, I wasn't surprised to find a message from Karen. She and Hal had tried to reach me over the weekend and wondered why I'd dropped out of sight, as if I weren't entitled to my own privacy, or had an obligation to always apprise the Gardiners of my whereabouts. After forty-eight hours of peace, Karen's email was a mosquito droning about my head. I shooed it away, excited about starting at Rizzoli.

CHAPTER FIFTEEN

A TRIP TO DC

If the Universe is hidden in itself, then
there can be no escape from it.
This is the great truth of things in general.
—Chuang Tzu, c.369-286 BC

Leonard wrote to me every day. His emails were jovial and innocent as he expressed his current happiness with phrases such as "I'm on top of the wind!" His writing style was still disjointed, full of odd abbreviations, misspellings, and rambling, but his daily notes now seemed harmless enough. He was full of chatter about how happy he was that we were friends and how well his life was going as he settled into his New Jersey home. His light, breezy banter, together with his curious phrasing, led me to believe that he hadn't received enough attention as a child, by what I'd read about his mother. His emails were childlike, with a child's mixture of neediness and "Hey, look at me!" The wealthy Mr. Nachman now offered me trinkets and baubles galore— cars and diamonds—and even asked if I wanted financial help. While publishing isn't the most lucrative of industries, I wasn't interested in my cousin's money and made sure to let him know that.

Work at Rizzoli was going well. I shared a one-room office divided into cubes with my boss and another publicist. We each promoted approximately a dozen books each season. It was a lot of books with overlapping campaigns, each book a complex world of its own. The phone calls and emails were unending—everyone needed something yesterday—but it was nevertheless a fun, but very demanding, job that served to keep my mind in the real world.

**

By mid-July, summer was in full swing and the Nachman corner of the world was blessedly quiet for a change, so I decided to take up Bobby and James on their invitation to spend a long weekend in the nation's capital. James Waters had recently purchased a beautiful new condo in Dupont Circle, and I could sleep on the couch in the living room. A getaway was just what I needed, and the thought of enjoying life with friends in another city was delicious.

The shuttle flight took off from LaGuardia, and from the window seat I gazed at buildings and houses fading into tiny squares on a grid, the metropolis of NYC dropping away fast. I observed the world below, a serene-looking place with normal people going about their daily routines. The madness had disappeared in the ether of the sky.

The DC shuttle is a twenty-minute flight. Having just enough time to finish a short beer, we soon approached Reagan National Airport in DC, the plane banking sharply. I was feeling better already thanks to the alcohol and the spin of the aircraft. Life for a moment was just fine.

James picked me up at the airport. It was good to see his tanned face beneath dark green aviator sunglasses. He was an easygoing, handsome middle-aged man, who was retired military. He worked for a consulting group which had government clients such as the US Army and the Department of Homeland Security. He gave me a big hug, took the handle of my bag, and led me to his BMW convertible. The ride to Dupont Circle was enjoyable, riding down tree-lined streets past gorgeous homes, monuments, and war memorials.

It was great to see Bobby in person, for a change, after our countless phone calls and emails. At six-two, he was an imposing figure, his short, reddish-blonde hair now peppered with gray. He looked healthy, well-cared for, and rested. After a long hug, he made me a drink, and the three of us sat down in the living room, shaking our heads in wonderment as we reviewed the bizarre events of the past ten months like retired cops rehashing the facts of an old case. James had been as concerned for my safety as Bobby, with Bobby calling James's secretary every morning to give her the latest on "Susan's drama up in New York." She would then pass along the news to the secretarial pool.

That night we had dinner at a Thai restaurant in a trendy part of town, making plans to barbecue on James's new boat the following day in on the Potomac. I felt relaxed in the company of these good friends, and I was miles away from the madding crowd. It felt good to feel safe.

The following day was glorious. The wind and salty air made me feel free and alive, and I realized even more how crazy my day-to-day life had become. I was enjoying myself as we dropped anchor half a mile away from Mount Vernon. Bobby grilled chicken and shrimp and poured a few drinks. The waves rocked the boat gently, working the alcohol deeper into my bloodstream and ushering me into a state of temporary bliss. No Rizzoli, no subways, no anonymous phone calls.

The next morning, I woke up refreshed and Bobby asked if I wanted to use his computer to check my email. Not wanting to sully my mini-vacation, I said no, but curiosity got the better of me a few minutes later and I signed on. It was the wrong decision.

Sharon had continued her charades over the weekend. Like the Energizer Bunny from hell, she assumed my identity once again and forged more emails using the bogus account she had created to represent me, asking Leonard for money. Leonard should have known by now to be on guard against his sister's emails, but he was vulnerable to her vicious pranks—Leonard, who could be whisked away far too easily on his capricious whims and who seemed naturally inclined toward flights of fantasy. By now, I could see through Sharon's petty, predictable tactics. Annoyed, I brushed off the email and evicted Sharon from my thoughts. I was still on vacation for another few hours, and I would savor every minute I had left.

I flew home that night, the plane tossed about by thunderstorms like a mere toy. So much for relaxation.

***

It was Wednesday, July 14. Leonard was in good spirits in a nighttime email. He seemed to be at ease with me, and unaware I'd already seen him wrapped in black nylon, he sent me a photo of himself in drag. He invited me to his new place and said he didn't want me to freak out if I saw him dressed like this, hence the picture. He claimed that he dressed up for "fun, magic, and make-believe."

His outfit was tame by Leona's standards, but it was still an eyebrow raiser. In this photo, Leonard wore a skintight, crushed-velvet miniskirt, accessorized by out-of-date pink granny glasses. He looked a bit secretarial, like an unfunny version of Dustin Hoffman's character of Dorothy in *Tootsie.* At the same time, the sight of Leonard displaying himself in his "fun clothes" was somewhat melancholic, an evocative image of someone trapped between two worlds. For the second time, I saw something etched in his face, something that resembled my own features. As a voyeur peering into Leonard's world of make-believe, I sensed that he was awkward in front of the camera, just as I was, despite his exhibitionism. There was an almost imperceptible look of hesitation in his face and posture, but it was there nonetheless. When he wasn't encased in black nylon mesh, he was far less frightening. In short, he was, like most of the population, human and vulnerable.

"Don't tell Hal," he wrote, like a kid begging his sister not to tattle on him.

I thanked him for sharing such a personal side of himself and reassured him that my own philosophy was "to each, his own." I expressed no judgment about his behavior, explaining that I'd grown up in New York City and had learned at an early age that everyone is different, even complex. His secret was safe with me.

CHAPTER SIXTEEN

I WOULD REALLY LIKE TO CHECK YOU OUT

A monster horrendous, hideous and vast, deprived of sight...
—Virgil, *The Aeneid*

My shaky contact with Leonard continued. While I was too trusting by nature, I also kept thinking of Leonard's vulnerability and the likelihood that, as a child, he'd been deprived of basic nurturance from a mother who carried around a doll she called Sondra, after her deceased daughter. I was still apprehensive, but Leonard now treated me like a real person and not a sexual playmate. As strange as he was, I had started to feel a connection to Leonard. Things were about as smooth as they were going to get with the "Lenster," and I thought that keeping in touch with him and remaining friendly were the best ways to manage the situation until there came a time, hopefully in the not-too-distant future, when I could extricate myself completely from all contact with Leonard and his family.

Some of Leonard's emails were sweet in a quirky kind of way. He gave me a nickname—Swan—and invited me yet again to chat via IM. Bobby and I both agreed that it was a charming moniker, summoning to mind an old-fashioned image of a graceful swan gliding across a still, silent lake.

The bird was an archetypal symbol of many interpretations, like the fable of the ugly duckling-turned-swan. Or perhaps the swan was a projection of Leonard's two-edged sexual identity—the imperfect male becoming perfect through a metamorphosis into female.

With my guard somewhat lowered, I received an email from someone named Bob who's email address was *felixxx_ nj@yahoo.com* with 'Felix daCat' as the moniker.

Hi Susan,

my name is Bob and I am a friend of your cousins. I saw your email addy when I was at his place and I thought I would write you to introduce myself I hope you don't mind. I am employed and I have my own place to live to. You are a very atractive lady and I would be pleased to meet you sometime.

I am doing construction work right now in the city and can come to brooklyn to see you someday after work if you want :)

I am helping Len paint his new place and will be able to pick you up sometime and drive you there. He is doing very good now and I don't have to go to his as much. I am into the arts to like you and also like rock music and good times out of doors. If you want to talk on the phn tonite let me know and I will call you on your 718#or you can reach me on my cell number if you want it?

I didn't know if you want me to come over this week or not so just let me know. I been to williamsberg before and could meet you somewhere. I would really like to check you out. I love dogs to!

peace,

Bob

I knew who this was instantly. Felix da Cat was none other than Robert McCottry, the shark-eyed predator who, with Lou Burr, had been convicted of the kidnap and rape twenty years earlier. Leonard's involvement had remained murky, with no indictment brought against him after being interviewed by the police. Felix was one of the criminal's aliases which Bobby had discovered on the NJDC website. The name, a hard contrast compared to the heinous nature of his crime, was printed indelibly on my brain.

But Karen had implied that the "Burr thing" was ancient history. Why was Leonard, the happy-go-lucky Wall Street entrepreneur riding on top of the wind, consorting with "Felix" twenty years after he'd been temporarily implicated in the actions of Burr and McCottry? I didn't think the doctors assigned to Leonard's case would be happy with the company he was keeping, but I reminded myself that even though I had earned Leonard's goodwill through my apology, he was still a man who'd been in and out of Greystone several times, someone whose ego and self-esteem were no more solid than a butterfly's wing. Trying to understand his motivations was useless. In one of his childlike moments, he may have thought mentioning me to McCottry was harmless. I was, after all, his understanding cousin with whom he could share his fanciful make-believe life. One thing appeared certain, however: Leonard had told McCottry about me. Felix knew where I lived, that I had a dog, and that I was interested in art. He'd seen my photo.

Bobby and I thought the email's wording to be very telling about the writer. The fact that McCottry boasted of being employed and having his own place spoke of someone who hadn't functioned in normal society for a while. It sounded like he had recently been a guest of the Gray Bar

Hotel and was either on parole or had recently finished serving his time. Of special concern was the cavalier way in which McCottry spoke of meeting me: "I . . . can come to brooklyn to see you someday after work ... I will be able to pick you up sometime . . . If you want to talk on the phone tonight, let me know." In Robert McCottry's mind, it was already decided that we would get together. I was "easy."

Like liquid fire, dread seeped into every cell of my body. I was in a freefall of terror, and if removing myself from Nachman influence had proved next to impossible, how would I fend off a convicted sex offender? The thought of a brutal rapist eyeballing my photo was bad enough, but the notion that he'd recently cast his footprints in my neighborhood was paralyzing. Gasping for breath, I forwarded McCottry's cozy introduction to Bobby, who called me within minutes. We quickly examined McCottry's "felixxx_nj" Yahoo profile, which had been recently updated and contained a picture of the felon from the early 1970s, his long, stringy hair hanging over a hippy T-shirt. Even in his youth, McCottry appeared maladjusted. There was a cadaverous look in his eye that didn't mesh with the innocence of the post-Woodstock generation. There was no hint of peace and love emanating from his hardened appearance. In the "What's New With Me" section of his profile, McCottry stated that he was "building a dungeon for a friend."

I sat in the chair facing my computer, immobile, as Bobby's voice, sounding like it was a hundred miles away, continued to drone through the telephone receiver. What the hell was I going to do?

One didn't have to be Sherlock Holmes to deduce that the friend having a dungeon built was Leonard Nachman.

My cousin had apparently wasted no time in getting settled in his new digs, ready for action. Jarring myself back to the here and now, I discussed with Bobby a likely scenario for what might have happened between Leonard and McCottry over and above what my indiscreet cousin may have told his felonious "buddy": Leonard was reading and writing emails at his PC while McCottry, working at Lenny's new home in New Jersey, gazed at an open window on the monitor and saw me. It was entirely plausible that the ex-con surmised that Leonard and I shared more than just DNA and that I was therefore as kinky as my cousin. Or maybe Leonard had innocently shown McCottry my picture and bragged about his fun relative in funky, edgy Williamsburg. However it had happened, gasoline had now been poured on a fire that had been brought under control in the past few weeks.

Completely petrified, I naturally wasn't going to respond to Felix da Cat. When Bobby and I Googled McCottry, we found a link to an old news story about two New Jersey convicts who'd attempted to sue the state government because they were displeased with the treatment they'd received in prison. One of the convicts was none other than McCottry himself. His partner in the jailhouse litigation was a criminal convicted of "atrocious assault" for nearly beating a woman to death and dumping her unconscious body off a high bridge. "Atrocious assault" was a real term in the penal code and designated an act that was malicious and cruel in the extreme. McCottry was far more than an ugly duckling. He was a creature of unfettered desire, a ravenous hunter without a conscience.

Given the tenor of his email, it was unlikely that McCottry was going to just leave me alone, and Bobby agreed that ignoring him might invite more unwanted emails. We decided that the best thing was to show the email to Leonard—not Hal or Karen this time around—and let him try to resolve the matter. Hal might well involve attorneys, and Karen might take to her bed again. I would contact the person responsible—Leonard—and hope for a swift reply indicating that he held some kind of sway over his seedy chum. I forwarded McCottry's message to Leonard, requesting that he keep my address confidential since I wasn't interested in getting any more emails of the same ilk.

Whatever action Leonard took on his end, it didn't work, for McCottry sent me a furious follow-up.

The subject line: 'Skank.'

To Susan F. the punkassd Brookland Skank

you couldn't keep your stinkin mouth closed. You gotta go tellin him I wrote you. well that is cool lady. Bitch's and hose like you don't matter no how. You all get what you deserve in the end.

LOL u 2faced bitch

I now had a convicted rapist, free to roam where he pleased, angry at me. Before I went completely round the bend, I sent McCottry's mail straight to Leonard, who said he was pissed at Felix for upsetting me. Leonard claimed that McCottry was sorry for what he'd done and that I wouldn't be bothered again.

I wasn't reassured in the least. The trip to Washington had been a minor detour around a pit of quicksand, which was now swallowing me, depriving me of air and movement. No matter what I had done during this nightmare of horror and deception, things had grown progressively worse each time I'd convinced myself that the worst was over. Frustrated and tired, Hal was no longer willing to run interference and handle his unpredictable brother-in-law. But where were the state-appointed guardians who were supposed to pick up the slack in watching over Leonard? Who was making sure that Leonard was taking his medication? Had he ever taken it at all, or had the mention of alarm clocks been another bit of vague rhetoric from Karen to keep me from knowing just how bad things were?

I was like a bull who had stumbled into a shuttered, cobwebbed china shop. Every step I took knocked over some precariously placed urn. When it hit the floor, dark matter issued forth.

CHAPTER SEVENTEEN

THE CAT DISAPPEARS

It vanished quite slowly, beginning with the end of the tail,
and ending with the grin, which remained
some time after the rest of it had gone.
—Lewis Carroll, *Alice in Wonderland*

By the end of July, Karen's emails signaled that she was doing well. Her description of life was idyllic. She was finally spending time by the pool, her younger daughter was taking swimming lessons, and she was baking raisin cookies for the kids to take to the arts and crafts fair the following weekend. She was a Stepford wife except for the random glitch in her programming caused by Leonard or Sharon. Karen was naturally very glad that Leonard and I were becoming friends since he "had so much to offer given a chance." I knew that she meant Leonard had good qualities, and I declined to tell her that I wasn't looking for cars or jewelry in a friendship, or that the present cordiality between her brother and me had resulted from my attempt to ameliorate a tense situation rather than establish any kind of deep rapport. Karen had a knack for disconnecting herself from the harsh realities of her family, such dissociation probably representing the principle way she'd survived the lifelong relationships she'd endured with her siblings and mother, and there was no reason to give her chapter and verse. She was lucky to have a stable husband.

As for Prince Hal, who had bolstered my hope on so many occasions, obviously put up with enormous pressure from his in-laws, far more than the aggravating gossip or Sunday dinners that spouses are wont to complain about. He'd actively dealt with Leonard's legal problems and, from what I could tell, had carefully monitored the mental health of both Leonard and Sharon. When I told him that I was quite appreciative of the way he took care of my interests in spite of all the problems he had to sift through, he candidly said that although he loved his family very much, there had been moments on business trips, sitting in a pressurized cabin five miles up, when he entertained thoughts of leaving the whole sordid mess and not looking back. I could sympathize with his sentiments, although I admired his "stay the course" attitude that had apparently always won out in his internal dialogues. The strength of his character was validated by actions he would shortly take.

Hal wrote on July 19, 2004, to say that, grabbing a flight on short notice, he was going to New Jersey "to help Leonard resolve an issue." He'd previously told me that he could no longer pick up the slack for his brother-in-law, but here he was again, running down to New Jersey to help Leonard. He was coming through Manhattan and asked if I would like to have coffee on Friday. I said "yes" since Hal was the one person in the extended family with whom I thought I could safely meet. Hal was my ally, and I relished the idea of meeting him. I sent him my phone number, unblocked my line, and waited with curiosity for the meeting. During the waiting period, Karen emailed me, and her letter made it immediately apparent why Hal was needed so badly in New Jersey.

Dear Susan,

It seems like we can't find any peace for long. Getting away to Maine has been a great relief this summer but there is always something waiting for us when we return.

Hal is going to New Jersey this weekend to help Len out again. Apparently a friend of his disappeared and has not been showing up for work. He was also helping Len with his medicine and painting his new place but now he's vanished. Hal and I think he just took off on the road but the authorities are questioning Len because he is supposedly the last person to see him. Bob and he have known each other for a while now and I can't understand why he didn't tell my brother where he was going. And to be honest with you Susan I am sick to death of people blaming my brother when something goes wrong or whatever. It is just not fair. Hal is supposed to meet with Len's community service counselor tomorrow and try to help schedule an appointment for him to talk to the police. He and Bob were friends for many years and none of this makes any sense. If Len knew something he would tell the police. Now Hal has to go down there again when he is very busy.

I have heard from Len that you and he are enjoying a nice correspondence and everything is nice between you. For that I am so thankful Susan. My brother has caused some problems in the past I know but he is still my flesh and blood and I love him and would do anything I could to help him. There are enough things to keep me busy this weekend while Hal is gone so I am not too worried. I hope things are good on your end. It seems like the summer goes by too fast every year.

Love, Karen

Bob was obviously Robert "Felix" McCottry, the maker of dungeons and friend of LenDogLenny. Karen's Stepford-like dissociation from her family was evident yet again since most people would be alarmed to find out their brother had rekindled a relationship with a felon, but I reminded myself that Karen's naiveté had been forged from years of dealing with repetitive, dysfunctional behavior from her brother and sister. Did she even know what normal was, or did she anesthetize herself with domestic routine? And for all her attempts to control Leonard's behavior, was there anything she could do to stop an adult man from associating with a friend even if the friend had a less than stellar reputation? If I had been in her shoes, perhaps I, too, would find myself baking cookies or taking to my bed. Maybe I would sigh at the mention of Bob McCottry and then watch my daughter's swim practice without a second thought.

The following day she said there might be another email problem since Hal hadn't received any reply to his invitation for coffee. She also claimed that Hal had flown into New York City and tried to call me but that my number had been blocked. He had therefore traveled on to New Jersey. Additionally, Leonard had told her that I hadn't answered any of his emails during the past week.

I had no idea what Karen was talking about. My phone hadn't been blocked, nor had I received any emails from Leonard. It seemed as if there was no end to the miscommunications in Karen's family.

Bobby concurred that "Bob" was Robert McCottry, and Felix's sexual overtures instantly sprang to our minds, as well as the fact that Leonard had confronted him twice. In trying to protect me, we thought Leonard may have precipitated a fight with McCottry. Had Leonard, in an uncontrolled moment, fallen into what Karen had once labeled "one of his bad personalities"? Had he physically harmed McCottry? Given the parole system, it was highly irregular for one of the most dangerous criminals on record in New Jersey to simply vanish, but he hadn't shown up for work or checked in with his parole officer. The thought of Leonard and Felix locked in a pitched battle wasn't a pleasant thought, but McCottry was missing and Lenny was being questioned by the police.

Conceivably, McCottry might have hit the road for reasons of his own. Criminals do that sometimes. He was an ex-con, and his predatory instincts might have resurfaced soon after he'd gotten a place of his own in the wide and unsuspecting world. But here was the million-dollar question: Would Brooklyn be the first stop on his flight from the jurisdiction of New Jersey? Did he want to see what Leonard's pretty little cousin looked like in person, the one who was into the arts like he was?

There was no way of knowing, and Bobby and I concluded that we'd done the right thing in handing the problem. There was no perfect way to handle people like McCottry, and I therefore decided to sit tight before responding to Karen lest she notify her sister, who might become enraged that I had been at least partially responsible for the police questioning Lenny.

Karen, however, wasn't in a patient mood. Two days later, she sent me a very pointed email, one that was uncharacteristically harsh for someone so faint of heart.

Dear Susan,

It must have been fun for you to hear all about my worries concerning my brother when you knew all along about this person that had disappeared. I had thought you were more sincere and honest. Why didn't you tell Hal or myself that you knew Bob McCottry or had heard from him at least? Also we wonder what is going on with you and Leonard that would lead you to be this way with us?

My feelings are really hurt Susan. I understand we don't know each other that well but I never thought you would hold back any information you might think useful to Hal or myself.

Thanks, Karen

Leonard had obviously spilled the beans to his family, and I was now the heavy. Karen's sarcasm was stinging, but how could she possibly think that any of this was fun for me, as if I were sitting back laughing after being contacted by a dangerous sex offender?

And then the realization hit me: Karen was virtually a surrogate mother to Leonard, and for precisely this reason I should have kept her in the loop. It wasn't that the decision Bobby and I had made to let Leonard deal with McCottry was illogical, but my credibility was on the line, and if anything really bad went down, my good word was all I had. Too many misunderstandings had transpired over the months, and I could understand how Hal and Karen would be displeased with my decision to stay mute. I emailed Karen, attempting to convey how conflicted I'd been about my decision to remain quiet, hoping that she would see what a difficult position I'd been in.

Hal sent me a short, polite reply, assuring me that he and Karen had my best interests at heart and requesting that I always be honest with both of them in the future. I replied by reiterating my feelings of ambivalence after receiving McCottry's "pick-up note." I'd been between and rock and a hard place, thinking I might be able to finesse Leonard into handling McCottry in a discreet, intelligent way.

The letter defused Karen's anger. She explained that her life had been a full-time struggle to keep her brother from incarceration, just as I had theorized. She admitted that it was wrong for McCottry to have written to me but believed she and Hal might have been able to "formulate a plan" to deal with such a sticky situation. The notion of having two siblings behind bars was too much to bear, even though Sharon was out on bail. "I just want to fall down and cry," she said.

In response, I told her I felt the same way: I was a wreck and wanted to cry since I'd thought the worst was over when Leonard and I had reached an understanding leading to more proper emails. I encouraged her not to think the worst and told her I was "here if you need me."

Even though I had become the centerpiece of chaos again, I found myself concerned with Leonard's well-being. He'd been worried about me, and he'd won my sympathy. I didn't want to see him get into trouble for anything, and I'd relaxed my attitude toward him. By the same token, I didn't want to hide my head in the sand like Karen. I reminded myself that I'd filed a police report against Leonard, and although Sharon had turned out to be the culprit, my cousin was nevertheless an unpredictable man who threw wild sex parties and occasionally had his neurotransmitters slowed down while finding himself locked in a suite at Greystone. Caution was still the watchword as I engaged in a mental high wire act spanning compassion and common sense.

To my great relief, Karen informed me that McCottry had been located and was now himself a patient at Greystone. He had, according to Karen, overdosed on some type of hallucinogenic drug. Until the past weekend, he couldn't remember his name, being admitted to the facility as a John Doe. Hal believed that McCottry might have tried to commit suicide. Greystone was turning out to be a busy place.

I didn't want to picture Leonard slipping McCottry a serious "down for the count" mickey. The thought of my cousin escorting the felon to the gates of hell was too terrifying to contemplate. I wasn't sure what had really happened to 'da Cat,' but I deliberately steered my mind away from Leonard's criminal potential. If he should ever commit a crime, I was likely to either get the blame from someone, or be the target of someone's wrath, regardless of how tenuous my connection was to the disturbed Wall Street *wunderkindt*.

CHAPTER EIGHTEEN

KINKFEST '04

What pornography is really about,
ultimately, isn't sex but death.
—Susan Sontag, *Partisan Review*, Spring 1967

In August, Leonard announced he was throwing a huge party.

Subject: i am Having a Party.

my Dearest Cousin,

I am looking for you on AIM as the beutiful *(sic)* Swan. See me as Lnachman1. I want to talk to you about a party. Do not worry about cloths *(sic)* I have everything you will need and will buy it. some weekends I have some people in from New York but soon I will have a Big Big fantasy party and you can meet them all. Alice in wonderland should be this theme and you can dress anything you want but can be Alice to *(sic)*. i have much to do now my Cousin before we meet face to face.

Much love,

Lenny

Lenny's fantasy gig was going to be a costume party, an "Alice in Wonderland" extravaganza. To Leonard, however, fantasy represented something more extreme than just a dress-up event. It sounded creepy, yet I was intrigued by the idea and actually considered attending. My interest in meeting this man absolutely went beyond reason. Every red flag was blaring away and yet despite it all, something was drawing me in. Something I needed to find, solve, or repair in my torn family.

He'd proven in our recent email correspondence that he could respect my boundaries. I reasoned that this might be my chance to meet a member of the family. Leonard offered something greater, although the risk was much higher. More than curiosity, it was a desire to connect with family that eclipsed my fear and apprehension. Leonard, more than any of them, held a fascination for me. I felt that all we needed to do was meet. I could look past the nylon and makeup and see the person inside, as I had looked beyond my family's aberrance. That having been said, I knew it was potentially dangerous. I would, of course, need a male escort, and Steve told me that he was up for an adventure since he had been informed of nearly every twist in my roller coaster ride with the Nachman family.

***

"More is merrier," Leona replied, supplying a link for the formal party announcement, "Lots of room to play. A performance for the cams. Anything fetish is okay." My cousin was to be the master of ceremonies in his hardcore fetish happening that was a mixture of kink and theater. It was exclusively for the daring members of Lenny's flamboyant universe, one in which inhibitions were nonexistent. The site listed who was scheduled to attend—apparently some members of the subculture had attained a certain amount of infamy—as well as details about music, activities, and playrooms. This wasn't going to be just a gathering of tired New Jersey swingers. It was going to be, by all accounts, the biggest sex party in the western hemisphere—a party with a name—and Leonard, who spoke of the event in his characteristic childlike simplicity, was going to be the ringmaster. It was playtime, and it wasn't hard to envision a professional financier involved in the underground party world of New York City. Politicians, doctors, lawyers, and actors were caught in compromising positions, figuratively and literally, every day. When it came to Kinkfest, there was nothing new under the sun.

I imagined Leona in a Mad Hatter costume as he stood in a room with black lighting, surrounded by pulsating music and bizarre creatures dancing fervidly in wild jerking movements. Tortured bodies that would gladly endure punishment generously meted out by their masters, slaves awaiting orders in this most secret of parties. And yet, like a moth drawn to the flame, I still entertained going. Maybe— just maybe—I could breach the gulf between Leonard and myself, if only for five minutes, while we stood in the ferocious darkness. He would see I wasn't afraid of him. The blood of my father and his ancestors would be just inches from me, and I would confront whatever odd traits were encoded on Fensten DNA. I had grown up in New York City, had spent my life in the East Village, uptown and Williamsburg. I wasn't frightened by the strange or the unusual or even danger, having been held up at both knifepoint and gunpoint. I even had a pair of red-sequined devil horns in the closet, a tame "costume" compared to what I expected to see. Besides, it seemed as if Leonard himself was looking forward to meeting me. I could do this.

Bobby tried to talk me out of going. He said it was a bad idea given the grief Leonard had caused me. To him, my steel resolve was, in reality, so much foolishness. Trying to tease me out of my boldness, he said that even though I wanted to slip in and out of the party virtually unnoticed, Leonard might stop the music and introduce me to the crowd. I would be center stage, track lights reflected in my eyes. Is this what I really wanted?

Two days after reading Leonard's party announcement, I was contacted by one of the principle players in Leonard's fantasy, Lord Mulgrave.

Subject: KINK FEST

Dear Sussane,

We look forward to meeting you this year at KINK FEST.

Mistress Leona has told us all about you. If you need a ride let us know we are in Queens.

Blessed Be,

Master Mulgrave and Cyrese

A photo of the couple was attached. Lord Mulgrave had an unsettling, penetrating stare, with reddish-brown hair parted in the middle, reminding me of a throwback from the Middle Ages. He had silver rings on every finger, his arms wrapped around the waist of his young and willing captive, Cyrese. There was no smile on the lips of this powdered, Mongolian-looking geisha, exact age and nationality indeterminate. Without thinking, I hit the reply button to say "thanks, but no thanks." Her gaze was mysterious, puzzling, silent. She didn't remain silent for long, however.

Subject: drive u

suSieQ

U might b misstress *(sic)* Leonas relation but that does not give u the oK to fuCk my mAn Lord Mulgrave. He wants u like he wants every woMan so do not flatter urself. Lay 1 hand on him or if IC u together u will not like what will happen to u. A bitch can dissapear *(sic)* 123 so b smart and watch yo ass. We will pik u up at ur house in Wb for the Sabbath & drop u off. get back on ur own.

P.out, Cyrese

Mistress Of The New Dawn

The geisha-goth was issuing a warning shot across the bow. Cyrese was okay with the idea of my attending Kinkfest, but she'd put me on notice. One false move and I could disappear—1, 2, 3. I was immediately shocked back to my senses. The mission was aborted, the countdown stopped. My curiosity about Leonard remained strong, but I wasn't going to have anything to do with Lord Mulgrave or his jealous slave girl. I wrote to Leonard and told him that, upon second thought, the whole affair was too wild. I summarized the message from Lord Mulgrave and Cyrese and said I wasn't into swinging or cam performances. Yes, I loved costume parties, but KinkFest was just too far over the line.

Leonard's reply merely said, "Do not worry, my beautiful cousin Swan. I will never let nothing [sic] bad happen to you at Kinkfest." He related how I could be driven to the "party loft" by Lord Mulgrave and then go to his house (Leonard's) the next morning. He was also still curious as to what costume I'd be wearing and wanted to know more about my escort. He was totally absorbed in the party, perhaps festooning the fetish loft with paraphernalia that I'd be better off not knowing about. He was "on top of the wind" again.

I'd made the right decision, however. Lord Mulgrave copied me when he announced a coming attraction.

Subject: FRAUSHISS JOINS KINKFEST!!!!!!

LISTEN UP EVERYONE.

FRAU SHISS IS BACK FROM GERMANY AND GOING TO PERFORM AT KINKFEST ON A PRIVATE FIRST CUM FIRST SERVE BASIS. SEE LINK HERE:

http://www.geocities.com/mastermulgrave/frau.html

MISTRESS LEONA KINK HAS MADE SURE THERE ARE ADEQUATE PLAY STATIONS. SEE YOU ALL THERE!!!!

BLESSED BE,

LORD MULGRAVE

This time the link led to a photo of a woman—Frau Shiss—smiling with what appeared to be feces in her mouth. It was one of the most disgusting images I'd ever seen.

I received several other messages on August 11. Offers— and stern orders in keeping with the theme of domination. Lord Mulgrave, for example, had specific plans for me. He was going to train me to work with "top shelf" clients, such as Jasper Crepes, who required needlework and geni-torture.

"You will learn service before you are served," he informed me tersely.

Pappagoose appeared in my inbox next, declaring that he needed a slave bitch for "kinkfestival." Roscoe Rhinefeld followed with a lengthy letter on creative uses, graphically described, for tampons and their applicators. Other photographs depicted a man's nipple being pierced with a syringe, and a naked man kneeling before two young leather-clad women whipping his backside.

The most chilling letter of all came from Cyrese.

Subject: Re: drive u

susieQ

u Best not b dissn no 1 little girly. If he is nuthn2u then y is he and FeLix tawking so much about u? if I find oUt ur meSsin with mah man Mulgrave you will be in a graVe 2 lol!!! btw I have giRlz that will bAck mah Azz up. so bWarnEd. B Cng U. lol.

P.out, Cyrese

Mistress Of The New Dawn

Felix was talking with Mulgrave. Fear crept over me like a fog, one which became denser after I read the next transmission from Lavinia deBraun satanically addressed from *ladylavinia666@yahoo.com.*

Subject: KINKFEST SLAVE

Slavegirl Susanne,

I have been asked to instruct you on service techniques and proper etiquette before you perform at KINKFEST.

I am a demanding dominatrix who uses strict application of BDSM practices.

You must be willing to submit to my will and take whatever I or my girls dish out.

Your first session will be FREE because you are friends with Lord Mulgrave and Master Felix. Anything thereafter will cost you the regular Slave fee.

Contact me here for more information about your FREE session. Time is running out and I need to break you in.

I ORDER YOU TO RESPOND IMMEDIATELY AFTER RECEIVING THIS COMMAND.

Lady Lavina

Bitch Goddess

Another mention of Felix—*Master* Felix—this one from Lady Lavinia, who held a whip across her gigantic breasts, which protruded above a tight black corset of leather and lace.

You are a very attractive lady and I would be pleased to meet you sometime.

Alice had fallen down the rabbit hole, and Wonderland was now a monstrous landscape, not unlike the grounds of Greystone. Emails continued to pour in—Bobbie Lyn was going to try to fit me in for some training sessions, and Lord Mulgrave himself said that a ball-gag harness could be mine since naughty slave girl Laura had run off again. (The harness fit over one's head, with a ball held firmly in the mouth via leather, studded straps that circled the head above the jaw line, connecting to other straps descending over the forehead and eyes.) As hideous as the contraption looked, I could only think of four syllables: Felix da Cat. He was free of the confines of Greystone and had spoken of me by name to an armada of sex ghouls who were now breathing down my neck, envisioning me in Leonard's windowless room and pain tubs. I responded to no one as I sat at my computer, numb, thinking of wandering through dark rooms among costumed figures, one of whom was Robert McCottry. That night I had a vivid dream in which I drove down a midnight road devoid of any other traffic, headed for New Jersey. When I arrived at an unknown house, I saw Leonard sitting in partial drag, purple granny glasses perched on his nose, near a corner window with a Japanese man. Leonard, nails painted glossy black, gestured that I should look at something in the corner, although I can't remember what object rested there. What was I doing here? Repulsed, I threw up deeply and violently in the dream world before waking. This was surely validation that my decision not to attend had been correct, for the dream held all the power of a psychic vision. I would be in great danger should I venture to my cousin's party loft, and it was time to be more emphatic with Mr. Nachman.

Dear Lenny-

There is some mistake. I am NOT into this scene and I am getting a lot of bad email that I don't want.

Please understand.

Thank you.

Susan

His reply was satisfactory. Leonard apologized, saying he'd been confused by my initial interest in the costume party. He assured me that I was "out of the list of mailings" and expressed his sorrow over the misunderstanding.

Karen emailed next, her letter almost an anomaly measured against the leathery overtures I'd received regarding Kinkfest. She'd enjoyed the previous week as she and Hal prepared to return to Maine for the last time that summer. She expressed surprise that I wouldn't be attending Lenny's party or meeting "his crowd" since he and I enjoyed the same "New York lifestyle." I had no doubt that the sight of Lord Mulgrave and his cohorts would put Karen into a rapid swoon requiring smelling salts and a day of recuperation. There wasn't much to say to poor Karen except that I'd heard Bob McCottry would be there, which was a definite deal breaker. I wished her a pleasant trip "down east," but I didn't have much to say about Leonard's party. I certainly wasn't going to enlighten her as to the true nature of Leonard's "crowd."

Another email caught my attention in a far more commanding way than Karen's homey, "come pay us a visit" message ever could.

Subject: sFensten?

Are you Susanne Fensten or Feinstein? I want to talk with you. Call me direct at 718-525-8928 between 10am and 3pm ONLY!!!

Carl

This was not a "Kinkfest announcement." There were no allusions to slaves or training sessions or rides to New Jersey. Carl Mulgrave—no longer a "lord"—wanted to tell me something, and there was a sense of urgency in his brief note. Had someone said something about me? Had it been Robert McCottry? Did Mulgrave want to warn me of some imminent danger?

I would really like to check you out.

Bobby and I checked on the web and found that a Carl Mulgrave resided in Queens. The phone numbers matched. I wanted to call but didn't since I had no idea who Carl Mulgrave was. For all I knew, it could be a set up. Once upon a time, Felix had run with Lou Burr. Was he now tag-teaming it with Carl Mulgrave? I wasn't going to find out.

CHAPTER NINETEEN

SELL THEM ALIVE

It was during the horror of a deep night.
—Jean Racine, *Athalie*

Autumn approached, Kinkfest was history, and once again I resolved to take another breather from the Nachmans. Ever persistent, however, Leonard wrote again to apologize for the emails his friends had sent prior to Kinkfest and to reiterate that he respected my wishes in matters relating to my personal lifestyle. What touched me was his plea not to abandon him. He truly wanted to be my friend. I got the feeling that Leonard, during a moment of reflection, had finally understood both intellectually and emotionally that I wasn't into his strange world of fantasy. He seemed to want what I had been after all along: simple, genuine friendship. Or in this case, maybe even a bit of kinship as well. All traces of enmity had been erased. If only Sharon would now come to her senses, I felt I could be free of the ongoing strife within her family once and for all. As usual, this was wishful thinking, for when one fire was smothered in the Nachman family, another soon flared up.

Over the course of a few days, Nolan's roommate had seen a suspicious man watching their house in Brooklyn, even looking in windows and asking questions of the neighbors. Their room was in a large home owned by the roommate's father. The roommate, who was aware of the troubles Nolan and I had been having with the Nachmans, told his father of the mysterious stranger lurking about the property. The news was not well received. The father did not wish to have unknown men casing his house as it could well be the prelude to a robbery—or worse. The owner didn't want Nolan's problems spilling over into the lives of his family, and Nolan was therefore asked to move. It was understandable that the father wanted to protect his property—our ordeal becoming increasingly dangerous, and at this point almost anything could be expected to happen—but Nolan no longer had a place to live. He didn't wish to stay with me. I believe he wanted to get as far away from me as possible by this time, it had all become far too much for him to deal with. He packed up and moved in with his own father in New Jersey. I felt guilty because his life had been uprooted, his grades weren't improving, and his commute to school would now be longer.

Hal fueled the fire even further on September 4 with more distressing news about Lydia Shoef, Sharon's traveling companion-in-arms and the very woman who'd sent me a caustic email, who had discovered shocking correspondence on her computer's hard drive. The explanation? Sharon had been using Lydia's PC to send email to Robert McCottry so her messages couldn't be traced to her own computer. (I believed, in all likelihood, Sharon had used Lydia's computer when masquerading as both Leonard and me.) Lydia's discovery had precipitated a fight with Sharon, just as Sharon and Tom must have fought shortly before their engagement had been broken. Hal believed that Sharon might finally be held accountable for her actions. He suggested that dark clouds loomed on the horizon for his sister-in-law, although he wasn't telling Karen yet of his plans to present the discovered emails to his lawyer in order to establish whether or not something could finally be done to rein Sharon in.

Lydia's conscience apparently prompted her to forward the discovered emails to Hal, who in turn sent them to me. The exchange began with a message from Felix to Sharon. Gauging from the contents, it appeared as if McCottry remembered Sharon from years past, perhaps from the incident when Leonard had been arrested and tried in connection with the arrest of McCottry and Burr for rape.

Dear Miss Barnes,

This is Felix aka Bob friend of Lenny who met you a few month *(sic)* ago.

I got your email from your brother Lennys place in case I need to write you sometime. Looks like it was a good thing I did. I know you have problems with her before and I thought you should know that he is planning on sending that bitch Susan Fenstein on a trip around the world. I found out he is sending her trip stuff to go to Mexico and other places by his money. You have always been straight with me so I thought I would return the favor. Maybe Lenny is not thinking with a clear mind? He wants to give her money and gifts and she is baiting him for more and more and more. I went by her place a week ago in Brooklan and they were all asleep or ? I do not know how many guys she had in there but people came in her building and out all night with her lights out. I just dont like to see Lenn hurt by this coniveing bitch. You can write me here if you need more info or i can give you my cell# to.

Please do not tell Lenny where you found out.

peace,

Felix

Apparently Felix had obtained a fair amount of information about me from Leonard's computer. As for the reference to a more recent meeting between Sharon and Felix, I thought it probable that both Sharon and McCottry had been hanging around Leonard's place after he was recently released from Greystone. Regardless, Sharon's reply made it clear that these two unsavory individuals were out for revenge, and I was their target. She asked McCottry to take pictures of me and warned him about my dog, finishing her directive with an offer to pay double if he could access Leonard's computer.

It seemed that accessing Leonard's computer would be easy as he had done it before, especially when I saw that McCottry had been most accommodating. He provided her with photos purported to be of me and my dog, and a shot of Nolan and I leaving my apartment building. He also sent a photo of Leonard at Kinkfest. He thought she should know what 'sick things' Leonard has been doing and added that he believed that Leonard tried to poison him, thanks to me, 'that little bitch.' He signed off 'peace, Felix.'

I could not open the attachments, but it didn't make any difference whether or not I'd seen the actual pictures. Felix claimed to have been near my apartment, had obtained the pictures, had spied on Nolan and me. The shadow of his evil had darkened my door steps. Almost as troubling was the fact that McCottry was taking a shot at Leonard for throwing Kinkfest, a party that McCottry himself had attended. Finally, the last sentence alluded to McCottry's belief that

Leonard had tried to poison him after learning that I had told my cousin about emails from "da Cat."

McCottry's stay at Greystone had obviously done nothing to change his criminal mindset, but he'd only been a John Doe admitted to a hospital after overdosing. He'd awakened with only one thing on his mind: revenge. He had been the one to serve time in prison, not Leonard.

But even the pictures were not enough to complete Sharon's preparations for revenge.

Felix,

Good work! Today I need to send you this software to download on a diskette and slip into his computer. Are you certain he broke the law at this party of his? I need more photos of him in his Leona persona to make the doctors listen. Then his little girlie in brooklyn can wonder what happened to her money train, lol lol lol.

I found out her boytoy goes into NYCITY when he leaves her shithole so he might have other hoes in there. Can you follow him next time and tell me where he goes exactly and how many hoes he keeps? I will fix that slut once and for all and with your help Felix. And my brother who wants to put that tramp over family will find time to think about it in a cell, lol lol lol. Try to find out exactly where he is sending her and her pimp and where you want me to send the first payment. Get a p.o. box quick, I will only send USPS money orders.

Sharon

Nolan was being followed into New York City after leaving my home. He was clearly in danger—and so was Leonard. I could only conclude that Sharon, jealous in the extreme, had decided that if her brother was going to be my friend, then he should be locked away in Greystone again. If she couldn't have him—and *control* him—then no one would.

I assumed that the disk inserted into Leonard's computer contained a keystroke logger program for the purposes of surveillance, allowing Sharon to learn everything Leonard did on his PC. Only Sharon knew what was on the disk, but one thing was for certain: she was far more than a troubled person who needed psychiatric care. I was now convinced she was definitely dangerous.

The final email in the exchange showed an almost gleeful McCottry.

> Now your talkin Lady, please call me tonite and we can set it all up. I can't wait to see that little broad squirm LOL. Her pimp will be my punk!!!LOL. p.o. box on the way. He's sending them his place in mexico and around the globe with gifts to. he was looking up diamonds when I last saw.
>
> Peace,
>
> Felix

McCottry, a violent man, always closed his emails with "Peace", which is exactly what he and Sharon had taken from me. My fear was intensified by the realization that the misperceptions of their sick minds could not be refocused on the truth. Reality is whatever such individuals say it is, and the thoughts of Felix and Sharon were now fueled with obsession. Obsessions sometimes come to a sudden stop with deadly consequences. Felix and Sharon were operating at fever pitch, apparently immensely enjoying all of this in a way that only two dangerous lunatics could. I felt as if I were being sawed in half, with Sharon and Felix at either end of an old-time two-handled tree saw. Both were dangerous when acting on their own, but as allies, they were doubly lethal. Their exchanges portrayed a firm resolve devoid of any moral considerations. They were evil.

I responded to Hal the following day, telling him that someone had knocked on my window late one Saturday night after I'd gone to bed. I wanted to be protected from the maniacal actions of McCottry and Sharon, who had crossed the line by miles, not inches. I was numb as I contemplated their unspeakable acts and future plans, expressing my opinion that Leonard, whatever his lifestyle might be, had not committed any crime and didn't deserve electric shock therapy. I also informed Hal that Carl Mulgrave had urgently requested that I contact him. Maybe he had important information on McCottry.

Are you Susan Fensten or Feinstein? I want to talk with you. Call me direct . . .

The words of this insistent note echoed in my head like a fire alarm. I was too afraid to actually call Mulgrave, but it was time to see why he wanted to speak with me. I sent him an email, spare as a haiku: "I am *not* looking for dates or to 'swing.' If you have something to tell me, let me know." His reply, sent from yet another email address, *cm11434@ yahoo.com*, manifested a tone totally dissimilar from his persona as Lord Mulgrave. And I was right. He had more information on Robert McCottry.

Subject: Re: Write me here if u get this.

Susan hi,

First of all I wanted to tell you sorry for what Cyrese wrote you. She had no rite *(sic)* to say anything and because she is a jealous animal she broke our trust and wrote you. Trust me she has been dealt with. Second I wanted to tell you not to go to KINK-FEST this year. There is a guy named Felix who is Cyreses uncle<not by law he did time with her father in prison> and he is plenty pissed off and says you squealed on him and got him drugged and put in a nut hospital in NJ. It is none of my business and I dont even care what happens to that lowlife animal. he showed me a picture of you and told that you are a hooker he was seeing. Leona asked me to give you a ride to Jersey if you were going and I said OK. Then I hear all this talk about Felix trying to get the Twelve Tribes cult involved and making you a work slave for them upstate and he was going to get paid by the commune. As far as I am concerned the 12 are nothing but a bunch of kiddy freaks and sados and no one deserves to be caught by them.

I am sorry I sent you some stuff to. I was fooled by him and then Leona put me right. I know you are Leona's cousin and all and that's kewl. He is a friend of mine and we have been doing business for a long time and you are OK in my book. They want to put Felix back in for possession so maybe he won't be a problem. I just heard from Leona that he screwed him over to so now I will find out what happened there. I wanted you should know and I tried to tell you not to come to the party and to say I am sorry for Cyrese's bad manners. Thank you for using this address to get back to me I want to be private. Felix is a very sick person and knows alot of sick people and I don't need him finding out through Cyrese. He goes by the name <the Cat> so if you hear anyone by that name get out of there.

Sincerely,

Carl

Mulgrave confirmed that there had been an altercation between Leonard and McCottry, who was "plenty pissed off" because I had "squealed on him and got him drugged and put in the nut hospital in NJ." The only encouraging sign was that the police wanted to pick up McCottry for possession of drugs, and as Mulgrave had written, "maybe he won't be a problem."

Maybe. It was hard not to be concerned by talk of the Twelve Tribes cult and McCottry wanting its members to become involved in converting me into a slave.

I thanked Carl Mulgrave for his apology in reference to the crude behavior of Cyrese and for "being a decent guy." But how was I going to function knowing that McCottry, if *not* apprehended by the police, held a serious grudge against me? And who was The Tribe of Twelve?

I was on high alert. Whenever I left home, I noticed everyone and everything even more so than usual. McCottry was out there, watching me, the click of his camera ticking off the seconds of my life.

Bobby and I Googled "The Tribe of Twelve" and discovered that it was a Messianic community founded by a former carnival barker and high school guidance counselor by the name of Elbert Eugene Spriggs. Both The Tribe and Spriggs were watched closely by law enforcement for child labor infractions as well as potential sexual abuse. Spriggs was a classic cult leader bearing an uncanny resemblance to Charles Manson. Bobby was horrified and didn't envy my having to tell Nolan of the latest developments.

Before I had the time to give Nolan a full disclosure of Mulgrave's latest correspondence, additional news poured in from Hal, who had received more emails from Lydia.

They comprised a further exchange between the two people on Earth I had come to loathe and fear the most.

Still photos were no longer sufficient for whatever sinister plans Sharon was hatching. She wanted McCottry to film me. She wrote, "I want to see her walk and see where she goes and who she talks to. What she eats and buys. Get everything and get some zoom shots of her face." She also requested that McCottry follow Nolan—she knew him by name—who the "gang upstate" could use for hard labor. McCottry replied, saying that he'd uploaded his cinematic handiwork to a server. He said that the twelve were "very interested in a child barer [sic] and she is prime." I would make a baby every year, after which I would be "done in and ate." Nolan, he said, would be excellent for fieldwork, such as growing vegetables. Before closing the email with his characteristic "Peace" signature, he thanked Sharon "4 the $." He may have been as interested in revenge as his co-conspirator, but he was still a mercenary at heart.

Zoom shots. Cannibalism. I had spiraled so far down the devilish circles of Sharon's inferno that I could no longer see daylight. When had McCottry taken his pictures and camcorder footage? How close had he been? It was as if he were a cinematographer making a clandestine documentary for his fiendish director—Sharon.

Sharon then blocked out the next scene for her forthcoming work-in-progress, one that was dark and macabre. She asked McCottry if he could still obtain chloroform. She was now moving inexorably toward her goal of delivering Nolan and me to The Tribe of Twelve, and she appeared ready to take the next logical step to get us upstate: kidnapping. In response, McCottry indicated that everything was in place. He assured Sharon that The Tribe would break us quickly.

Matters had taken a turn toward slavery and possible homicide. This was no longer just a matter of receiving unwanted email with porn attached or mysterious hang-up calls. Our lives were in danger. Swallowing my fear, I gave Nolan the unabridged version of the latest developments. He was shaken and extremely angry. All along he had told me to leave this alone and yet I somehow couldn't. Now there was nothing I could do to turn back the clock. The wheels for the hideous actions Sharon and Felix were planning to take had all inadvertently been set in motion the previous October by my simple posting on Genealogy.com.

I was terrified. I called my local precinct again, explaining my crisis to an officer.

"There's a plot to kidnap me and my boyfriend, and we need help," I said.

"Oh?" said the voice at the precinct. "And how exactly do you know this?"

The doubt in his voice was obvious.

"I heard it from family members who discovered the truth through emails stored on a friend's hard drive." As the words left my lips, I realized that this thumbnail sketch sounded absurd.

"Uh huh. I see."

There was a slight pause.

"Ma'am, you need to call the FBI," the cop said.

I hung up and found the phone number for FBI headquarters in downtown Manhattan. I dialed the number, which connected me to a woman with a matter-of-fact tone of voice.

"What's the nature of your problem?" she asked.

I tried to remain calm as I described my dire situation with a bit more clarity, but it was soon obvious I wasn't getting through. After listening to my story, she suggested I call the local police. I told her that it was the local police who'd told me to call the Bureau in the first place, but she was obviously just someone who screened hundreds of calls a day. My plea for help had reached an immediate dead end. My options seemed limited. I didn't know how much time I had left before an arm, appearing from nowhere, clamped a damp handkerchief over my nose and mouth as I slipped helplessly into a dark and potentially endless sleep.

***

Hal emailed the next day, throwing a lifeline into the inferno.

Dear Susan,

I wanted you to be one of the first people I told the good news to.

Our lawyer Mr. Walters called a little while ago and also sent a fax. McCottry's car was identified as one seen leaving a burglary at a chemical lab last week. They picked him and another man (no it was not Leonard) up early this morning and is in custody. Now we don't have to go to court later this month on the charge that Len "poisoned" him. This is great news because it saves us a bunch of time and worry having to fly back and forth to NJ and also in lawyer fees. I thought you would be particularly happy to know McCottry is off the street and heading back to prison sooner than expected. I am told they found the stolen chemicals on his property in a garden shed.

Karen just got off the phone with Len and he is bouncing off the walls with happiness. You may not know this but we were very afraid this latest drugging charge would have been the end for Len. He has been walking on thin ice ever since the Belarus case. Our lawyer is also preparing paperwork for the court in regard to Sharon and her threats that were found on Lydia's computer. He said none of it will be able to be introduced in the matter between she and my wife but "could serve to show how her psychological outlook affects her life and those around her". In all honesty I do not want to take on the responsibility of raising her kids, but if she goes to prison we will assume guardianship.

That is the news for now. I will write with more information as it comes in.

Hal

Carl Mulgrave confirmed Hal's news, that McCottry had been "popped." I was relieved, because I had already planned to visit the 90th Precinct in person that night after work since there was too much at stake to allow voices over the telephone to tell me that nothing could be done.

I sent numerous questions to Hal. Was Sharon aware of McCottry's arrest? Was there anything I could legally do to ensure that she be kept away from me? Were the police aware of what she had intended to do with the chemicals? Had Hal's lawyer in New Jersey alerted the police, providing a full explanation of the kidnapping plot?

I breathed a sigh of relief. It had been a hell of a day. Literally.

Carl sent me an additional email to say "Yes, they got him and one of The Twelve for stealing chemicals for meth.

Stupid cat had a gallon of trichloromethane in his back yard."

I Googled "trichloromethane" and my knees went weak. The chemical had a more common name: chloroform.

I told Hal that the stolen chemicals found in McCottry's garden shed were chloroform. Shocked, he asked my permission to send his lawyer and New Jersey authorities any emails I had pertaining to the kidnapping plot, preferably all in a single file. I cut and pasted Carl Mulgrave's communications into the emails Hal himself had sent courtesy of Lydia, feeling relieved that the authorities might finally take a more active interest in what had clearly been a serious threat to Leonard, Nolan, and me. McCottry may have indeed wanted to manufacture amphetamines, but it was important that the police knew the principal reason he had trichloromethane in his possession.

Hal forwarded my emails to his lawyer and told me that, if justice was served, he and Karen might be forced to care for Sharon's two children. In a lighthearted moment, he wrote, "A house of 5 women. Pray for me too." I sympathized with Hal's plight, but it seemed to me a small price to pay to reclaim our lives.

I reminded Hal that I had printouts of McCottry's Yahoo profile and pointed out that The Tribe of Twelve was also a group of cannibals. I didn't think it was possible for Hal's lawyer to have too much information.

Robert McCottry, who was fond of "out of doors" activities, was back indoors, and Sharon was about to face the music while standing in front of a judge.

We had escaped this malevolent plot, at least for now.

CHAPTER TWENTY

A POEM 4U

All poets are mad.
—Robert Burton, *The Anatomy of Melancholy*

Given my odyssey through the disturbed minds of so many people, perhaps I should no longer have been flustered by emails from the people who'd darkened my inbox since my genealogical inquiry, but such is the nature of terror. It stalks one relentlessly.

Leonard and I were sent the same email by Cyrese on September 9, 2004. The subject line was "luv uR nu adre$s, LOL," a sarcastic reference to my new email address. Her text was as follows.

> U miTe thiNk uR CleVr mi$s talKal0t bUt blaBrm0uths g0t 2b shUt
>
> mY Unc$ g0t p0pPed, ok s0 whAt?
>
> it$ aLl go0d, paYbaK wiT ju$t 1 sh0t
>
> LOL, Cyre$e
>
> a poem by Master Felix ,learn it.
>
> *what i dream of doing to her an her pimp, a..*
>
> Tie them up, tie them down, kick his head, tear her gown

Slap his face, bite her tits- Up till now they ain't felt shit

Fingers crushed, toes cut off, windpipes smashed, bloody coughs

Broken jaws, cuts and scrapes- This goes far beyond just rape

Bleeding cunt and ass torn dress; shit bitch fag, and she's a mess

I'll fuck them out of there last breath, I won't stop till after death

Pathetic tears, such a waste- Here's my shit, have a taste

Beg all they want but I won't stop, a table leg crammed up her twat

And something nice completes the task- a tent stake pounded up his ass

He can't die yet, I'm not quite done, don't act like she ain't having fun

The stakes pulled out, but then replaced- I think I rather fuck his face

As I come, they will go- End there life with one last blow

lol lol lol lol LOL, lol

Bobby and I thought it probable that the poem was something that the Mistress of the New Dawn had found on the internet. Regardless of where it originated, Cyrese claimed that the poem was authored by McCottry, and it didn't take a stretch of the imagination to realize that he was calling the shots while in jail. The reach of criminals in prison to the outside world is well known, with entire crime syndicates run by mobsters and others serving long-term sentences. McCottry wouldn't have had internet access while behind bars, but a few telephone calls to Cyrese would have been sufficient to instruct her in the art of keeping pressure on the bookish slut who'd ratted him out. As the prelude to the poem stated, it was time for "paYbaK."

Hal sent a brief but shocking note on September 10 saying that Leonard had been shot at earlier that afternoon. His report was vague, but he explained that a bullet had shattered the driver's side window of Leonard's automobile. Leonard had escaped unharmed, although Karen was understandably distraught. A little while later, Mulgrave wrote to say "Head's up!" since he'd heard that "something was going down." I presumed that he had heard from Cyrese that some wicked plan was in the works before the actual shooting had taken place, although it was equally possible that his warning alluded to a wider plan of revenge that also included me. Was I going to be next? Had "paYbaK" begun? According to an earlier email from Mulgrave, Cyrese's father had served time with Felix, who she called "uncle," and given Sharon's close association with McCottry, it wasn't hard to imagine Cyrese teaming up with the redoubtable Ms. Barnes. Leonard told Hal that the person who had fired the shot at his window was a woman. Privately, I doubted Leonard could have been clear in what he saw through a window fractured into a spider web glaze while adrenaline wisely compelled him to hit the accelerator.

I replied to Mulgrave, telling him that I was okay but frightened to the point that I wished I had somewhere to go—just about anywhere would do—to escape. Carl Mulgrave, a devotee of domination and bondage when he wasn't being "a decent guy," continued to be supportive.

Subject: Re: Re: Write me here if u get this.

Susan hi,

I heard someone tried to clip Leona. This is terrible shit. If you speak to him let him know I am asking about him. He wrote me yesterday and said he was going underground. Tell him I love him and will do whatever he wants. He will know what that means. why don't you and your man take a trip somewheres nice for a while. Take a load off your mind until the heats off? Are you sure you are OK?

be cool,

Carl

"Cool" was the one thing I couldn't be. Cyrese's email indicated that "ju$t 1 shOt" was payback, a fact Leonard had learned firsthand. In an effort to keep bullets from spitting fire through my own window, I dragged a heavy antique mirror weighing two hundred pounds from my bedroom to a spot that nearly covered both windows. It had inch-thick beveled glass and was backed with heavy wood. It reflected my state of terror—literally. When I gazed into its silvered surface, a thin, haunted, deeply unhappy figure stared back. I was a hostage of fear. Although McCottry and Sharon had not literally chloroformed me, I was nevertheless smothered by guesswork as to who might be outside my door or beneath my windows. Exactly where these phantoms were, however, was almost a moot issue. They were already inside my head. I stayed inside for most of the weekend, darting out only briefly for a few errands.

Hal brought me up to speed the next day on how Leonard and Karen were faring.

Sept 11

Dear Susan,

Leonard called us last night from a safe house where he staying and my guess is he will end up in a hotel someplace in N.J. for a while. He sounded very upset and cried on the phone with Karen. He is also worried about you and wanted me to write you to let you know he is alright. He wanted to know if you got his E-mails or not?

He just kept saying that he saw "her", so I am assuming it was a woman who shot at him. Last night he still had broken glass in his hair before he showered so the shot must have come close to his head. Mr. Walters told us this morning that McCottry is going to be put away for a long time beginning Monday he gets transferred from the lockup to the detention center. His charge against Leonard has been dropped in lieu of his stealing the chemicals.

Right now I am trying to calm my wife down because she gets so upset concerning her brother. Her sister asked us to watch her kids this week end but I said it was not a good time for us. It was strange that she did not want us to know where she was going and by law she is not allowed to leave the state.

I was relieved to hear that McCottry's charge against Leonard had been dropped, and I hoped that Hal's attorney could ensure that "da Cat" would indeed be put away for a long time. Mr. Walters had been telling Hal for weeks that he had enough evidence to deal effectively with both Sharon and McCottry, but the wheels of justice were turning slowly. I was also dying to find out if the woman who'd taken a shot at Leonard was either Sharon or Cyrese, and I asked Hal if he knew.

He didn't, for when he answered, he asked if I could get in touch with Cyrese's boyfriend and find out if she had been involved. He informed me that Karen was sobbing into her pillow, blaming herself for everything. I didn't envy Hal, who was attempting to take care of his girls while his wife appeared to be flirting with a complete nervous breakdown—assuming she hadn't suffered one already. In a follow-up email, Hal said that he'd tried to call me twice, but that he'd gotten static on the first try and an answering machine on the second. Given my jittery nerves, I had begun to block my line again, unblocking it for a few minutes at a time should a friend want to call. I didn't have an answering machine—only voice mail—but there was no message from Hal, and as for the static, I guessed that a blocked line might conceivably produce static. I had no other theory as to why Hal consistently could not reach my number.

The emotional weight of these latest concerns took a heavy toll on my relationship with Nolan. He didn't like living with his father and stepmother in New Jersey, and he was always on the road, commuting to school and his job. He was tired of the ceaseless melodrama, and I couldn't blame him. When we were together, we were less talkative, and the silence grew palpable. I kept new information to myself, our relationship slowly dying as I withdrew into my world of gloom and hyper-vigilance.

My life was now a 24-7 news cycle, with updates every half hour. Hal emailed me shortly after his last "check-in" to tell me that a rock had smashed Leonard's car window, not a bullet. The mechanic replacing the glass had found the rock on the back seat. A teenager, part of a larger group, had thrown the small, hard projectile, missing Leonard by an inch, and it wasn't hard to ascribe motivation. Leonard would be an easy, desirable target for mean-spirited adolescents if he were driving around in light make-up and earrings. He might even have been wearing a costume from a party the night before, a few pieces of glitter still in his hair. It wasn't hard to imagine bigoted slurs as a rock sailed through the air.

According to Hal, Leonard felt silly and was sorry he had alarmed everyone. He was also afraid.

my Cousin,

my sister is trying to get in here i think and i have not answered the door or phones.

Do not trust her or take her lies. my nerves are better now but she is trying to see me i think and I do not want her so now I have to call Harold. Do not see her or let her in to. She is a bad liar.

love,

Lenny

There was no danger that I would listen to anything Sharon had to say. But I felt for Leonard, who, like me, was a prisoner in his own house (assuming he had returned home).

Hal emailed that he and Karen were trying to reach me. I had received a hang-up call shortly before his email and decided that I needed to get out of the house. I told Hal that a friend and I were going to a neighborhood café for lunch. I needed to settle my nerves and told him I was re-blocking the phone. Undeterred, he emailed again, asking me to unblock my phone. I released the block, and within minutes someone called and hung up immediately.

I'd had enough for one day. I blocked the phone and went out with Steve. I'd known him for twenty-five years, and I filled him in on the latest developments even though it would have been nice to talk about ordinary life.

CHAPTER TWENTY-ONE

ARE YOU SUE?

Damaged people are dangerous. They know how to survive.
—Josephine Hart, *Damage*

Finding peace and quiet proved impossible. Sharon, McCottry, and Cyrese were driven by some flawed dynamic, like a malevolent, dark current in an underground river pulling swimmers away from light and any hope of survival. The emails I received over the next few days from Carl about Cyrese proved that the current was as strong as ever.

According to Carl, Cyrese was abusive and out of control, breaking plates and trying to beat on him. He was trying to get rid of her by the weekend. The good news was that "da Cat" might be caged for at least ten years.

Leonard, always struggling to keep his mental problems in check, was also vulnerable, and Sharon was taunting her sibling with threats. Leonard sent me the following in answer to my inquiry as to how he was doing.

My good Swan,

I am not good to. I have been called so many times last night by my bad sister so I have to un-plug my phone now., She is trying to make my cra-zy threats hospital and jail for sexual expressions. Now she called my doctor to say i am suicide and do not answer to her call or doorbell. But I will not be crazy thanks to her. Now I have to felt sad and afraid of her. Harold is sad to and Karan is happy. my family sucks bad for me.

so Sad Lenny

I thought it was ironic that the very person who had been so incensed at my initial contact with Leonard, a woman who thought I was responsible for having Leonard sent to Greystone, was herself now attempting to drive Leonard back into the grim confines of the horrid psychiatric facility in New Jersey. My angst over his fate deepened.

***

On a cool Saturday afternoon I walked my dog along North 9th Street and Wythe Avenue. It was a quiet stretch just a couple of blocks from my place. With Mini Me as my companion, I was enjoying a few moments of peace when a red Ford Bronco pulled up near us, the engine idling. I looked at the plates since I was still watching every detail any time I left my home, although I was interrupted before I had time to commit the plate to memory.

"Are you Sue?" a woman asked, opening the door and leaning out. She was a thirty-something bleach-blonde with a rough-cut Queens accent. I was glad Mini Me was at my side.

Not many people call me Sue. This woman didn't look at all familiar. The scowl on her face spoke of urgency and anger, and it was evident she wasn't looking for a teatime companion. I thought I saw someone in the passenger seat, but I couldn't be sure. Maybe Mini Me wouldn't be enough protection after all. I felt trapped.

She will make good babies and keep making one every year until she's done in and ate.

"No, I'm not," I said bravely.

If she didn't know exactly what "Sue" looked like, then I wasn't going to play the obliging stranger and help her out.

The woman looked puzzled, irritated. "You're not Sue?" she asked, squinting in annoyed frustration.

"No." My face was expressionless.

She studied my frozen stare for a few tense moments. "Okay, no problem," she said, her face relaxing and she sped off.

I felt like a hunted rabbit. My impulse was to run, but I thought it best to remain calm and let the Bronco disappear even though my heart was pounding. I couldn't let her— or them, as the case might be—know which way I was headed, assuming she didn't have my address already (and it seemed as if everyone between Massachusetts and New Jersey already knew where Susan Fensten spent her days and nights cringing in fear). But I had to at least *try* to throw them off by not heading directly for my front door. I swiftly turned the corner, which was only a few steps away, and headed down Wythe and then left onto North 8th. Mini Me and I moved at a quick clip, with my mind on the suspicious Bronco and its occupant … or occupants.

Had there been somebody in the passenger seat, somebody staring at me from the shadowy recesses of the vehicle? Had the rough-looking blonde been alone?

As I continued walking, I was so immersed in my thoughts that I hardly felt my feet touching the pavement.

I couldn't wander the neighborhood forever, so I walked quickly to my building, keys in hand as my eyes darted back and forth, searching for any sign of the red Bronco. My hand reached out, inserted the key, and turned the tumblers in the lock.

I was inside, but my mind raced with a dozen questions. Were these people friends of Cyrese or McCottry? What were the odds that a total stranger would peg me as "Sue" in an almost deserted neighborhood? Had the blonde recognized my dog and me from the picture I sent to Karen and which had been passed to so many eager viewers? Did she mean me harm or was she perhaps trying to warn me of something?

Sue. SusieQ. Susan B. Fuckstein. My name, twisted in so many emails, seemed foreign, alien. But maybe that's what stalkers do best in their quest to instill fear: they make their prey dissociate by peeling away their identities, their confidence in the familiar.

I called Bobby, a reflexive reaction anytime something new or bizarre poked its head out of the unknown, and the incident with the blonde certainly qualified as bizarre. Bobby was of the opinion that he wouldn't have been able to live in the same building any longer if he were in my shoes. He would be too afraid and have to move.

I couldn't hide something this serious from Nolan, so I told him that someone very real had approached me in the neighborhood—no disembodied voice in an email— someone who asked for me by name. I could tell that he'd had enough, that he was ready to call it quits and leave.

I can't say that I blamed him.

***

More bad news pertaining to Nolan came from Carl on September 18.

Susan hi,

I wanted to say hi and see how your doing? Some new things have happened in the last day I wanted to talk to you about. She keeps calling here for Cyrese and I want to put a stop to her leading her into darker waters. I found some more pictures and a map from the computer of Brooklyn and Jersey. Susan can you tell me who a "Nolan G." is and also if you know a "Vincent S."? want to see this Barnes lady put away.

Carl :)

Sharon and Cyrese knew Nolan's last name, and if they had maps, I assumed they intended to use them. Despite the severe strain in our relationship, Nolan and I checked in with each other daily. Meanwhile, Sharon was providing Cyrese with money, drugs, and a full-time job as accomplice. I asked Carl if he could send me the Visa slip with Sharon's name on it, but he said that he didn't have it anymore. He said he was still in the process of giving Cyrese the boot but felt that he had to tread lightly so as not to agitate Cyrese's father. I told Carl to keep Lenny's whereabouts secret if my cousin indeed moved to a loft. He knew Leonard was feeling down because of Sharon and was about to lose his car "thanks to all this shit," so I didn't have to spell out the danger that his friend might be in.

The only good news to come from Carl was that McCottry was being transferred to Ancora, a psychiatric facility in Hammonton, New Jersey. He had landed in a mental hospital, and I thought it could actually be for the better since he might be kept under closer watch, with his movements and communications severely limited. This was doubly important because I'd heard that McCottry was enraged when his freedom had been revoked so soon—and because of me.

I told Carl the story about the red Bronco, and he piqued my curiosity with his reply.

Susan hi,

Listen I think I know who this might be. Was there another woman with brown hair with her or a dog guard in the back part like a gate? I will check back later.

Carl

If there *had* been another person in the Ford, I felt sure it was a woman, although I was equally certain there had been no dog in the vehicle. It didn't surprise me that Carl might know who blondie's partner was, even in a city like New York, the world became a smaller place once one bored into certain inner circles. The nightlife for the damned was the perfect camouflage for criminals and those who fed on the fringes of their activities.

***

More emails. The bad kind.

I received the lyrics from U2's "I Threw a Brick through a Window" from *jelly@jello.com*. Sharon or Cyrese was telegraphing me a message, a little "Lobbing a brick through your window wouldn't be so hard to do."

When I told Hal of this email he responded:

Susan,

Forgive me for getting back to you so late I have been on the road. This concerns me regarding the "woman who asked you questions" and this threat of a "brick through your window". I do not like it in the least. Without sounding too nosey I wonder if there is any way you could move? In my humble estimation a change of address would do you good. More later.

Hugs and support,

Hal

I told Hal that I would keep him apprised of all developments, but that I was unable to move and could not accept Leonard's charity. In all truth, I wouldn't have known where to go even if I could have afforded to relocate. Was any place safe?

CHAPTER TWENTY-TWO

THE FREEZER

Is it progress if a cannibal eats with a knife and fork?
—Stanislaw Lec, *Unkempt Thoughts*

By the waning days of September, I had endured many levels of shock. At times, I descended into deeper states of numbness and disbelief. At other times, my body's fight-or-flight response was stuck in overdrive. Threats of murder and cannibalism have distinct effects on the nervous system.

On September 24, several news items from Hal arrived in the space of a few hours as one email after another poured into my inbox. First, I learned that Carl had been attacked and was in the intensive care unit. His sister Janis had alerted Leonard, who in turn told Hal.

Dear Leona,

I am writing to let you know Carl is in the ICU at Mary Immaculate after being stuck with a morphine needle. The police have been over his house twice now and Cyrese is nowhere to be found. I will let him tell you about it but he wanted me to let you know and to tell your cousin that he was hit. A car pulled up on him and that's all he knows. He is in ICU for another day. He stopped breathing in the ambulance and now he has trouble feeling his feet. I am going back tonight to see him so if you

want I can give him a message or you can call him
when he gets a room. Sorry to be such a downer.

Janis

In subsequent emails on the same day, more details
emerged, although they were far from complete. Carl had
been given a "hot shot"—a syringe loaded with one or more
"knockout" drugs. A neighbor had seen him lying on the
sidewalk and called 911. He was breathing on his own and
had mumbled something about "the twelve." Cyrese was
missing, and most of her belongings had been cleared out
of Carl's place. As Janis had succinctly put it to Leonard,
"What the fuck are you two up to now?"

Bobby and I speculated on Cyrese's whereabouts upon
reading an email from Lenny to Hal in which he said he
believed she, too, was involved with The Tribe of Twelve via
Sharon and Felix. Leonard seemed to have some knowledge
of The Tribe, stating that they were "a devil cult . . . who
ate a mother and kid this summer." He also wanted to know
when Sharon would finally cease to be his signatory so that
he could get his money and find another place.

It was obvious that Leonard was petrified. He advised
me to be extremely cautious—no problem, I was already
"there"—and told me that he was checking into a hotel for
the night but not to tell Hal. His nerves, he said, were shot.

The Tribe was figuring more and more prominently in
unfolding events as evidenced by an email I received directly
from Janis after I expressed my concerns to her about Carl's
medical status. She said Cyrese had been arrested in upstate
New York while "living with a bunch of people" and was
being detained for questioning by the police. She said Carl
was improving, but it was the last two sentences of her

email that were especially puzzling: "If you don't mind me asking this, could you please tell me what Cyrese could have stashed away in a freezer in Carl's garage? The police took the whole thing, drip pan included."

Bobby and I had been correct. Cyrese had been with The Twelve.

***

Janis emailed on September 25 to say that the police were becoming more and more interested in Cyrese's involvement with The Tribe of Twelve. As for the mysterious contents of Carl's freezer, Janis provided a clue in a second email that arrived later in the day.

Leona and Susan,

I saw Carl tonight and he is doing good and the doctor told him he can go home by Monday. He is out of ICU and in a private room. When I got there 2 detectives were leaving. He said they think Cyrese's uncle had a corps in the freezer for a while. Yes a corps, a dead body. They are investigating him on a murder. This is getting to fucked up for me guys. He told me to tell you thanks for all the good wishes and that he will be back up in no time. The good news is he can feel his feet and was walking a little bit earlier. I am not staying at his place anymore after hearing about the dead body, lol No way.

The cops told Carl that when they arrested Cyrese some of the people there tried to hide her and it turned ugly. They are getting all of his phone records from the time she lived with him and seeing who she called. I have a feeling but Carl won't tell me that they found something really bad up at that farm. I am just so glad my brother is ok.

Thanks you guys for caring.

Janis

The only response I could make to Janis was, "It's a nightmare" and that I was glad Carl continued to improve. He'd been very kind to me once we'd gotten beyond the initial awkwardness of Kinkfest, and I was genuinely sorry to see him targeted. It wasn't as if I couldn't sympathize. But a corpse in the freezer? The word "nightmare" seemed an understatement.

I emailed Karen next, assuring her that I believed in God and prayer "in my own way," adding that I was now ready to move, although I wasn't sure how I could afford to relocate. Despite my deep, lifelong ties to New York City, I didn't think I could bear much more. There were too many pitchforks in the fiery circles of this inferno. The police believed there had been a corpse in Carl's freezer—Cyrese's stash for her "uncle" Felix. I might have regarded Janis's information a bit differently—maybe even with mild skepticism—if I hadn't seen the many emails between Sharon and Felix, emails that addressed a single stated goal of getting Nolan and me upstate, where cannibalism was practiced by The Tribe of Twelve.

Predictably, Karen was upset, feeling that she couldn't keep saving everyone. She also said that Leonard was "still MIA," but I intended to honor his request not to divulge that he was temporarily staying at a hotel. Furthermore, her email contained information about the genetic predispositions in Sharon's family (and by extension, those in the family of

Morris Feinstein). Speaking of Sharon's daughter, Karen wrote:

> I am also a little worried about her own child Jolie. Every pet this little girl ever gets ends up dead. Hamsters, fish, two birds, and even a house cat. Sharon said it looked poisoned. When she is here she is a bad loser when she plays with our girls and something usually ends up mysteriously broken by the end of the night.

Dead animals, possibly killed by Jolie. Broken objects, a sign of violent behavior. I now began to think that the only person who'd acted with wisdom and common sense was Tom Schoef, who had broken away from the family months ago. Perhaps he'd seen the warning signs far more clearly than I had. I am sure Nolan would agree.

I needed to move.

***

Leonard was back home but was still committed to moving, although it was unlikely that he would find relief from the meddlesome and harassing Sharon unless she was no longer his signatory. Hal and Karen were still reluctant to completely remove Sharon from their lives even though Karen had said on more than one occasion that she was finally realizing the depth of her sister's illness. Karen, the quintessential caretaker and enabler, was psychologically enmeshed with her siblings. Why the Gardiners allowed Sharon to even set foot in their home was beyond me.

Hal related developments about Sharon and McCottry, although his report was, as usual, long on optimism and short on specifics. Sharon was going to be brought before a judge the following week. He said McCottry was "also facing new charges that should seal his fate for a long time to come." Sharon was stirring many cauldrons, but I was unsure which of her actions Mr. Walters was trying to counter. As for McCottry, Hal had already told me that he'd been slapped with new charges for his kidnapping scheme, so was he now telling me that additional charges had been filed? Was McCottry now in trouble, like Cyrese, for the contents of the freezer or administering the hot shot? I trusted that Hal, in the midst of trying to keep his family functioning, was doing what he could to find legal remedies for the insanity that was spreading like a plague, but the vagueness of everyone's reports was wearing on my nerves. There was always a new development—a new mystery, hurdle, or impediment—and it was exhausting to repeatedly update my friends as I fed them new information.

I needed to move, and if people tracked me down using the internet, then so be it. It was a chance I'd have to take.

My growing resolve to leave was reinforced by Leonard's next messages. He said that McCottry had once taken him to a river to see the skull of a dead girl. He was convinced that his former friend was eating people and was into "devil worship and fire lust." He also believed the police would be wise to question McCottry about a missing priest.

According to Janis, Carl was coming home that afternoon, hopefully to an empty home. Cyrese had been released, but she wasn't allowed to go near Carl's place, although the police didn't have any evidence to link her to his assault. The hot shot, she said, had been administered by two women. One had engaged Carl in conversation while the other actually gave him the injection. When Janis informed Carl that the police had taken the freezer from the garage, he quickly stopped talking. The mention of two women administering the hot shot was of concern, for it made me wonder if they were the same people in the red Bronco who had asked for Sue.

The freezer was becoming a central issue, and at least three people appeared to know its contents: Carl, Cyrese, and McCottry.

***

When people know they've succeeded in frightening you—know they've got you impaled on a sword of fear—the mind games begin. Emails now arrived from anonymous senders. Then came two rhymes brimming with the consumption of human flesh, sex, and violence. These messages had been sent for pure shock value, nothing more, since the murderous, cannibalistic poems Nolan was supposedly "recommending" referred to how he and I would both be killed and eaten. The third message was also allegedly from Nolan. Two pictures were attached displaying a woman on a BBQ spit, obviously faked, the other was a nude woman face down in some grass and leaves, and her skin was chalky blue white.

From: Nolan Grey NGrey_pimp@yahoo.com

Subject: EATEN ALIVE

The tribal cook shouts out commands:

"Don't turn the spit too slow!"

"Alright, let's butter her up again,

this time from head to toe!"

Was the body on the ground someone posing? Many sexual cults are focused on death as an aphrodisiac, so it wasn't out of the realm of possibility. That said, it looked like it could well be the corpse of a young woman.

It was time to go to the authorities again.

CHAPTER TWENTY-THREE

THE TRIBE OF THE TWELVE

Tell us, pray, what devil
This melancholy is, which can transform
Men into monsters.
—John Ford, *The Lady's Trial*

I returned to the 90th Precinct, wondering how I could possibly explain the photo of the dead girl, threats of cannibalism, and kidnapping plots without being regarded as crazy. I explained the nature of my visit to the desk officer, and, as I sketched out the story, my words sounded surreal, as if I were recounting the plot of a slasher movie. Trying to take it all in, the officer eyed me for a moment and asked me to take a seat. I waited a very long time before I was allowed to speak to a Detective Fronenberger, a seasoned cop. I quickly sensed that I didn't have a great deal of time to lay out the facts before he would shut me down, so I explained my situation as succinctly as I could while trying to retain some sense of desperation and urgency. Before speaking of cannibalism or kidnapping, however, I told him I'd been to the station before to complain about sexual harassment.

"Well?" he said, narrowing his eyes. "The prostitution report—what about it?"

Cops have a way of making a person feel guilty when they're not. I countered by telling him that not only was I *not* a prostitute but that I hadn't even been in Massachusetts in over twenty years. My answer seemed to quell his skepticism, so I proceeded to describe the unsettling encounter I'd had with the gravel-throated blonde in the red Bronco, and how Carl Mulgrave had been hospitalized after receiving a hot shot from two women who might have been the occupants of the Ford. When I told him that I didn't have a plate number for the vehicle, he said there wasn't much to go on.

I pressed on, showing him the emails and the photo of the dead girl, explaining that there were some bad people who knew where I lived and who'd been watching me. Despite my belief that the body looked like a genuine corpse rather than someone posing, he quickly responded by saying the picture could have been downloaded from a website. He studied the picture again and left the room. I had no idea whether he was soliciting another opinion, looking through files of unsolved homicides, or simply stalling for time. When he returned fifteen minutes later, he said he understood my fears completely but that there wasn't much he could do. A few emails, hearsay, and a graphic picture, possibly from the internet, wasn't enough to warrant police involvement. His hands were tied.

I told him plainly that I was sinking into despair to the point of moving from the city. He told me I shouldn't take such a drastic step just yet, but I wasn't soothed. By this point, I had few remaining concrete or emotional resources at my disposal. Fronenberger said to stay in touch. Stay in touch about *what*—everything the police either didn't believe or couldn't investigate?

On the way home, I carefully weighed the various dangers facing me. I felt that something was most definitely going to happen, and if my body turned up, at least the cops would have somewhere to start their investigation. Like other potential victims before me, I was leaving clues for those who would find the crime scene if the worst-case scenario played out. Others would have to deal with it. I'd tried and gotten nowhere.

I had no sense of reality any longer. I was mired in total despair. Carl Mulgrave, on the other hand, felt almost jubilant.

"I Made IT!"

Leona, Susan hi,

Well I made it lol. I want to thank you both for thinkin about me. It's been a real hard time the last few days. I found out a lot of shit I didn't want to know and now my life has changed.

I just wanted to let you know I'm home and OK and I will write more tomorrow. I'm very tired and still not feeling to good :(My advise to both of you is keep your eagle eye open until this thing is closed. There is a lot of shit about to come down.

Carl :)

What Carl knew about what was soon to "come down" was anybody's guess, but the cops had interviewed him by his bedside, and I had the sense that there was more to Carl's personal story than he felt he could safely share.

Hal had come into possession of more emails from Carl via Leonard. Carl was less guarded when speaking only to Leona, which was understandable since the two apparently went pretty far back.

Cyrese was on the loose and doing web design for The Twelve, although I didn't have the stomach to look at the link. Carl was further tipping his hand by saying that the stash in the freezer wasn't a deer "killed illegal," as Felix had told him.

Leonard had also received a copy of the link and tried to assuage any fears I might have regarding his own behavior by telling me that he "like [sic] all food and most veggies and fruits," like a kid reassuring his teacher that he's a good boy who always does his homework. He himself continued to be afraid for his own safety, and with each email he sent, the contrast between the harassing personality he originally displayed and the frightened, concerned man I had come to know became sharply delineated. I was still his swan.

Leonard had good reason to be afraid. Sharon was using her freedom, which I hoped would be short-lived, to masquerade as Nolan, warning Lenny in the sternest terms to cease all contact with me.

From: Nolan Grey <Ngrey_pimp@yahoo.com>

Subject: BACK OFF

To: LeonaKink@yahoo.com

Cc: LeonardNachman@yahoo.com, LenDog_NJ@yahoo.com

STAY AWAY FROM SUSAN YOU SICK PIECE OF SHIT.

IF I FIND OUT YOU ARE IN CONTACT WITH HER YOU WILL PAY.

NOLAN

Hal remained the nexus for most communication and news. He told me that Sharon was due to stand before a judge again in a matter of days, although until then she was "free to work whatever evil she wants."

Hal advised me not to look at the link to Cyrese's web designs, explaining that they were old drawings and pictures of medieval woodcuts depicting demonic creatures eating people. The web page, he said, was a call to "a feast for the fall season," which included "slaughter and fresh kills." He suggested Nolan and I get away for a while until "this thing blows over." As much as I respected Hal, his sentiment was naïve. Things weren't going to blow over, with criminals bowing and exiting, stage left. We were in far too deep. As for Nolan, he was contemplating going to Atlanta, even if it meant withdrawing from school for the semester. Because of me, he'd been exposed to a maelstrom of criminal activity that had steadily worn on his nerves. He had reached his limit and needed a change, and I understood that. By the same token, I didn't want to be abandoned at my most vulnerable moment.

On September 29, Carl sent me a very long email that reiterated much of what I already knew, but it also contained new details that helped create a more coherent narrative of the myriad events that had unfolded so quickly.

Susan hi,

I want to be straight with you Susan because you need to know some things. I don't know if you or your cousin are taking any of this serious but I am. I was almost killed and I'm not taking this shit anymore. OK I admit I knew Cyrese and her uncle were into some weird shit but I kept my nose out of it minding my business. Felix sold dope and Cyrese got in it with him for a while, OK then he took her upstate to meet some friends of his and she came back a different girl. I am telling you Susan if you saw her before you would never know her now. Her old man Maurice is a real badass and has connections on the outside. He's doing time in northern Cali. but the bars and concrete don't stop his reach. I spoke with him a few times when he call'd for Cyrese and we got along OK. There is a group of people living upstate here that are very bad. Evil is more the word Im lookin for. They call themselves the "Twelve Tribes" but that's a bunch of shit. They aren't near God or Israel or anything good it's all a front.

OK they make homiopathic stuff and look innocent and all but they aren't. The guy that runs the place now did time with Manson out in Cali. (yea Charles Manson) and still keeps in touch with the "Family". This is a spin off of a spinoff of an offshoot from Manson's own people. The 12 my ass. Cyrese ended up babysitting and taking care of the kids for a while and doing Web design for them. Then she told me some whacked out story about a barbecue pit where some baby was roasted. I didn't buy into it at the time but now I know she wasn't bullshittin. Somehow this Barnes lady got in touch with them up there and got a deal going with Felix to try to have you and your boyfriend bagged and tagged. OK I think you know that much now so far. Maurice was going to get a payout from his buddy who runs the 12 I think for the "new meat" and "breeder woman" meaning you live but make babies for them to eat. Yes I said EAT. OK I know this is wild shit but check it out, they do rituals all the time and need humans to sacrafice. Check out "Incarnate Nation." I don't think Cyrese had anything to do with any killing but she got herself in deep knowing about all this shit.

Last spring before the weather got real good Felix asked me to store a deer he and a friend killed illegal in my father's old freezer. I said OK and that was that. I never use the thing and never will now, lol. But seriously I thought they had a deers body in there. A few weeks later they came and took it out while I was at work. OK so what? It weren't no deer Susan. While I was in the hospital the police came and took a bunch of shit from my place including the freezer. I knew it were empty cause I looked in it a few weeks ago and there was just some dark blood down on the frost. I figured it were from the deer. Now I am involved in a murder investigation. I got a hotshot where they tried to kill me and now I am gonna have to testify to everything I know. The cops told me that morning they could arrest me right there in my hospital bed for conspiracy if I didn't cooperate. OK so I did and now we are waiting for DNA evidence to come back to see if ol'Felix or his friend is a killer. I think Cyrese is calling me from her old man's place out on the island. Her stepmother owns it and they stay in touch. I am not accepting her calls because I do not trust her or want anything to do with her or her fucked up life anymore. Her name is "Cyrese Bork" by the way but she uses a few aliases. So if you see that last name come up on your caller i.d. (if you have it) do not accept it, it is Cyrese or her fucked up mother.

OK the other thing is I am moving out of here. This is sad for me because my dad bought this place back in 1965 and it's been Home ever since. To much shit has gone down here and now the neighbors are looking at me sideways and I get cars slowing down to look cause they know this is the house the Crime scene people took a freezer out of. How would you like to be known as the Killer in the neighborhood? Lol. I can just imagine what Hallows Eve will be like this year. Cyrese would usually go full speed ahead and decorate this place for a party but not this year. I am turning out the lights, locking up the doors and leaving for a couple of days. Another reason and I guess the main point I want to make to you is Halloween' is coming up and from what I can put together these people upstate were lookin forward to having your boyfriend to cut up and eat. When Felix got popped Cyrese went crazy and because she thinks I am helping you and Leona out she told her buddies at the commune.

Susan I didn't see it coming I feel so dam stupid about it. I was minding my own business thinking about work the next day and BAM I got stuck in the back and and when I turned around the other bitch hit me in the upper arm. I still have 2 bruises where they got me. Felt like one of the needles broke off in my back for a few days but it was just swellin. I have been also haveing bad night mares at night and cant feel comfortable anymore so the doctors told me to get out of here wich I am doing very soon. I have a detective who is working on this and he told me that when they went up to pop Cyrese the elders there gave them a hard time saying she wasn't there and all this shit. Guess where they found her? Lol, hiding under the floorboards in one of the kids she was watchings room. Lol, yep like a rat under the rug. She had maps of N.Y. N.J. and P.A. Also she had a description of you and what your boyfriend look like, names and address and all to of some other victims. My point is I guess that this ain't over. HallowsEve is coming up and I feel like they are going to try something.

OK Felix is in the can and Cyrese is supposed to be in contact with the police until they call her again. But there are other crazies on the loose like those bitches who stuck me and who knows who else. Watch any calls that come in from 518 area code or 516 it might be Cyrese or some of the 12 looking to see if your all home. I am not trying to be paranoid or to scare you I am dead on serious. I almost died Susan and I am not taking any more chances. I advise you to keep a weapon handy and like I say why don't you and your boyfriend get out of here for a while or take a trip? I would not be around on All Hallows if I were you. Cyrese and her friends always celebrate the Sabbath and with things the way they are I can imagine what they are planning. I knew she was a bad girl and all that but I never thought she was involved in murder, blood sacrafice or Satanism for real. I figured she like the look and jewelry and image of it all, boy was I ever wrong. Everything got real bad when this Barnes lady started to call here and I told the police that "It's Leona's sister in Massachussets". You know that anyhow but this bitch is the one who got things stirred up. I wanted to get rid of Cyrese for a while anyhow but Barnes just helped it happen a lot sooner I guess. Susan do you think Cyrese is still talking to her and that is where the money is coming from? I gave the police Cyreses paperwork for the p.o. box she opened and I think they will trace some money to Barnes. The det. here in NY won't say anything about her because right now I think they have there hands full with what they got upstate.

These people are sick and Evil. I thought I saw a lot in my time but this shit is off the charts. Human sacrafice, torture, slave labor and forced child-birth? No thank you. I am a simple country boy when it comes to any of that. OK I have my little perversities but nothing that isn't consensual. OK and one more thing. Did you know that your cousin was involved in a bad scene a while back with Fe-lix and another guy and some girl they got? Don't worry it ain't murder but might have been if the poor thing didn't get away. Leona is kewl and all I love him like a brother but that always bothered me a little bit. I hope this don't shock you to much but I thought you should know that to. I can tell you more later if you want. Susan be careful and you and your boyfriend watch your backs please. If you can get out of here for Halloween' then I suggest you do it. Let me know if there is anything I can do. right now I am going through all my shit to see what I am gonna keep and give away.

Be kewl

I had originally envisioned Cyrese as Carl's kinky girlfriend. She had been threatening me from the beginning, but I obviously had no designs on "her man." Kinkfest came and went, with Cyrese representing nothing more at the time than a minor player in the larger drama. Her "old man," however, was Maurice Bork, a "real badass" doing hard time in California. Her honorary uncle was none other than Robert McCottry, who'd introduced her to dealing dope and an upstate cult that had a taste for serving unusual fare at dinnertime. Enter Sharon Barnes, an old friend of Felix from the days when Leonard was suspected of raping a young girl with McCottry and Lou Burr. Already under psychiatric care, Sharon had turned sullen and vindictive when her wedding had been canceled and her control over Leonard had, in her own mind, been compromised by his correspondence with me. The stage was set—and so was the dinner table. She made plans with McCottry to have Nolan and me abducted, and through McCottry she'd acquired a secondary accomplice with knowledge of The Twelve, Cyrese Bork. When Felix was "popped," Cyrese became enraged at me and had picked up where her uncle had left off. By cooperating with the police and snitching on both Felix and Cyrese, Carl had barely escaped arrest, resulting in the confiscation of the infamous freezer that had, in all likelihood, contained human remains courtesy of Felix and his buddy Mika.

As for Kinkfest, it had served as a conduit, bringing Mulgrave and Cyrese into my life at the same time that McCottry, newly released from prison, was building a dungeon for Leonard, who had told him about his "best cousin" in New York. When I pissed off Felix, I gave him the perfect motive for cooperating with Sharon. It all made a lot more sense now.

But the cause and effect reached back even farther. The pivotal character in every event that had transpired—the stalking, the threats, the emails, the mysterious phone calls—had been Leonard Nachman. He was the hub where all the spokes connected, and yet I placed no blame on his shoulders. He could not have foreseen how his ebullient banter about Kinkfest would link me straight to a criminal underworld that dovetailed with his fetishism.

I had no idea what to do. To the police, everything Carl had described was either hearsay or "make-believe." According to the letter of the law, there wasn't anything they could do, although Detective Fronenberger wasn't standing in my shoes. He hadn't been stalked, hadn't picked up the phone to listen to silence on the other end of the line. Malicious, sick people hadn't cruised past his home in the middle of the night, nor had he received emails promising that he would become a victim of ritualistic cannibalism.

Leonard, Hal, and Carl had all told me to be careful but not to worry—things would be fine one day. All I had to do was take a holiday. They meant well, but they were wrong.

My days were surely numbered.

**

Hal's next update was predictable. The results of Sharon's hearing were not what he or I had hoped for. Karen had been a reluctant witness at best—as usual, Hal provided no specifics—but the result was Sharon received a $25,000 fine but no jail time. She had also been charged with crimes pertaining to Leonard: stalking, harassment, criminal practice, and the intentional infliction of emotional distress. Mr. Walters had only succeeded in proving electronic harassment, for which Sharon received mandatory charity work in lieu of imprisonment since she was a widowed mother of two. There was one hope remaining: if New Jersey pursued the kidnapping charges brought against McCottry, then new charges might also be filed against Sharon for complicity. But there was a glitch. With McCottry already incarcerated, the authorities were in no hurry to prosecute him for intent to kidnap. The only positive outcome of the hearing was that Sharon had received a restraining order forbidding her to approach Leonard. The trial information from the Commonwealth of Massachusetts, with commentary by Ken Walters, was forwarded by Hal.

Hal,

She did it again. They gave her a fine of $25,000.00 and issued a HRO for Leonard. When she comes near him or it can be proven she is behind any subsequent suffering due to her actions she will be arrested. There was not enough evidence to show she ever left the Commonwealth, yet there was considerable interest in this subject. I got the feeling the panel wanted to throw the book at her but judiciously they could not. Because of the utility records we were able to establish electronic harassment, reflected in the penalty. She should have gone to jail for 6mos. at least, but they introduced her 'charity work' and the fact she is 'a widowed mother of two'. Stir of humor when 'Felix deCat' was introduced. If New Jersey pursues this with McCottry, then Barnes will be brought up on charges at that time. If McCottry is not brought up on these serious charges, Barnes will not be either.

You know the drill Hal. The paperwork went in about two weeks ago and I could tell by the panel's expression when we walked in that they had plenty of time to see everything for themselves. The consensus is that Barnes had something to do with everything we showed, but legally there are protections in her favor. Leonard could not prove loss of wages, nor can anyone else I assume. When we do its back to court; I think we will have a very strong case. With the Jersey case coupled with what your relative sent us from New York and what they heard today I believe she will be fully prosecuted. I will add that $25,000.00 is a good sock in the jaw. Something to smile about. The court has ruled on this matter (see below).

Ken

SMC-03782791
COMMONWEALTH / NACHMAN v. BARNES
September 30, 2004
Present: Aaron, Walters, Lynch, Greaney, & Ireland
Stalking, Harassment, Practice, Criminal, Intentional Infliction of Emotional Distress.

Instructions to jury, Assistance of counsel, Cross-examination by prosecutor, Argument by prosecutor. Evidence, Judicial discretion, Relevancy and materiality, Cross-examination, Credibility of evidence.

Complaint received and sworn to in the Civil Division of the District Court Department on September 15, 2004.

A pretrial motion to dismiss was considered by Kenneth J. Cote, Jr., J., and the case was tried before Nancy Dusek, J.

Abraham J. Mayer for the defendant.

Deborah Ahlstrom, Assistant District Attorney, for the Commonwealth.

Facts of the Case

Sharon Barnes (d) willfully and maliciously engaged in a knowing pattern of conduct or series of acts over a period of time directed at her brother: Leonard Nachman (p) and others, which seriously alarmed him and caused him to suffer substantial emotional distress. Defendant took pride in degrading Plaintiff for her own amusement.

Questions Presented / Conclusion:

(The harassment must be such that a reasonable person would be placed in fear for their physical safety. The nature of online communications permits a high level of abusive discussion).

1) Is there evidence that the defendant traveled across a state line? NO

2) Is there evidence that the defendant used mail, email, or telephone? YES

3) Is there evidence that the defendant communicated an intent to injure or harass the plaintiff? YES

4) Is there evidence that in the course of, or as a result of, such travel or communications the defendant placed the plaintiff in reasonable fear of their life, or of serious bodily

injury, or of the death or serious bodily injury to a member of the plaintiff's immediate family? YES

5) Is there evidence that the defendant communicated a demand or request for a ransom or reward for the release of any kidnapped person? NO

6) Is there evidence that the defendant communicated a threat to kidnap or injure any person, with the intent to extort money or any other thing of value from the plaintiff? NO

7) Is there evidence that the defendant communicated a threat to kidnap or injure any person? YES

8) Is there evidence that the defendant communicated a threat to injure the property or reputation of the plaintiff or of another or the reputation of a deceased person or any threat to accuse the plaintiff or any other person of a crime, with the intent to extort money or any other thing of value from the plaintiff? NO

9) Is there evidence that the communications took place in interstate or foreign commerce? NO

10) Is there evidence that the defendant knowingly used an electronic communications device to make and then transmit a communication which is obscene, lewd, lascivious, or filthy, with intent to annoy, abuse, threaten, or harass another person? YES

11) Is there evidence that the defendant made a telephone call or used a telecommunications device, whether or not conversation or communication ensued, without disclosing their identity with intent to annoy, abuse, threaten, or harass any person at the called number or who received the communications? YES

12) Is there evidence that the defendant made or caused to be made the telephone of another repeatedly or

continuously to ring, with intent to harass any person at the called number? YES

13) Is there evidence that the defendant made repeated telephone calls or repeatedly initiated communication with a telecommunications device, during which conversation or communication ensued, with the intent solely to harass any person at the called number or who received the communication? YES

SMC-03782791 - Docket Number: 94
Argued: Sep 30, 2004 / **Decided**: Sep 30, 2004
Judicial Court Room 1401, Boston, MA 02108

Hal had told me twice that McCottry had been "slapped" with new charges. He had promised time and again that Sharon would soon be behind bars on countless charges thanks to the information and emails provided to his attorney. Now he was telling me that Sharon was free and that "the new charges" against McCottry were not going to be prosecuted with any swiftness. Was I surprised? Not at all. The system existed for criminals, not victims.

Perhaps Hal, Karen, and Leonard were content to exist in perpetual limbo. By all accounts, Leonard and his siblings had endured chaos since childhood. As for Hal, he was never going to forsake his family despite his occasional temptations to leave. Their lives constituted a nightmarish circus that was never going to fold its tents. This may have approached normalcy to them, but for me it was a nightmare that kept getting worse.

I decided to move to Washington, DC. It was the only place where I had friends. If I was hunted down, at least I wouldn't die alone.

CHAPTER TWENTY-FOUR

QUIETLY MOVE AWAY

I can face death, but I cannot face watching
myself disappear from within ...
I don't know who I am anymore.
—Claude Jutra

The growing sense of isolation within this grim vortex tilted the vacuum of the centrifuge in the monster's favor. With each escalating twist and turn it became harder to talk about and I became more vulnerable. Part of me wanted desperately to hide my ordeal, as I had in past abusive relationships. The story was so bizarre and exhausting my small circle was wearing thin. The stress was unbearable. I felt I had to move but was conflicted and needed to talk with one of my few and oldest friends. Steve said I should absolutely not be bullied from leaving my home, my city, and my life. I trusted his judgment, by this point I had lived in Williamsburg for twenty years. I was paying "1980s rent," and had a marvelous view of Manhattan from my corner on North 7th Street and Kent Avenue. For the first time in my life, I had a garden. A simple thing, to be sure, but not something available to most New Yorkers. I was just one stop from Manhattan, a four-minute subway ride. I loved my quiet perch along the banks of the East River rounding the 'elbow' of the island. How could I possibly find a better home?

My mother naturally wanted me to stay in New York. I'd told her about my ordeal without putting too fine a point on the more macabre elements of the story, and her inquiry of "Do any of these people know where I live?" went straight to my heart. I didn't want to be too far away from her, but I was hard-pressed to think of a way out of my dilemma.

Bobby, who was also a native New Yorker, continued to feel that I had no option left but to relocate, as painful as that might be. Nolan was in agreement. He not only felt that it was the best thing to do—he earnestly believed that it was the *only* thing to do.

When I told my boss at Rizzoli that there was a strong possibility that I would have to resign because of being stalked—I painted my story in broad strokes—the news was met with a grave look of concern. She, too, felt that I should remain in the city but trusted that I knew best. If it were necessary, she'd be sorry to lose me. I suspect it was hard for her and others to put themselves in my shoes. Their worlds were comfortable, predictable. By contrast, my life was phantasmagoric. In my deepening alienation from everything that was normal, I envied everyone who wasn't me.

Bobby invited me to stay with James and him at Dupont Circle so that I could look at apartments. I still wasn't one hundred percent convinced that I was ready to leave Brooklyn, especially since Washington was not a publishing center and my employment opportunities would be very limited. I had little money on hand, and I would be starting from scratch. In preparation for the trip, I looked at online listings for apartments in DC, and found them to be nearly as expensive as those in New York. Assuming I found suitable digs, they would probably be smaller and not have a backyard for my dog. I had been afraid of being murdered, but a part of me was already dying as I looked at the online descriptions. How had things come to this? On the way to Penn Station I ruminated over the pros and cons of moving, fear driving me forward while a voice deep within told me I would be making the biggest mistake of my life.

Penn Station was crowded, and having never taken the Acela before, my preoccupation with making the correct decision made it difficult to find where I was to board. On the train, I again wondered if moving would solve anything at all. The age of privacy was over, and anyone could be found with the click of a keyboard. By leaving Williamsburg, however, I would at least be removing myself from immediate physical danger. My misgivings were at war with the primal survival instinct in the recesses of every human brain.

I arrived in DC late, worn out, and looking terrible. I was thin and pale again from constantly worrying, my clothes hung limply on my small frame. James and Bobby were quite worried about my haggard appearance, but they looked past it, acting cheerful. At their home, we had a drink and a snack as we talked about how the surreal events surrounding my life now revolved around Sharon, Carl, Cyrese, and McCottry. We tried to laugh at the outrageousness of the situation—twenty-first century cannibals, hot shots, and unknown packages of meat in the freezer of a fetishist—but the laughter was edgy. A tinge of the morbid hung over the conversation. I forced a few smiles, but my mind kept returning to my own private hell.

That's not to say that Bobby or James were intentionally insensitive. James even offered to put the utilities in his name for any apartment I might find. Utility records were accessible online and, by using search engines such as Zabasearch.com, anyone could be lead to the city that I lived in with a quick search. He genuinely cared about me, for he and his secretary had continued to receive daily news about my situation from Bobby.

The following day, Bobby took me through a few neighborhoods within my price range, but they weren't the most ideal places to live in Washington by a long shot, and some were clearly more run down than parts of Williamsburg. With no job leads, I resolved to simply use the weekend as a getaway, all the time dreading my return home, where my inbox would surely contain the psychodrama of Hal's false hopes, Leonard's delicate emotions, Karen's tone of resignation, and Carl's grisly news bulletins. I knew that Nolan expected me to bring back solid job leads, but that wasn't going to happen over the course of a brief weekend, if ever. Despite our floundering relationship, I knew that Nolan cared for me, but I wasn't a magician. I couldn't just snap my fingers and produce a new life in DC.

That night, Bobby and James took me out to dinner, where I sat at the table with approximately ten gay men immersed in the latest gossip. It didn't take long for someone to ask about my ordeal, and I once again forced a smile, gathered my courage, and made polite replies even though I was trying to forget my pain for a few hours, not entertain the troops with my true crime adventure. With each new question, someone else's ears tuned in to the conversation until I was the topic of the evening. Little did these people know that I was ashamed of these current events in my life, that I felt degraded after months of being referred to as a slut, a baby factory, and ultimately a piece of meat that would be good for nothing but sacrifice when the time came. I was on public display, but the people at the table couldn't truly empathize with the helplessness I was feeling. They hadn't been turned away twice by the police, nor were they facing unemployment or being uprooted from everything that made them who they were. At a table of ten, I still felt as if I was eating by myself.

This time, there was no redeeming feature of my jaunt down to DC. No gentle waves as Bobby grilled shrimp on James's boat, no fascination with the architecture and monuments of our nation's capital. My thoughts were turned inward, my life slipping away with each passing second. Maybe this was how people ended up in Greystone.

CHAPTER TWENTY-FIVE

BOUNCE TEST

Great whites have three basic attack modes. A "bump and nibble" approach seeks more information about an object. The "bite and split" attack inflicts a serious wound, then the shark retreats to observe its result. Most devastating is the "break and crush," where a shark leaps out of the water and pounces on its prey. When it hits, it sounds like somebody smashing up a wicker chair.
—Sean van Sommeran, *Pelagic Shark Research Foundation*

One bleak afternoon while walking Mini Me, I happened upon one of the many neighborhood characters, a woman I'd seen several times before. In her fifties, she was someone who, like a lot of others, had gotten her tail caught on a rusty nail in Williamsburg, rambling through life, stopping occasionally and clinging to it for a while. I was more than familiar with lone drifters who tapped into deep wells that others didn't know existed. With dark, wide-set eyes, she had black, wavy hair and a classic theatrical face. She reminded me of an Egon Schiele painting, her features ashen and exotic. Her black beret, cocked sideways, was not a cliché or an affectation. She was the genuine article, a soul in transit, both troubled and wise. I'd spoken with her before when buying her jewelry, so I greeted her without hesitation. She asked me how I was. I didn't look very well since my skin resembled chalk, and I made a reply that reflected my despair.

"Not so good," I said.

"What's the matter?" she asked, lowering her eyelids. "Boyfriend trouble?"

I laughed despite myself, shaking my head at the idea. "Romantic pain? I wish! I could handle that standing on my head."

"Then what is it?"

"I'm being chased by cannibals." I said it flat out, a remark that I wouldn't entrust to anyone except close friends or those who existed partly on the other side of life and had their own strange tales to tell.

The chilly October wind stirred, and a can blew across the lifeless landscape. She looked straight at my face, unblinking. Her eyes grew serious as she stared at a man standing nearby.

"Don't say that out loud," she warned. "He could be a cop. He could be one of *them*."

She took me seriously, but my statement had opened a Pandora's box full of paranoia. She started to rant about pedophiles and cops, believing that cops were rapists— and maybe cannibals, too. They couldn't be trusted. Her charming eccentricities had quickly boiled into something I didn't want to deal with at the moment, a stream of consciousness that too closely resembled the loose ideas and logic in so many of the emails I'd received for nearly a year. I told her I'd be careful and hurried off.

I'd been taken seriously, however, even if only for a few moments, and her credence made me feel human again. Few would have been able to mentally stomach my story, even in passing. Anyone would think I was crazy if I mentioned cannibalism.

***

Carl checked in with a brief update for Lenny and me.

Leona, Susan hi,

I just got word that Cyreses old man Maury is being investigated big time to!!!

They got a supena for California to take the mail out of his cell and Bingo! they see the shit he and Cyrese were writing back and forth, Lol can you believe how dum she is? I can only imagine what they said cause both of them are whack jobs.

Her mother (step) left a message this afternoon telling me to "mind my own buisness" and all this shit. So I am changeing my number and then selling this place.

Well, thats my update. I trust you both are doing OK?

Carl :)

Cyrese and her father might have been exchanging snail mail about any number of things, all of them illegal, but prisoners often correspond in highly sophisticated code rivaling CIA ciphers, so no one would really know what they might be up to. Was it possible that Cyrese was asking her father how to get me killed—or eaten? Nothing seemed out of the realm of possibility at this point. I agreed with Carl all the way. It was time to get out.

Leonard wrote to tell me that he was making a present for me, one that wouldn't be destroyed by his sister. It was some kind of earthen-clay sculpture with sticks attached. He was also contemplating living at a loft in New Jersey, but he still checked into hotels on the weekend for safety's sake. He seemed more like a child with each passing email, such as when he said he would live at the Sugar Factory (the loft) "like Willy Wonka, lol."

***

I was at work when the phone on my desk rang. The caller ID read "Anonymous," which wasn't unusual since my phone rang all day, every day. When I answered, a woman angrily cried, "I want to smash your face in!" Then the line went dead. I felt the smack in my face as sharply as if the woman had been in the room with me. The traveling carnival of the damned, complete with distorted funhouse mirrors, had come to Rizzoli.

The very same day, Nolan was at school when an anonymous call rolled into his voicemail. When he checked the message later, he was horrified to hear what sounded like someone being brutally tortured. He accidentally deleted it before I could hear it.

I wrote to Karen, telling her how distressed I was that Nolan and I were being harassed by telephone yet again. I said straightforwardly that I was at risk because her sister was still free.

Karen sent a reply on October 4, a message, coupled with good wishes, which contained implications that I was being stubborn and judgmental about her sister.

Dear Susan,

I understand how you feel but please don't put it all on me.

If anything, I have tried to keep everyone calm and together as a family. I am raising two daughters while all of this is happening and sometimes I think you forget that Sharon is my sister. We spent a lot of time together growing up. And even though I realize she has deep psychological problems I still want to help her. I wonder if all of these "threats and stories" are true sometimes.

The man in N.Y. who got hurt was a drug addict I feel who might have gotten too much stuff running through his system? Why blame that on Sharon too when she was all the way up here in MA? None of it makes sense to me.

I am sorry to hear you and your friend got annoying calls. We have Caller I.D. and a block on the line so I don't have to put up with those kinds of things. Your telephone company usually runs a deal now and then on the service. You might look into that.

I still have not heard from Len and I am worried. He usually calls me by now and it's been 3 days. Do you know anything? Is there something I should know?

Hal is being civil with me although there's little or no conversation still. He blames me for not helping when my sister was in court last week, but how could I?

You know how it is Susan, I'm sure, having had a sister you know the value of that bond. I did have a long talk with her the other day and she sounded very airy and light as though there was nothing to brood over. I think she is putting all of this behind her and moving on. I wish you could too.

Can't you forgive and forget, move on and meet life's challenges with a new outlook?

I hope so. My sister can be a lovely woman' when given half a chance. Did you know she is musical? Yes, she taught herself to play the piano when she was young and has even composed some of her own arrangements. You see all of this is going away and new times are here. I do love the holidays and hope you and your friend will come up this year. Don't say no this time dear cousin.

I wish you a wonderful week full of sunshine and happy surprises.

Love,

Karen

I wasn't blaming her for anything. I was well aware that she was stressed from taking care of her family. This had been one of her constant themes, although she obviously couldn't begin to empathize with what I was going through. Her entire family was well protected within its madness, but I was alone. Sharon was her sister, but to me she was a major threat.

The rest of the email revealed the Karen whom I had come to know from a distance, someone detached from reality. I didn't think Sharon was "moving on" with her life—I didn't believe she was capable of doing so without intensive psychiatric treatment—nor was I even remotely tempted to give her "half a chance." But Karen, in her perpetual naiveté, had convinced herself that "all of this is going away."

It struck me as inconsistent that Karen, who had upbraided me for blocking anonymous calls, was explaining to me that the phone company ran deals so that I could block annoying calls. And after taking me to task for my views of her sister, why had she reverted to her ongoing saccharine invitation to visit her family? As much as I *could* deduce about the troubled housewife, she was more than a bit enigmatic.

I replied by saying that the calls and emails weren't just annoying; they were criminal in nature, death threats even. I made it clear that I would continue to pursue solutions through law enforcement until justice was served. Her response was glib and rambling.

Dear Susan,

What can I say dear cousin? I am being blamed by one and all so you might as well join the bandwagon. Alright I see a man is now dead but I still cannot understand why this has to be my sister's actions? There is no proof or evidence she was anywhere near this man. I am so tired of all these frightening stories affecting our lives. My sister was here at her home when he committed suicide. I know that for a fact. Now Len is moving again and this time he and Hal won't tell me where. Isn't that terrible Susan, I am his sister and I care about him but they are afraid Sharon will find out somehow. I will go visit him when he gets settled so I don't know how they expect to keep me in the dark for too long, Lol. This is all such nonsense everyone moving here and there. I have lived in the same house for over 10 years, why can't other people do it? I suppose I am just more stable than most when it comes to family and keeping a home.

I just want to forget about that awful man who died and everything else that is ugly in our lives. It does not concern us I tried to tell Hal but he is now coming off like Prince Valiant trying to save the day, Lol, if he only knew how ridiculous he looks with his paper files and faxes to the lawyer. I swear Susan the man thinks he's a lawyer sometimes, LOL. Why doesn't everybody just settle down and enjoy life on its terms. Look at me, I have had a very hard time of it with my brother's problems and my sister acting up the way she does. But I am normal, lol, I think.

Susan I hope you know the beauty and the value of having children of your own sometime soon. Do you think it will happen? I hope so although not everyone is capable of being a good parent. Take me for instance, I try to give my girls a good life and even after doing everything right out of the book I still run into problems. That's just life Susan, you have to roll with the punches.

I am sorry to know you are having all these problems right now. Are you going to move too like Len and everyone else, Lol? Are you and your boyfriend going to move in together or will you buy something this time? You can always come up here and use our guest house or stay in Boston in our other place for a while.

Please do not be mad at me like the others cousin. I only do what I think is best for all concerned. My sister has not even mentioned you the last few times we talked and I think she has put you out of her mind. I wish you could do the same with her.

These calls you claim you received could have been anyone and did you ever stop to consider it was a wrong number? Think about it Susan, Lol, you live in the busiest city in the world and when a wrong number comes in or someone says something off color you take it as a threat to your life?, Lol. Crossed telephone wires happen every day. I even got a wrong number yesterday myself. Well here come the girls so I will sign off for now. Let me know how you are doing. I hope things improve and get better very soon.

Love,

Karen

The statement that she was "more stable than most" was laughable. Her casual manner throughout the rest of the letter, however, was not. She had previously admitted that her sister was disturbed, but now she was in defensive mode again, with Sharon a victim instead of a perpetrator. As for her "crossed lines" theory about my annoying calls, I could only shrug and let Karen be Karen. It was useless to tell her that people dialing wrong numbers didn't scream threats into the phone. Furthermore, if she believed Hal worthy of ridicule because he was collecting evidence, then there wasn't much hope that she was going to understand my plight.

***

Nolan's own personal nightmare was also getting deeper and darker. The day after my "bounce test," he received a voicemail in which a man's voice told Nolan that he needed to go to my apartment immediately. The caller alleged I was going to be raped, Nolan would be forced to watch, and then we were all "going for a ride." Nolan called me from school in a panic, stating that he was going to leave class in Brooklyn and drive into Manhattan to pick me up at work. We would then head straight to my place, pick up some clothes and my dog, and spend the night somewhere safe until we could figure out what to do. While waiting for Nolan, I called Steve and asked if we could crash at his house.

Nolan and I raced to Williamsburg, grabbed some clothes, and waited for Steve to get home from work. While waiting, Nolan was adamant that I should never return to my apartment again. The situation was totally out of control, and I apparently had no way of dealing with any of the dangers that were impacting his life and mine. I was getting very angry at this point, however, as if an internal cog had clicked firmly into place.

"Fine," I said. "We'll go to Steve's for one night just to get out of the way, but I'm not leaving my house for good."

I had no sense of the future, no ability to predict what might happen next in all of this craziness. The only thing I did know for sure was that I wasn't going to be chased from my home. I wasn't going to move to Washington, nor was I going to start looking for safe houses or new apartments in New York. What were my stalkers going to do? Bust down my door? Okay, let them. I was of a mind to kill anyone who came near me. I'd use a baseball bat, my hands, or the rage of eleven months to protect myself. The new internal gears had started to move. I'd grown defiant. I was tired of running scared, and it was time to fight back.

***

On Friday, October 8, I told Hal about the harassment at my office and that someone pretending to be Leonard had sent me an e-greeting. A cryptic response arrived from Hal the same day.

Susan,

I have been in meetings all day I am sorry to get back to you so late. I know it would not be from Leonard as he is still mourning the loss of his friend. I am sure you are upset by it also knowing him briefly. Susan can you please forward me the "greeting" you got so I can add it to the file. Was it threatening? If it is from Sharon there has to be a way to prove it. I will write more from home this evening.

Hal

The loss of his friend? Who was this deceased person I had known briefly? My reply therefore read, "Who? I don't know what you mean." His answer was short and to the point.

Susan,

Leonard's friend Carl is dead. There is some talk of suicide and Len is very upset. I am sorry, I thought you knew.

Hal

Hal also said Leonard would be moving the following month since extreme measures were called for in the wake of the tragedy.

I stared at the screen, thinking that the killing was now close at hand. It was no longer removed, no longer a question of a mystery package in a freezer or the practices of an upstate cult. Carl Mulgrave was dead, and I wasn't buying into the notion of suicide any more than Janis was. Her email to Hal was most emphatic on this point.

Hi Harold,

Carl was found shot in the head last night with a suicide note still in the typewriter. **He did not kill**

himself. Before he died he found out he was writing to a fake detective set up through a remailer by someone who wanted information from him. And that's not all. I suspect his ex-girlfriend Cyrese Bork. The coroner is ruling it a suicide and there is no investigation right now. My parents are both sick and this is probably going to kill them too. My brother would never dream of killing himself. Yes the gun was his and it was in his hand but the note sounds nothing like him. I have the feeling your brother in law Leona and his cousin got into something they shouldn't have. Carl was not into drugs or crime and none of this makes any sense to us. I can send you a print-out of his note if you think it will help? I am leaving for the funeral home now.

Janis Mulgrave

I felt that Janis had known her brother well enough to decide whether or not he'd been suicidal. I knew from his emails that Carl had been afraid, but I also knew that he had done everything possible to protect himself. Suicide seemed highly unlikely. Janis suspected that Cyrese was behind it, and I couldn't help but think of one of Carl's last emails, in which he stated that Cyrese had been writing to her "old man." On top of that, someone had pretended to be Detective Loria in order to find out what Carl knew and what he was up to. Whatever the impersonator had found out, it apparently didn't please her.

Leonard was naturally petrified. Writing to Hal, he said, "He id [sic] not kill hisself I am afraid now very bad."

LNachman1, the man I had once reviled, was consumed with grief and sadness. His joyous winds had dropped, and he was falling fast and hard.

***

I began another round of phone calls to the police. I first called the precinct in Carl Mulgrave's neighborhood in Queens. I began to lay out the details of my situation when the officer interrupted me, saying he was going to transfer me to someone else. Another officer, sounding like someone higher in rank, listened as I related the background of my complex story and then explained that a friend had landed in the hospital the month before as a result of a hot shot loaded with some kind of drug. I added that the police had found a dead body in the freezer of his house in Jamaica, Queens, and that the freezer had been confiscated, together with the drip pan. Now Carl himself was gone, having been found dead from a gunshot wound in his car in Union City, New Jersey. The officer informed me that no open investigation matched the details I was providing. He asked where I lived and why I hadn't contacted my own precinct, and I told him that my previous complaint had gone nowhere. He wanted to know who I'd spoken with, so I gave him Detective Fronenberger's name. He took my name and telephone number, and we hung up.

In desperation, I called Fronenberger again. He seemed annoyed, and I learned that he'd received an angry call from the commander of the Queen's precinct, who had called him, demanding to know why I wasn't getting any assistance in Brooklyn. I guessed he'd gotten chewed out pretty badly since I'd spoken of murder, and now he was running out of patience. Nevertheless, he said he'd look into the matter and get back to me. A short while later he called to say that, according to the medical examiner, no dead bodies had been found in New Jersey. That's how the call ended. I was deeply frustrated. This wasn't another stolen car, another routine burglary. I needed the police, but they didn't seem to need the information I was providing pertaining to numerous possible crimes.

Had the woman in the black beret been right? Were the cops in on it?

Of course not, and I quickly banished all such paranoid thoughts from my mind. But there was no explanation as to why the police had no record of Carl's death, regardless of how he had died. A gunshot to the head? The coroner would definitely have conducted an examination, suicide or not. The police, of course, were fallible, and that was Bobby's conclusion: the police were bungling and inept. Paperwork may have gotten lost, or perhaps someone in Carl's family, for reasons unknown, wanted the gruesome facts covered up.

CHAPTER TWENTY-SIX

FALL SLAUGHTER

Murder, like talent, seems occasionally to run in families.
—The Physiology of Life (1859)

When I arrived at Rizzoli the following Monday, I realized how easy it would be for someone to simply walk past the receptionist, whose other duties sometimes took her away from her desk. When a visitor stepped off the elevator onto the second floor they saw nothing but a reception desk and a main corridor leading to the various offices. Anyone could walk in, and now that I was certain Sharon and her associates knew where I worked, I was more than a bit apprehensive. A security guard was stationed in the lobby, but he couldn't be expected to stop someone who dressed and acted normally from getting on an elevator.

I received an email from someone claiming to be Leonard, but the grammar, spelling, and tone didn't match his style or personality. As was my custom more times than not, I forwarded it to Hal.

> one snitch dead make it 2 more life is short for the pimp n whore
>
> they call for help that never comes no one listens to rats from the slums

snitch L in bed with a crack in her spine soon to r.i.p. in a box o'pine

twenty two days till AllHallowsEve 2 souls for the fire and a dog to cleave

girlF likes to blab and make lots of noise her mouth n twat full of cum from the boys

a drag queen will choke on a ball in his throat the mad Man watches a gun in his coat

the Devil wants two now three make it five There will be no peace while they all are alive

LOL LOL LOL LOL LOL *Happy Halloween* You Pieces Of Shit !!!!!LOL LOL Felix says HELLO LOL LOL

The vulgar lines, together with the rhyming pattern, had all the hallmarks of Cyrese's earlier poetry. I was becoming a prisoner within my own mind. The indomitable Ms. Barnes had managed to transform my imagination into a private Greystone. No walls, no doctors—just a sense of unending confinement, of being watched by someone taking delight in my pain. This must have been how Leonard had felt on so many occasions in his life. On October 10, he sent Hal a brief email that said, "today I went see [sic] my dead friend in a casket . . . Harold I do not want to die to [sic]." The sheer despair in Lenny's words was heartbreaking—and matched my own.

***

The Tribe of Twelve was preparing for All Hallows Eve, and I received the following email at work from louburr_ nj@yahoo.com which offered me a free ride to attend a barbaric, savage ceremony.

Dear Susan,

How nice to hear from you Im very flatterd. Yes of course I will take you to the feast thankyou for asking me. You and your freind can ride up in my new van with us. Can I ask you how you got my email address? I am just curious cause I don't give it out to much. So you are Leona's cousin huh? He told me about you a while ago when we talked. Did Leona give you my address? And were you at KinkFest this year? And if you were I am sorry I don't remember you I guess. Tell me more about yourselve and if you can send me a picture (recent) that would be good. Here is one of me at FleshPot this year lol. I was trying to be like Ed Gein lol! if you know who he was. I didno't think Leona was into this kind of thing so I am just surprised is all. You understand what goe's on there I assume so we are cool on that right up front. Do you have and Incarnate Pass or need one for your freind? Susan I look forward to meeting you and if you would like to meet or talk before the Slaughter you can always give me a call. Would you like to call me? I can give you my #and you could always just say hi if you wanted. And send me your home address so I know where Im going lol. Don't forget that picture hon!

Kisses back, Lou B.

SFensten <sfensten@rizzoliusa.com> wrote:

>feast.

>never been to the Fall Slaughter and always wanted to go.

>address where to pick me up. You will enjoy the
ride there, I will guarantee that LOL!

>Kisses,

>*Susan F.*

Someone was impersonating me again—someone who
had written to Lou Burr and feigned interest in attending
The Tribe's Fall Slaughter. BurrLou Burr and McCottry had
been convicted of raping a young woman when Leonard
was in college.

Another criminal now knew who I was and had my
email address. I already knew that Leonard had allowed my
name to be spread around liberally regarding my possible
attendance at Kinkfest, but thanks to Leonard's party (if not
for other reasons) McCottry and Burr were still in contact
with each other, a deadly duo that Leonard should have had
the good sense to avoid. Leonard's judgment, of course, was
erratic and not to be trusted when it came to his fetishism,
or perhaps despite flare-ups, the bond between the three was
everlasting.

This didn't mean that Leonard had remained on good
terms with Burr, however. Three emails demonstrated quite
clearly that the two men had issues, and I was one of them.
Burr asked Leonard if he had given me his address and "if
this chick is for real."

Dear Lou,

NO I did not give anybody your Email I promise. I
think my bitchy sister is trying more tricks. Do not
believe her please Lou please. Now I think she
wants to kill my cousin and ate her friend, a guy. i
do not care what you do but please please do not
see my good cousin get aten or hurt. Please tell

them to eat somebody else. I am not fooling, my sister has some plan. I am getting out of here now too and only people i trusted are knowing. Carl is dead and so many bad have happened I need to get out. No more partys and no more nothing.

Len

Burr's reply didn't mince words.

Leona,

You don't beg me bitch I do whatever I want and you know it. If this bitch wants action then I will give it to her. She wrote me remember I didn't write her so fuck off all of you.

Yeah Carl is dead so the fuck what? he was S.T.U.P.I.D. and didn't know how to keep his trap shut. And speaking of him guess who just called me? Cyrise wants me to meet her out on the Island tonight. What do you think that bitch wants? I can't protect you anymore Leona your on your own. If there's money in it I'm there. I'm hungry bitch we all don't live on Park Avenue like some people.

Lou

I shouldn't have been surprised that Cyrese was friends with both McCottry and Burr. As Maurice Bork's daughter, she evidently commanded a lot of respect within the criminal community, a respect that also extended to the members of The Tribe. The most troubling aspect of Burr's letter to Leonard, however, was that he wasn't buying the explanation about Sharon, his "bitchy sister." He was ready to give me "action," and I took him at his word that he was willing to try, even without my consent. Men like Burr took what they wanted. Lou Burr's initial contact, asking if I needed a ride to the Fall Slaughter, was similar to McCottry's first email:

polite, with an improper sense of familiarity and a hint of flirtation. It was not a good omen. Leonard naturally forwarded Burr's stinging response to his brother-in-law.

Harold,

ok now see how he threats me ? will my good cousin be ok now? ?

He is with these people who ate some people and i bet Felix told him something to. now Carls ex-Bitch is calling him to make more trouble for me. see what he says here to me.

Lenny

Hal wrote to say that he thought he knew who the man was—it was old news to me—and that he didn't know how Burr had gotten my email address. In the meantime, Burr proved to be a persistent man when I didn't give him a response.

Susan:

Its not nice to say Hi and then run away. Naughty naughty, lol!

Daddy Lou

Susan Fensten wrote:

>

>write me here too if you want to talk private. OHHHHH!!!!

>or *brooklynusa@verizon.net*

>Susan

I sent the message to Hal, telling him I was overwhelmed and didn't know what to do. He emailed me the following morning, once more complaining about not being able to get in touch with me. His emails to me were allegedly bouncing back to him, and he said that his lawyer was going to contact the Brooklyn police soon if I didn't respond. His phone calls weren't going through either. I always appreciated Hal's concerns—but I had no explanation for what were becoming cyclical notifications about phone calls and emails being blocked. If there were problems, I could only assume it was on the Gardiners' end. They had complained once before about problems with Yahoo, so I decided to let the matter pass.

Of far more importance was the fact that Hal had gotten tough with Lou Burr on my behalf. He reiterated what Leonard had already explained, telling him that it was Sharon or one of her helpers who had sent him email under my name.

Dear Lou,

This is Harold Gardiner, Leonard's brother in law. You remember me I am sure.

I wanted to advise you of the situation you are in right now. My sister in law Sharon (Len's sister) is impersonating a relative of my wife's, who is Len's cousin also. Her name is Susan, and for some sick reason Sharon has taken it upon herself to hurt or harass her every chance she gets. Sharon or one of her helpers wrote to you as Susan to get you to write to her and annoy her.

Please understand that our relative Susan did not write to you and wants nothing to do with you or anyone else you might know. There is no reason to write or phone her after this point. Lou I realize you have done your time and paid your dues to society, so you know what to expect if any further harassment or harm should come to Susan via you.

Be smart and walk away now before you get involved in something that is heading down a dead-end street.

Best of luck

I printed out this email and showed it to my boss at Rizzoli. A look of grave concern washed over her face. There was nothing she could do, but it made me feel better that she was taking the matter seriously since it was affecting my concentration and ability to work.

Burr's answer was as contrite as an altar boy's—if one assumed that altar boys occasionally used foul language outside of church.

Harold, I understand and I am sorry if I made anybody uncomfortable. I spoke to someone last night who told me some wild shit that I just don't need to be a part of right now. Rest assured I am minding my own business. Please accept my apology for my mistake. I appreciate you taking the time to explain this all to me. I am out of it.

I was, for now at least, content to have some measure of reassurance. Besides, there wasn't much I could do except to keep my aluminum baseball bat close at hand. I was scared out of my wits given that the upstate cult was staging a "Fall Slaughter," and Nolan and I had been on the menu for several weeks. Hal had said that a hundred missing persons were linked to The Tribe.

***

If my life in 2003 and 2004 had been a movie, the editor would have had a tough time doing his job. Scenes were dissolving into each other with rapidity, and the fade-ins and fade-outs were constant.

Hal said he and his lawyer were about to meet with Sharon one last time to confront her, threatening her with prosecution and jail time if she continued disrupting lives. She was meeting Hal for lunch, not realizing that Walters was going to be there. I wanted very badly to believe that this confrontation would lead to lasting results, but I couldn't convince myself. Sharon was so far over the line into criminal activity and mental illness that I didn't think anything except a psychiatric facility, preferably one within a prison, could deter the scorned woman from her quest for meaningless revenge. Ken Walters had succeeded in doing nothing thus far except obtaining the proverbial slap on the wrist for Hal's sister-in-law, and the idea of reading Sharon the riot act seemed almost ludicrous. I told Hal that, while I longed for our collective nightmare to come to an end, Sharon was, in my estimation, a sociopath and could manipulate her way out of taking responsibility for anything, as when she had sobbed profusely when taken away in handcuffs a few months earlier. "The proof," I said, "will lie in the days and weeks to come.

The response was almost too good to be true. I had expected Hal to say, "The meeting is not what we had hoped for." To the contrary, Hal felt that he had obtained complete closure on the matter of Sharon Barnes' behavior.

Susan,

It's over.

Whatever it was, I think Mr. Walters and I were able to put a stop to it before it went any further. Sharon was waiting for me when I got to the restaurant (she was having a mixed drink) already. We exchanged some small talk and just when she asked "what our lunch meeting was all about?" Mr. Walters walked in (thank God).

In a nutshell it was explained to her in a very convincing manner that "if there are any further disruptions in our lives, Len's life and yours, she will be prosecuted to the highest degree of the law." In the beginning she acted defiant but every time her children were brought into the matter she relented and listened. There is enough evidence to tie her to several things that would merit the law's attention and we (Mr. Walters and myself) are at the point of pushing for full prosecution.

I had a long talk with Karen last night and spoke to Len this morning. Everyone agreed this last ditch effort to find reason within their sister was worth a try. In my humble opinion I would say our talk today worked.

Please don't think ill of me Susan for not going right to the police with our lawyer, but for my family's sake and out of respect for the past I decided to try one more attempt at being nice. Sharon understands that if one more thing happens and is linked to her in any way she will not be seeing her children for a very long time. Children are not allowed to visit inmates and a few years behind bars is what she is looking at if she continues on this course. I also felt that prosecuting her would only drag this out longer because she is a vindictive woman with lots of money at her disposal.

There were a few strained moments when I thought she was going to walk out and leave or at the very least throw her drink in my face, lol but she did not and I have a gut feeling that it's finished. Believe it or not we all shared a joke regarding the food making a reference that "it was no better than prison food." We all shook hands when it was over and I will probably see her again this evening when she comes to pick up her kids. She is busy with community service this afternoon and Karen watches them every Wed.

There are more details that I will get to you in time, but I wanted to write you immediately and let you know that I do believe Mr. Walters and I achieved our goal this afternoon. I looked her in the eye as we were leaving and reached for her hand and asked her "it's over?" and she said "it's over."

I know you must be thinking, yeah right, but I feel in my gut that we were able to drive the facts home plain and clear to her. I just spoke to Karen a few minutes ago when I got back to the office and she told me Sharon had called her after we met and was "sobbing." She feels her sister is finally understanding the mess she has caused in everybody's lives especially her own and that of her daughters.

With hope,

Hal

Hal was convinced that a corner had been turned with his devious sister-in-law. I didn't share Hal's hope. A little talk over lunch wasn't going to solve anything. No mention had been made for quite some time about her receiving medication or psychiatric care, which seemed a crucial component in assessing what she might do in the future. A mild intervention consisting of a scare tactic over lunch wasn't going to work on a sociopath.

The monster herself wrote me on October 13.

Subject: Goodbye

Susan Fensten,

Big surprise to hear from me direct I bet. No this is
not an apology.

This note is to inform you that you can get back
to your so-called life again. I still don't like you or
what you represent but I want nothing more to do
with you or your kind.

I hope to never hear about you ever again.

Sincerely,

Sharon

When Sharon said she wanted nothing more to do with
me, I didn't believe her. I was convinced that whatever she
had previously planned was still in the pipeline. If she had
people like McCottry or Burr helping Cyrese to carry out her
directives, how could her actions be traced? Hal told me that
her letter was mere bluster and that Sharon always wanted
to have the last word. *"Next time,"* he said, *"she could tell it
to the judge."*

Next time? What had happened to the "connection" Hal
had made to Sharon's humanity, to the person she used to
be? Part of me wanted to hope that something had changed
in the long, complex equation formed by the hundreds of
emails I'd received for an entire year, but my cynicism
regarding Sharon hadn't wavered. She was dangerous and
needed to be locked up.

I thanked Hal for everything and wrote back:

Dear Hal-

More than anyone, I wish for this to be over. I am going to trust you on this. My only caveat is that Sharon is quite the sociopath and is able to dodge taking responsibility whenever she needs to. She was also led away in handcuffs 'sobbing' once before. Please don't think that I don't appreciate your incredible efforts, **I do, very much so***, but I don't trust HER. I've suffered tremendously because of her and I don't think I will ever forget it.*

The proof of this will lie in the days and weeks to come. If we can all go back to ‹normal,' then no one will be happier than I.

Thank you Hal from the bottom of my heart for everything you've done over the last months and particularly lately. I really want you to know how grateful I am to you. Thank you for taking care of Burr too--the prospect of fending off yet another psycho was looming terribly for me.

You may use my office email address in the future if you like, but I can only check it at work. Pending further impersonations, I will be going back to using publishingnyc@yahoo again, so please ignore my request to use publishingnyc_usa@ yahoo. I panicked after I saw "Lou's" email last night. Please let Lenny know too. And I don't think I'll be clicking on any yahoo greetings anymore either--please tell Karen, I know she liked sending them.

Tonight I am going to get a bottle of my favorite imported Belgian beer and raise a toast to you Hal and to Mr. Walters too! Please thank him for me when you have the chance.

Exhausted, relieved, hopeful.

Susan

When he replied, Hal had other information for me besides his views of Sharon. He spoke of Lou Burr, and although some of what he divulged was information I'd known for quite a while, new details emerged about the ex-con.

Dear Susan,

Thank you for this kind note, I appreciate it. Please do not "trust me" because I can't make any guarantees especially when concerning my sister-in-law. You will think this less cavalier I expect, but my main reason was selfish by nature. You see Susan I do not want two more children. I do not like Sharon's oldest daughter (Jolie) and never feel comfortable when she is in our home. If Sharon were to go to prison there is no doubt that we would take in her children as we are the official guardians by law.

Of course I wanted to fix things for you and Leonard at the same time, but I am no knight and I certainly don't wear shiny armor, lol.

Having said that, I still believe that Sharon got it. There was a connection made I hadn't felt in quite a long time and this afternoon I remembered what she was like as a person again. I know that sounds bad but you have to understand what she has done to me and my family over the years.

Although it was not said outright, Sharon understood that I was giving her one last chance to stop. When everything had been explained to her very cut and dry, you could see her demeanor shift and it looked as though she understood the importance of this chance. Like you say Susan, "time will tell" and I am very hopeful that we can all put this behind us and move on to better times. The hollidays are coming up and I would like to enjoy them for a change.

Burr is a very sick man. If you knew his record you would cringe. Len got into trouble with him and {you better sit down} McCottry a while back where a young woman was hurt. I feel she was lucky to live, to be honest with you. Leonard was spared any real punishment because the prosecutors could not prove he raped the woman also. Then some time later after he was released from the prison, he and Len got back together at a hospital in N.J. called Greystone Park. That is where Len was committed a few months ago when he sent you all of that vulgarity. Sharon had everything to do with his being locked up and for that we are all still angry. The electricity does something to them Susan, they come out different. I don't know how to explain it. After he and Burr got back together as "friends" (I suspect they were lovers) Len began getting into trouble again. His biggest mistake was the child pornography charge he faced which I believe was really the work of this "Lou."

Leonard has never expressed any interest in children in the whole time I have known him. I think he can take or leave our girls too. He never mentions them or asks about them (which hurts Karen). I don't think he even sees children when he goes out around town. They don't exist in Len's world. Burr and I had a run in at Leonard's old place when he was in the hospital. I was there with a buddy of mine cleaning up when we found Lou Burr and another man involved in a scene I will not describe to you. They had a key to get in obviously. We made sure the young lady was sent safely on her way and warned both of them to get out and never come on his property again. Leonard doesn't even know this so please keep it between us.

Burr understood that he was seconds away from going back to prison and I could tell he was thankful to get away with just a good scare and a warning. He knew who I was when I wrote him this morning.

Susan, I never received your request to use another email address for you. This morning, email bounced back from 3 of the known email addresses I have for you and I was a little nervous. If you are keeping this open for now, that is fine. I will continue to mail you at *publishingnyc@yahoo.com* and only write you at work if it's very important.

Which I hope I don't have to do.

It's late now and I need to finish up some other work, lol, the kind they pay me for.

Please let me know how things are going and if there is anything else I can do.

That beer sounds good.

Cheers,

Hal

Burr had also been a patient at Greystone—and at the same time as Leonard. That was certainly news to me—and an odd coincidence—but it was now apparent that the paths of Leonard, McCottry, and Burr had intersected frequently and in numerous ways. They had all been tried for rape, they had all been patients at Greystone, and they had all shared an interest in fetishism. At least Leonard didn't share Felix and Lou's interest in The Tribe, although Hal was now implying that Burr was a bisexual pedophile. A final detail related by Hal was that he had encountered Burr one day while cleaning up the filth at Leonard's old place (perhaps during one of the "hose-downs"). Burr was in the house with a young lady. Hal and his helper sent the woman on her way, warning Burr not to set foot on the property again.

Was this bit of "Burr history" supposed to encourage me after he had warned Burr and received an apology? Why was Hal telling me this?

**

With Burr having been taken care of—hopefully—Leonard was back in the clouds. He was busy with his art again, sculpting a head—a cross between his and mine—out of cadaver wax and putty. He assured me that he was not one of "those bad ones," an allusion to The Tribe. It was also his way of telling me that he hadn't killed anyone to obtain his materials.

Leonard was being Leonard, and there wasn't much to say about his creative pursuits. If sculpting kept him out of Greystone, so much the better.

It was October 17. Halloween was fourteen days away. So was the Fall Slaughter.

CHAPTER TWENTY-SEVEN

YOU HAVE A VERY SOFT VOICE, SUSAN

And they found no more of her than the skull,
and the feet, and the palms of her hands.
—*II Kings 9:31*

There are some days in New York City when its hardness and gloom are inescapable. October 19 was an overcast day, and I looked out the window of my office at the lifeless stone sculptures on the old gray buildings on Park Avenue South and wondered if I was looking at a grotesque sculpture of my own life: unmoving, dark, impenetrable. My spirit had no light, no energy. Would I still find myself reading threatening emails a year from now? Two years from now? I wanted to fight, but I wasn't sure how.

That morning, I received an email from a Detective Hernandez of the NYPD from *NYPDhernandez@most-wanted.com*. He wanted to speak with Nolan and me about "the case."

Subject: Your Case File

Miss S. Fensten,

Your file was given to me to review and I would like to meet with you and your boyfriend N. Gray in person to go over a few facts of the case.

This meeting is confidential. Please meet me at the corner of Kent Ave./Franklin St. and N.14 St. this evening Tuesday October 19 at 8pm. I will be driving a tan station wagon. Do not bring your dog please.

Det. A. Hernandez - NYPD

case#: SF8485KLMU44MG7O5M1

www.nypd.org

Everything about the email was wrong and deliberately so. The proposed rendezvous point was at the bottom of a dark, empty industrial street a few blocks from my home at the edge of the waterfront. The only witness to such a meeting would be the silent, massive fortresses. If Detective Hernandez wanted to speak with Nolan and me, why not come to the door and show me his badge? Besides, it was nearly impossible to speak to a cop on the telephone, let alone in person. There was no need for this kind of secrecy, normally reserved for undercover operations pertaining to vice and gangs, if the police were finally interested in my case. Detective Fronenberger hadn't been overly concerned with my plight, so why should I assume that he had suddenly given my case to someone who was taking an avid interest in all of my emails? And since when did anyone, let alone a police officer, drive a tan station wagon? It didn't add up.

What *did* add up was that sitting in an unmarked car late at night on a deserted street with someone who requested I not bring my dog was a set-up, quite likely the very same kind that had resulted in Carl getting a hot shot. Carl had, after all, been in touch with the mysterious Detective Loria, who had turned out to be a total fake. There was no way either Nolan or I would honor a request for such a meeting.

A closer inspection of the message revealed that it had been sent through a website that provided phony return email addresses. No legitimate detective would have used such a bogus-sounding email address. I called the 90th Precinct and asked to speak with Detective Fronenberger. Somebody was impersonating a police officer, and I believed the possible parallel with Carl Mulgrave's scenario deserved attention. Maybe this is what I needed to finally get Fronenberger's attention. He wasn't at the station, however, which was probably just as good, because I would go the precinct and speak to someone in person. They could dismiss me if they wanted, but I was still firmly committed to standing my ground rather than moving to Washington, DC, and forfeiting my life.

I forwarded the email to Hal and then called Nolan, who picked me up at two-thirty and drove to the 90th. When we arrived, Nolan took a seat while I spoke to the female officer who had interviewed me during my very first visit to the precinct. She offered no sympathetic treatment this time, but rather told me to be seated. I sat, watching her whisper to a plain-clothed female officer, probably a detective, who guided me into a room off to the side. Displaying a deadpan expression, the officer listened only briefly before taking my number and informing me that someone would call me.

Someone.

I'd been given the brush-off again, and I had the distinct impression that my reputation had preceded me before I even stepped foot in the station that afternoon. I was the crackpot with a handful of emails and a story about porn, schizophrenic relatives, cannibals, and hot shots. On the way home, I replayed the visit in my mind and imagined the young policewoman leaning toward her colleague, saying in a hushed tone, "It's her again."

The brief trip was quiet since Nolan had very little to say. He was terrified, but the tension only made him more withdrawn. He had formerly spoken of going to Georgia, and it seemed to me that part of him was already there. He was worried about me—that hadn't changed—but he wanted this to be over.

As we passed North 14th Street, I glanced at the meeting spot proposed by "Detective Hernandez." The street was desolate. It was a cold October night, and even the overhead lamp was broken on a street with block-long warehouses, a street that ended at a chain link fence or at the lip of an embankment on the East River. It was the exactly the type of place where you'd expect to be assaulted. I wasn't particularly worried anymore about being chloroformed, but I had begun to think that Cyrese knew more people than I had previously suspected. She knew Lou Burr, who might be the tip of the iceberg. How many dark forces roamed the night, and for what purposes?

***

It was déjà vu all over again. I received the following at work the next day.

Subject: for Susan F.

Miss Susan,

Keep this note between just us o.k.?

I am not trying to bother you but I wanted you to know that since we made each others aquaintence why not be friendly like and get a drink or something? I will be passing by your hood this weekend and could stop in to say Hi. Give a guy a break and say Yes, o.k.?

Your uncle Gardiner wrote me and told me about the mistake I made and I am very sorry if I offended you. I can pick you up at your house and we can go wherever. I am a very nice guy once you get to know me. Ever since I seen your picture I have been thinking about you and how nice you look. I know you must be a very good person Susan. I would like the opportunity to get to know you. How about it? I am willing to let bygones be bygones are you little lady?

The email was reminiscent of Robert McCottry's note to me months before, in which his tone had been simultaneously presumptuous and southern gentlemanly. Yeah, sure, I was gonna be his little lady and give him a second chance. We'd go out to eat, have a few drinks, and then he would show me things I couldn't imagine, such as a blow to the head or a needle loaded with morphine. To him, it was a done deal. Unfortunately for him, and fortunately for me, I *could* imagine his real intentions.

The phone at my desk rang a moment later. When I answered, someone hung up. An email followed immediately:

Subject: You have a very soft Voice Susan

I might just have to surprise you little lady and come up behind you when your walkin your doggy, lol. Would you like to feel my strong arms around your sweet body? Don't forget to take my call tonight.

Big Lou

Big Lou had called just to hear my voice. I felt sick and hot with fear. I was in a cat and mouse game with a sexual predator and he was winning. He had me right where he wanted me and I was as terrified as I was powerless. Burr and his crew knew my neighborhood well, down to the intersections with dead ends and broken streetlamps. Shaking, I called Bobby right away, but he said he felt helpless. He was in DC; I was in New York City.

I was becoming an expert on finding information on the web, thanks to Bobby, so I searched for Lou Burr's profile on Yahoo's search page. Burr wasn't the least bit shy about his interests.

The fact that an ex-con would post such a profile proved that criminals are sometimes truly stupid, but Burr was no doubt part of a Yahoo group that shared the same interests, from Meat Puppets to Kinki Kids. In all probability, he was one of a thousand (or more) people who had similar profiles. The pictures on the profile were in keeping with the many I had already received.

The photograph superimposed over the bonfire on the bottom left appeared to be a decapitated woman with a stump of an arm, and the woman on a spit was in the same position as the woman in the picture sent to me previously.

For the moment, there was nothing to do but shut down my PC and go home.

I always took the stairs at work because I didn't like waiting for the elevator. I was more terrified than ever when I walked into the stairwell, my feet echoing on the metal and slate steps.

You have a very soft voice, Susan.

I continued down the stairs, no one above or below me.

Would you like to feel my strong arms around your sweet body?

I didn't feel any better out on the street. It was another cold October night, and I was happy to land on my doorstep after practically running the three blocks from the Bedford Avenue subway station.

CHAPTER TWENTY-EIGHT

THE FBI

So on this windy sea of land, the fiend
Walked up and down alone bent on his prey.
—John Milton, *Paradise Lost*

As quiet as he had been throughout most of this madness, Nolan was becoming more hands-on after living through months of tension revolving around fake detectives, cannibalism, Carl's murder, criminals, and numerous threatening phone calls. He'd also been discouraged by our latest trip to the 90th Precinct and decided to take action. He called FBI headquarters in Manhattan, and, miraculously, he connected with someone who wanted to hear the full story. The agent who returned his call had heard of The Tribe of Twelve, although he wasn't aware of the cult's link to cannibalism. I was relieved that the Feds were going to give me a chance to explain my story. The FBI's normal sphere of jurisdiction deals with terrorists, bank robbers, the Mafia, white-collar crime—even Martha Stewart—but here I was, armed with my pile of crazy pictures and email threats. Because of Nolan's persistence, however, I could again dare to believe that I mattered in the great scheme of things. We were scheduled to meet with the agent in three days.

That afternoon Bobby and I were exchanging emails discussing how senior citizens are vulnerable to online scams when I told him the news.

Oh yes, can you imagine how many senior citizens are rooked ONLINE? sad.

Oh get this... Nolan made a call to the NY FBI earlier this week. They called back today and an agent wants to meet with us next week [at the FBI HQ downtown. NOT on a dark empty street corner!]

He said he's heard of the 12 Tribes. He said they are not known as cannibals, but he knows of them and he wants to see all my emails! So it looks like we've got at least an ear.

I am quite surprised we got a bite. I was willing to move on and forget this crap, but if the FBI wants to hear, then I'll give them the story. Even though I want to leave it all behind, in truth, if Nolan and I had been so stupid as to meet the fake cop, we could have been hurt or worse!

Let this be the LAST chapter of this grotesque carnival.

Bobby replied that it was great news and that these people must be stopped.

Meanwhile I received another hang-up call at my desk.

By 5 p.m. that day Hal sent me an email. He said he was getting the feeling that Sharon was "running out of steam." No explanation was given, but then Hal never proffered any explanation the first time around. I didn't think Sharon would *ever* run out of steam until she was behind bars or lying in a coffin, but I was more interested in my impending meeting with the Federal Bureau of Investigation than Hal's vague updates. My mind had shifted gears. For now, I wasn't going to tell any of the Nachmans, not even Hal, that I had contacted the Bureau. No information was safe once it found its way into the hands of the clan in Massachusetts and New Jersey. The more I had tried to find clarity with my inquiries or forwarded emails over the months, the more harassment I received. The "forward" and "reply" buttons had perhaps become my greatest enablers, and nothing was going to jeopardize what might be my last chance to find justice.

***

After work on Monday, the 25th of October, Nolan and I went to FBI headquarters at One Federal Plaza. I went through the rigorous building security carrying a laptop case filled with printouts of emails, internet profiles, and pictures. Every character in the *dramatis personae* who had emailed me since the previous October would be presented to the authorities. On the elevator, I breathed a sigh of relief, hardly daring to believe that I was finally going to speak with someone other than a harried local precinct detective.

Nolan and I were escorted to a small, sparse interview room with a table and three chairs. A metal bar was bolted to the gray wall so that suspects could be handcuffed to the rod while interrogated. We waited for what seemed an eternity before Special Agent Waller walked into the room, introduced himself, and sat down. He was thirty-ish, dressed in a well-tailored suit, and was more handsome than I expected an FBI agent to be.

After many rounds with law enforcement, having had to explain my plight over and over, I intrepidly placed my carrying case on the table and launched directly into my story, starting at the beginning by explaining my post at *Genealogy.com*, pausing only to answer questions. I watched the agent's face as I began introducing the various characters in my saga, sorting through the large stack of papers before me. Would he think I was crazy like the cops at the 90th seemed to?

For the next three hours, the agent listened patiently, taking many notes. Gaining even more confidence, I plunged into greater and greater detail. The agent stopped me occasionally to inquire about the relationship between various characters, asking how I originally met them online, or to request their contact information. His eyes widened when I produced the New Jersey Department of Corrections offender profiles of McCottry and Burr, printed from the website. These men were "in the system," and he studied the sheets carefully as I related their role in the cyber-stalking.

I did my best to deflect attention from Leonard, for whom I felt increasing protectiveness and who, I had come to believe, was just as much a victim as I was. I certainly didn't omit him from my story, but I placed far more emphasis on Sharon, who seemed to be the nexus from which emanated so many spokes of darkness and danger. I explained her relationship to McCottry, and how, together, they had planned to kidnap Nolan and me in order to transport us to The Tribe. My account also focused intensely on Cyrese, who had played such a dominant role in the unfolding events after Kinkfest, and who was connected with so many other people, especially McCottry and Sharon, and who had been corresponding with her imprisoned father, Maurice Bork.

It was a long haul, but I managed to touch on everyone, including the "good guys" such as Hal, Carl, Lydia, and Janis.

It was liberating to lay it all out in the open, from the pornographic pictures and sexual harassment to the multiple threats on my life and Nolan's. Agent Waller asked me to follow up with him by providing him with a written summary of everyone involved and a chronological order of how the events had transpired. He gave us his card, and we thanked him profusely as he escorted us to the bank of elevators where two other agents were waiting.

He believed me, and the hope I experienced on that evening was, unlike the promises of Hal's lawyer, genuine and solid. On the way down, I told Nolan that just being inside Bureau headquarters made me feel safe for the first time in months. The two agents who had stepped onto the elevator with us laughed, one of them saying, "It's not as safe as you think." I chuckled nervously.

My apprehension returned on the way home, where I didn't feel safe at all, but at least I had my foot in the door with the FBI. At least, as I had thought before, if something *did* happen, there would be a record. One way or another, justice would be done.

In the next two days, I typed up a three-page summary detailing the chronology and cast. I then faxed it to Agent Waller, who would now have more than an oral recounting of my tale. He would have the hard copy of the most bizarre experience of my life.

CHAPTER TWENTY-NINE

THINGS GO SILENT

The cruelest lies are often told in silence.
—Robert Louis Stevenson

Agent Waller had taken my report and was studying the many emails I'd given him, as well as printouts of the criminal records and mug shots for Robert McCottry and Lou Burr. This simple statement of fact—that he was aware of my story and was actively checking it out—came back to me again and again for one simple reason: it was true. For months I had been fed a steady diet of information that was decidedly surrealistic. The characters were unpredictable. Their stories were at times plausible; at other times, their actions were bizarre and contradictory. Metaphorically, I was standing near a fault line, the ground shifting one way and then sliding back again. But I was now certain of at least one rock-solid fact: Agent Waller was looking at my case. I had been in the same interrogation room with him, had spoken to him, had shaken his hand. His involvement was a constant I could rely on despite whatever might happen in the future.

For this very reason, the day after I met with Agent Waller—it was now Tuesday, October 26—I began feeling not so much less afraid as "not alone." I felt freer to walk the streets because I had the backing of the Feds. Leaving my office and stepping out for lunch was now a less fearful experience. The threat had not been eliminated since I was well aware that the Nachman family and their surly friends were still "out there" somewhere, and there were so very many of them. At least if something happened to Nolan or me, the FBI would have leads to follow that might yield hard evidence of any foul play. It was comforting to know that even if we were kidnapped or found dead—and I still considered that a very real possibility—those responsible would be caught in the end.

Not surprisingly, some of the same old stunts were still being attempted. I received a Yahoo notification that someone was trying to access my password. With even Lou Burr being pranked, it seemed as if there was no stopping Sharon, despite Hal's claim that she was running out of steam.

Meanwhile, I kept in constant touch with Bobby as usual, who was naturally eager to hear all the details of my meeting with the FBI. He also wanted to know if I had notified Hal of my trip to the Bureau, and, if so, what his reaction had been. I told him that I intentionally had not informed Hal of my actions because I didn't want to tip anyone off. I thought my reply spoke for itself: I didn't want to jeopardize my relationship with the FBI and its budding investigation now that I, with the aid of Nolan, had finally gotten the ear of law enforcement.

What ensued was a flurry of emails and phone calls between Bobby and me in which he, not uncharacteristically, showed himself to be the quintessential busybody and gossip. He seemed offended that I hadn't told Hal. His initial response was "Well, I'm sure Hal, of all people, wouldn't tip off anyone you didn't want him to." I told Bobby that as much as I liked Hal, I was going to pursue my legal route with stealth. I knew for a fact that Hal didn't want to raise Sharon's two kids, which explained his reluctance to prosecute her. I added that it had come down to me or them, and I was opting for me. It was time that I acted in my own self-interest. Hal, Sharon, her children—they simply didn't figure into the equation anymore. I feared for my life and it wasn't my job to clean up someone else's "mess" or to inform anyone what steps I was taking to protect myself.

Bobby continued to make a case for the loving kindness of Hal and seemed surprised that I wouldn't keep him in the loop.

> True, that makes sense about not wanting to raise her brats, but I just found it funny. Here the man has done so much to assist you and keep you apprised and even help you out a couple of times and you went behind his back to the Feds. Oh well, you didn't plan on keeping in touch with them anyhow...

> What a group. I tell you we went over the story again last night and the whole thing is soooooooooooo unbelievable, a nightmare of fantasy and fact. Very, very unbelievable.

Bobby's logic didn't add up, and I told him so. Dealing with the "group," as Bobby had termed it, had indeed been nightmarish—almost unbelievable, except to the FBI. Hal had been a terrific help when it came to having support, but he obviously hadn't produced any significant results, nor did I expect him to in the future. In fact, quite often after he became involved, things became worse. I was within my rights to pursue using law enforcement, and how I went about it was my own business. Protecting my self-interest did not constitute going behind Hal's back.

Bobby backed off, but only slightly.

Went behind his back by not wanting to tell him, that's all...you said you are afraid he would 'tip off' someone, hahahaha, imagine? "Hey Lou, get out of town, she's got the Feds on your tail" Anyhow, I'm sure if he and his lawyer felt the FBI were needed they would have called them in a long, long time ago, I think they are using the US court system instead. But it's sooooo slow. Also I thought he asked you a while ago to let him handle this as he has some kind of plan or process he was following. You probably got him dumped with 2 kids to raise now. LOL!

Despite the "LOL" and "hahahaha," it was apparent Bobby was trying to goad me and lay a guilt trip on me. He didn't seem to understand that the matter no longer properly belonged in the hands of Hal or his lawyer. What they believed to be necessary was totally irrelevant. I therefore shot back the following:

I don't see this as me dumping the kids on him at all. I don't need to report my every experience with the police, as I have already been to them several times and had not told Hal about any of it. I don't think he'd really 'tip Lou off.' I don't know what he and his lawyers are going to accomplish, but since it's a local matter to them and they are not prosecuting FOR ME, why would they need the FBI? 'Let Hal handle it'? Sure, he got her to say 'it's over' but it is not over.

There was a time I leaned on Hal for help, but after all was said and done, he and his family were "fortress Nachman," and I was an outsider looking in, never quite sure what they were doing. Besides, Hal had his own internal family problems to deal with, and while he may have cared about my welfare to a greater or lesser degree, I didn't interpret his actions as being altruistically "for me." I had also had enough exchanges with his family to feel relatively certain that they hadn't told me everything. That was my intuition, which was bolstered by the lengthy email trail I'd given to the FBI. Transparency wasn't a strong suit of the Gardiner or Nachman clans. As far as the ordeal "being over," that was equally false since someone had been trying to access my Yahoo account. Sharon's claim to the contrary counted for nothing.

Bobby, of course, had an answer for everything.

Of course you have a right to contact the law. No, I meant he asked you to allow him to handle it or at least keep him apprised of your doings and this little trip to the FBI and some other things you've done seem kind of sneaky. You said you didn't want him to know, and I'm trying to imagine him telling Lou and Sharon to be careful, the FEDS are on them!

Anyhow, I'm sure you know what you're doing and now that you've gotten the FBI in on it you should yield some results. It will most likely steamroll over any of the hard work he and his lawyer were trying to do, but then again you are perfectly within your rights to seek the help of law enforcement. I just doubt he will be very happy with the result.

So now I was being "sneaky" by trying to protect myself? That was ridiculous, and I didn't appreciate Bobby denigrating my actions by referring to my "*little* trip to the FBI". His opinions were becoming sarcastic and fickle. He realized that the court system was slow; he was sure I knew what I was doing; he acknowledged that I'd had a perfect right to contact law enforcement; he was sure that my plan would yield results; and he validated the nightmarish quality of my experiences. On the flip side, however, he believed my actions to be clandestine moves that would destroy the alleged hard work and advocacy afforded by Hal and Ken. And he was sure Hal wouldn't be pleased with the results produced by my contacting the Bureau.

But to call me sneaky—well, that was typical Bobby again. I told him he was off base and that, in point of fact, Hal had never requested that I keep him fully apprised of my dealings with the police. Besides, Hal had tried it his way, but I hadn't seen any fruit borne from his efforts. Bobby didn't seem to understand that I no longer cared what Hal thought.

Bobby clearly saw that I was irritated and tried to explain the logic of his thinking.

> OK, I thought you meant Lou when you said you were afraid he would tip someone off. Well, I doubt he'd call Sharon and alert her, and anyhow what good would it do, the file is in the Feds hands now. She can't back track and erase her steps. I was confused when you said tip someone off and that you're using stealth. I don't know the man, but from what I've read the last year he seems like he's been a friend to you. I'm sure he'll find out soon enough via the authorities.

Bobby couldn't resist getting in a good hard jab at the very end, implying that Hal would soon learn that I was not his friend since I had not told him of my consultation with the FBI. Bobby was being a bitch, and he was making me angry. I was starting to recall why I had moved away from the friendship in the first place. I told him point blank that I didn't know why he was arguing with me. Consequently, his terse apologetic statement tried to parse words as he said, "You said 'stealth' sorry …. That just means undercover or unseen …. 'sneaky' has a negative connotation, sorry."

I didn't know what results my meeting with the FBI might yield, although I was hopeful. My life had been interrupted for too long, and it was high time that I put myself first. Bobby had said nothing thus far to convince me to break my silence or inform Hal of my actions. His next email opened with sarcasm.

Oh please, no one's arguing with you.

I might not be as bright as you, but from all the emails you sent me from this guy it seems like he's been trying to handle this on his own, mainly because he doesn't want to get saddled with Sharon's children. I think the exact words he used was "I am no knight in shining armor, my reasons are selfish" for handling it the way he has been for so many years. It's a family thing. He and Karen have "tried their hardest to keep people out of jail" etc.

And as for who he was going to 'tip off' I still can't figure that one out, but like I said you must know what you're doing and now that it's in the Feds hands it will be taken care of. I'm sure if the authorities wanted Hal to record Sharon they would have come up with that one a while back too. I think Hal probably assumed you were talking with local law enforcement, but when you and Nolan went to the Federal Bureau of Investigation to lodge a formal complaint, you kind of raised this to another level, and James I were wondering what he felt about that.

You told me you didn't tell Hal because you didn't want to tip someone off, hahaha ok, I was just wondering about that, that's all. No argument and I know how having one's motives questioned can make someone defensive.

Like I said, I might not be as bright as you where all of this is concerned, being an observer from the sidelines, but my overall impression was that Hal was trying to work things out and was also looking at you as a confidante.

I think the FBI will blow everything he's tried to do out of the water. And you know, maybe that's a good thing. The man obviously wasn't having any success. She paid one fine, spent another night in jail and still she keeps on ticking.

Anyhow, no argument, I just found it interesting Hal was one of the people you wanted to use some 'stealth' with. He seemed so helpful and nice the last email or two you shared with me. Can't wait to hear the Feds findings. I think you blew the top off this family once and for all.

He was again employing an inconsistent approach as he reveled in pouring over the details in a re-petitive manner. He understood my position and yet he couldn't figure out why I didn't trust Hal. He understood why I was defensive but Hal had tried to keep people out of jail. It was good that the FBI would finally blow everything out of the water but why would I use secrecy with Hal. Hal hadn't had any success but he'd been so helpful. Reading Bobby's emails was like watching a swinging pen-dulum. His opinions vacillated, every few sentenc-es, between validation and criticism.

Bobby and I had *always* batted theories back and forth ever since my early contacts with Karen, Leonard, and Sharon, and I was used to his penchant for being difficult. He and I had discussed the endless possibilities as events unfolded over the months, and maybe he was playing devil's advocate. Besides, gossips never want a juicy conversation with lurid details to end.

As for the allusion to Sharon being taped, Agent Waller had indeed suggested it as a possibility, but I told Bobby that I doubted it would come to that. I reiterated that Hal's problems were his own and that Sharon should have thought of her children before she decided to repeatedly break the law.

As for raising matters to a new level, he was dead right about that, and my next email offered no apologies.

This is the level it needs to be raised to.

All I could think of last night was that agent reading everything. I mean, he's got the whole kit and caboodle now. If she left me alone, none of this would be necessary. But enough is enough. I know Leona won't cry when she [Sharon] is rendered in 'captivity' again. I also was thinking of the possible scenario; a knock at the door; she opens it and there are two crisp-suited FBI agents standing there with their gold badges gleaming in the early morning light. Who knows what will happen. I am very anxious to hear back about the agent's findings. I was admiring his business card this morning while I was on the L train.

Somehow, Bobby didn't grasp that it was time for a new approach. I wanted all of this to stop. It needed to stop.

Nolan had gotten through to someone with clout, someone who was interested in what had been happening to me. The fact that he was a federal agent seemed to get under Bobby's skin. Additionally, the Bureau had jurisdiction over matters related to kidnapping and cults. Things had been raised to a new level long ago by the parties involved. What Nolan and I had done was to raise the *response* to these horrific events. If Bobby didn't "get it," that was too bad. At this point, I was as unconcerned with his approval as I was with Hal's.

***

On October 27, Bobby wrote to me to ask how I was doing. I informed him that things were fine and that I hadn't received any email from anyone since Monday. Fall is a busy season in publishing, and I was getting back to the growing pile of work on my desk to the extent that I was able to do so. I had been living inside the dark world of threats and cyber filth, while working in a publishing atmosphere that accentuated glamour—book parties, famous authors, high-profile media, and press releases about books on art, food, architecture, and other subjects of refinement and sophistication. The contrast was more than a little disorienting. I was at my wit's end, and consequently my productivity had suffered.

I wrote Bobby that afternoon, responding that it was a typical crazy day work-wise, and I mentioned that the FBI agent had called to request additional information on McCottry. Waller was still waiting to hear from the facility currently holding him, but the most recent information indicated that McCottry hadn't been released since 1991. Waller had said he would be making calls "all around" this week to get a more comprehensive picture, which might reveal an updated arrest record. Whatever else Agent Waller might learn, the fact that McCottry had been locked up since 1991 put a new twist on everything. It was a game changer, especially if Waller found no updated information on McCottry, and I didn't expect that he would. If Robert McCottry had been incarcerated during my long nightmare, then he couldn't have emailed me, built a dungeon at Lenny's place, or been at Kinkfest. It meant that someone was lying to me, which was much less frightening than someone trying to kidnap me. Removing this single piece of the puzzle was like turning off a switch that fed power to everything that had been happening to me. It was like the proverbial house of cards collapsing.

Bobby didn't see it that way.

Well it's great he's focusing on McCottry who's already locked up behind bars - but what about the other ones who are loose and able to cause harm within the next four days? Does he know Halloween is on Sunday? What's so important about McCottry if he's not bothering you? Last I heard over a month or so ago he was locked up.

Yes, McCottry was locked up, but Bobby wasn't focusing on the chronology. A simple truth had come to light: There *were* no "other ones." With just one person removed from the sordid mix, the entire depraved odyssey I'd lived through was beginning to unravel. I knew that *some* people existed, such as Lou Burr and Robert McCottry. Also, Burr and McCottry had arrest records that had been confirmed. Each persona, Karen, Hal, Sharon, Cyrese, Karl, Lou and Leonard had all buttressed in great detail the existence of McCottry and his state of freedom outside of prison in their lives throughout the entire saga. But the rest were suddenly imaginary, specters of the mind. If the story around McCottry was fake, then all of it was.

But whose mind had invented the story?

I could easily have said to myself at this point that there was no longer any use in staying worried and tense. It was all a hoax, a cruel joke, but nothing to be really concerned about. Why should I be worried about people who didn't exist? Why not ignore it all?

Because someone was out there, fixated on me. Someone might not be trying to cause me physical harm, but someone certainly was intent on destroying me. One or more people had gone to a great deal of trouble to terrorize me over an extended period of time, and the extent of their efforts had gone far past the level of a misguided prank. The adrenaline and cortisol—"stress chemicals"— which had been coursing through my bloodstream for quite some time were far from imaginary. My health had suffered, and I was physically tired and emotionally weary. My mind and body struggled to distinguish between fantasy and reality. For me, it had been real—all of it. Someone was quite intent on making me fear, each day that I woke up, that it might be my last. The questions remained: Why? And who was at the other end of the computer?

CHAPTER THIRTY

HALLOWEEN WEEKEND

Still as he fled, his eye was backward cast,
as if his fear still followed him behind.
—Edmund Spenser, *The Faerie Queene* (1596)

On Thursday, October 28, Bobby sent me updates about his personal life and social calendar. It was fluff, but it was better than arguing with him *ad nauseam* about my alleged ill-treatment of Hal. He had errands to run—the post office, gym, and then shopping to buy a cigar box sampler for a friend's birthday party. His rambling reinforced how little responsibility he had in his life. He had far too much time on his hands, which explained why he could spend hours giving me a hard time about the characters in my personal drama for the sheer hell of it. I was busy writing a more detailed account for Agent Waller while Bobby was tracking down "tobaccy smokes" for a friend. His cavalier manner was totally in keeping with all of the bitchy and repetitious emails he threw my way every day. He had nothing better to do.

He included the following, however, at the end of the email. It was clear he'd enjoyed the saga and didn't want the soap opera to completely disappear.

James and I talked about it a little more before we went to bed and our heads were swimming with 'what if's' and 'what-abouts.'

Nothing makes sense, unless the agent is wrong. If he's right, the whole thing is thrown off its axis. Anyhow keep me posted. It's almost more interesting now than it was before, and the best part is you're not being harassed or annoyed either. I wonder what's up with Leona ... no news? Can't you write him and just say Hi or something, see what's up?

I responded with "Nothing makes sense now, but it will. If the axis is off, then fine." I then added the following:

Also, no word from anyone since Monday. According to the 'story,' Len's moving and probably busy. Maybe Hal took the family out of town early for Halloween like he said he was going to. But no other tricks as of this morning. Don't feel like writing Lenny or Hal. Since I am learning new things via the FBI, I will let them make the next move, see what they have to say. Busy as hell today at work. I'm glad things are 'quiet,' so I can get some work done, or at least try to ...

I've got a lot to do tonight too. I have to finish writing that synopsis for the FBI agent tonight and I have to pack for the weekend. We are leaving from work tomorrow to head out to the New Jersey hotel I booked to avoid being at home on Halloween.

Sure ain't fun reliving all this and writing it out. Ugh.

The operative word in my email was "story," for that's exactly what it all was now: a fabrication, even though I still referred to the principal players in someone's cyber play by name. Bobby had been right about one thing, however: the play had lost coherence. It was "off its axis." He couldn't have put it better. But he was off the mark about the agent being wrong. Waller knew what he was doing, and hence my firm belief that things were soon going to make sense.

The following morning, Friday, Bobby's email was again full of chit-chat about his DC social life. Meanwhile, I sat at my desk at work, furiously attempting to complete the outline of events for the FBI. I was determined to get it to Agent Waller before Nolan and I headed to a hotel in New Jersey, where I would have no internet access. I told Bobby that I was trying to finish my report, which, apparently, was too much for the incorrigible busybody to resist. Bobby shot back the following:

Ok great doll....hey I'd love to see it too if it's not that private, would be cool to see it all laid out, etc.

"Doll" had no intention of sharing the report with Mr. Ironside. I felt I owed it to Agent Waller to follow his instructions to the letter, not only did I want everything to remain strictly confidential, but I was determined that the best course of action was to respect the law and Agent Waller's requests for confidentiality. This was my big chance—maybe my *only* chance—to resolve matters, and I wasn't going to blow it. So I was resolved my report would remain private.

At first, Bobby didn't press me on the issue. He simply asked, "What's cooking … you guys still heading out of town this weekend?" I told him I was exhausted but we were leaving right after work.

Bobby was like a fish that couldn't wiggle off the hook. The story had snagged him the way a soap opera grabs a viewer and doesn't let go. "What about what you wrote for the agent? I thought I'd ask to take a peek one more time if it's not too personal."

Of course it was personal! I replied, "I'd like to hold onto it for now. You know the whole story anyway."

Bobby seemed confused and wrote back "Huh?" My own response was even shorter: "?" Bobby did indeed know the whole story. He'd been privy to every detail from the beginning, but it was driving him crazy that he didn't know chapter and verse of what I was serving up to federal law enforcement. He didn't ask specifically, but he might have been worried that I had mentioned his role as confidante in my report. But I hadn't. I kept my summary to just the facts of the story without veering off into my social circle. He was a very private individual, and he was observing the entire drama from an enviable safe distance. I doubt if he would have wanted his name mentioned in the report.

The social banter from Washington now evaporated. Bobby seemed indignant, hurt even.

> It's just kind of funny. Every day for almost a whole year you've sent me updates and actual emails from these people, and now when you took the time to get the whole story down on paper (for an FBI agent no less) - it's something you want to hold onto.
>
> Not sure what I did wrong, except try to be a friend to you.

Oy - when I think of the hours and days I've been upset by all of this.

I couldn't deny that despite the prickly manner in which Bobby had challenged my actions of late, he had, from a much broader perspective, been there for me the entire time and had indeed seemed to be genuinely upset at what I had gone through. He may have been a bit cavalier at times and caught up in being a DC social butterfly, but he'd certainly spent hundreds of hours talking with me about the whole sordid ordeal. As he noted, he was my friend, and friends had disagreements. I reassured him that he didn't need to feel upset or take it personally. I must have gotten through since he made no further reference to the report for the Feds, but rather sent wishes that Nolan and I have a great weekend.

After work, Nolan picked me up at the office, Mini Me already in the car. I instantly felt freer as we drove through busy downtown traffic to the Holland Tunnel. With bustling Manhattan all around, it felt good to be anonymous and unnoticed. I was not accessible to the monster, that nameless someone—or "someones"—who had invented so many characters and reached through the computer screen to hijack and terrorize my emotions. Whoever was responsible didn't know where I was or where I was going. I had packed up and hit the road, headed in another direction. I felt safer just knowing that we wouldn't be anywhere near Brooklyn on Halloween. In fact, part of me wished that we could just keep driving and not go back home—ever. Ironically, we were heading into New Jersey, the state from which Len Dog, Big Lou, and Felix da Cat emerged, but I was nothing more than another traveler on the highway. For a couple of days at least, I'd have nothing to worry about.

***

It was back to work on Monday, November 1. I was greeted with an email from Bobby, who asked if I had discovered any broken windows, firebombs, or bullet holes upon returning home. This was the norm from Bobby, illustrative of his dark and sometimes callous sense of humor. I told him my home was just as I'd left it. Even better, I'd found no emails in my inbox upon returning, which meant that I'd received nothing for the entire previous week—nothing on Yahoo and nothing at work. I was pleased, but at the same time, it seemed rather odd that all correspondence had suddenly ceased with no apparent reason.

Even Bobby agreed.

As for no new emails, that is odd, but what isn't regarding this case?

Hardly anyone believed the brief synopsis I gave when asked. James's friend from work, Darcy, was funny. We were sitting out on the back deck enjoying a lovely eve and a cigarette when she turned to me out of the blue and said - I know what's been happening up in NY. And I looked at her like WHAT ??? And she said with your friend Susan. And I was like...uh huh....and she said James has been giving me updates. And then I realized she was the gal at work who was interested in all of that, but for a second I looked at her like she had a big 12 on her forehead. Hahahahaha! Anyhow glad all is well and quiet.

Peace, it's marvelous!

It didn't surprise me that Bobby had been compelled to keep discussing my case, even if it was with a colleague of James's. His appetite for all the juicy details was insatiable.

I could have done without his reference to "The Twelve," but what should I have expected from someone who asked if my home had been fire bombed? His "hahahahaha" style was both glib and conversational, which is to say that it was Bobby through and through. As usual, he'd ended with some form of expression that he was glad I was well, and I took the sentiment as sincere.

I was still baffled by the fact that things had gone silent for so long, an entire week, even with my professional emails. In this case, a week felt like an eternity, waiting to hear from Waller. But he was supposed to meet McCottry soon, and I was curious as to what information that avenue might yield. I remained cautiously optimistic.

In the midst of the silence Bobby reported a blip on the radar. He related that he'd seen Leonard online on Saturday afternoon—another rapid fire "on and off." Bobby surmised that he had probably just been sporadically checking email, but thought that I would have received something from him by now. It sounded like Leonard all right, and I hoped that maybe they had all finally decided not to contact me anymore. I related this to Bobby, and the fact that I actually said "they" even though I now had a strong preliminary indication that almost everyone was probably imaginary.

I remained anxious to hear from Agent Waller. The person was largely silent—flying under the radar, as it were—but I was positive was still there nonetheless. I'm not sure which can be more unsettling: all-out chaos or the ominous silence of a person you know is watching you.

The next day, on Tuesday, Bobby said that Lenny was online the previous night and then again that morning. He hypothesized that Leonard "must be fishing for new Kink."

It was certainly plausible, even though I now had reason to suspect that the online presence might not be anyone named Leonard Nachman. It was dawning on me that the fact that I had never talked to or met Leonard, or anyone else in the family, which hadn't seemed that odd before, now caused me to doubt if any of this was real. But if he was indeed a real person and looking for a new "kink"—it meant that I might no longer be his focus. Also, the FBI would have a trail to follow if he was remaining active online. From this perspective, Bobby's observations didn't necessarily represent bad news.

I felt encouraged that Waller must surely be hotly pursuing new leads.

Bobby continued to refer to the perpetrator of this hoax as "they," as did I. It was natural. Personal histories had been created, and it was difficult, if not impossible, to refer to what had happened without mentioning people by name, or at least as a collective "they." Bobby therefore sent the following:

> Have you written? Maybe they've tried to write you and there is a block? who knows...trying to find a rational reason in any of this is difficult.
>
> F'n nuts!

My email address hadn't changed, and that kept me wary in the extreme. I wrote back.

> *No I haven't written. As of lately, I'd rather let sleeping dogs lie. It's never been a matter of my initiating or not, with so many 'entities' abounding. It just seems as if a 'switch' has been flipped. Of all the many plausible scenarios, they could have all decided to cease contact with me, but if they*

wanted to write me, my email is still the same.
There is no block at my end. It just makes me more
suspicious that this whole thing was a massive evil
joke.

Did this silence represent the calm before the storm? Would events resume at a more terrifying pace, like someone starting up the dangerous and garish rides at a county fair midway? I wanted to let sleeping dogs lie, but sometimes a hungry pooch awakened in a very bad mood. Why this sudden stop in communication now that I had met with the FBI? I hadn't told anyone except Bobby. His opinion was that if I was correct—that things were not at all what they seemed—then the scenario was "even more sinister." But he wasn't totally convinced that this was the case. Bobby was mistrustful of the FBI, and law enforcement in general. He couldn't distance himself from the many characters we'd discussed, as if he were psychologically enmeshed with them, and he therefore continued to make comments such as "By now Hal should have written with an update or something. I assumed Lenny was just busy, but nothing from anyone. Where is Cyrese or Burr or the rest?"

I replied, reiterating that "with da Cat never 'out of doors' it changes a lot." In other words, McCottry had not been on the street since 1991. And that, I agreed, was most certainly sinister. I added that I was eating better, laughing more, and taking care of myself. Between the temporary safety of a weekend in New Jersey and the absence of horrid emails in my inbox, I was able to recapture a bit of my energy and humor despite my ongoing concerns. I was miles away from *joie de vive*, but knowing that Agent Waller would be getting back to me with more information soon was enough to help me assume a slightly more relaxed daily rhythm.

Bobby reminded me that I had been almost unrecognizable at one point, looking gaunt and waxy. As he said, "You can't come from something like that without showing the effects inwardly and outwardly. It's just plain math."

There was no argument there. The day I found out that I'd gotten through to the FBI, it felt like I mattered. And since it was appearing likely that I'd been duped, I thought I'd be able to accept that possibility once I had some closure.

Bobby remained dubious, however.

Duped? Could be, but I find it hard to believe that everything was manufactured ... I mean there was so much. Lives, family histories, names, places, particulars, dates, some verifiable facts ... oy!

Plus the way certain things came to light; by accident some of the time, etc.

On the surface, I understood his logic. It *was* hard to believe that so much could be manufactured, but the fact that McCottry had been incarcerated while several "characters" insisted that he was roaming the open roads of America took things to a new level. It wasn't likely that he'd been released and then recaptured and transferred. If all these people claimed that they had been interacting with him outside of prison, this wasn't a possibility, so they were all lying, or maybe all of it was a lie? It seemed inconceivable, but what else was the answer? Yes, Agent Waller was double-checking facts on Robert McCottry, but he'd seemed confident that the man had been out of circulation since 1991.

Things had definitely started to unravel. Echoing a sentiment of Bobby's, I felt that I'd lived in dark territory, a landscape of worries, negativity, and dashed hopes. Agent Waller represented a ray of hope in the distance, but I wasn't free of the dark territory yet.

CHAPTER THIRTY-ONE

THE GREAT WHITE AND THE SEAL

Your play's too hard to act; there are no living people in it.
—Anton Chekov

Thoughts of Agent Waller meeting Robert McCottry played through my mind. Although the story that had taken shape for nearly a year was now breaking apart, the fact that Agent Waller was going to meet 'da Cat' made this realization all too real. Remembering his mug shot caused a shiver of fear to dance down my spine. Waller wasn't just going to shuffle paperwork or make a simple phone call; he was actually going to travel to the prison in New Jersey and speak face-to-face with a hardened inmate. This was truly going above and beyond the task at hand and given the vast array of cases handled by the FBI, I was thankful that the Bureau had ascribed importance to my peculiar case. Even the smallest detail obtained from McCottry might yield a treasure trove of information, or maybe McCottry would provide no answers at all, leading to a dead end. But either way, I wanted to know so that I could put my mind at ease to stop being afraid. In the long run, I trusted Waller to do what he said he would.

Given Bobby's prickly, peevish nature, he continued to parry and thrust with me via email and telephone, alternately questioning my motives and then offering me solace, although his support was becoming increasingly laced with sarcasm and harsh criticism for my actions. I sometimes wondered whose side Bobby was on and why I remained friends with him. His barbs left me feeling uncomfortable, alone in a hell that he himself couldn't experience given his physical and emotional distance from my problems. On most days, I believed that, at some level, he genuinely cared for me, but, on others, I wondered if maybe I was just entertainment for Bobby. My other friends were concerned about my welfare, but they understandably didn't have the patience—or the stomach—to put up with such a complicated saga, complete with the filth that had assaulted my inbox. Bobby, on the other hand, knew every actor in this sordid drama inside and out—every turn of the worm. He was a difficult confidante, but he was all I had on a day-to-day basis.

It was mid-November, and I reminded Bobby that Agent Waller was going to speak to McCottry soon and that I hoped he would "dig up some of the truth." Bobby lapsed into his supportive role, full of almost jovial speculation about the cast of characters we'd watched for what seemed like endless months and how they had gained so much credibility.

I know it! That is what is so weird about this, otherwise it seems somewhat plausible. But ya know what? I kind of miss Leona and his crazy little notes. He was endearing in some ways even though there was an element of danger about him.

I was forced to agree with his opinion of Leona and stated that, "To tell the truth, I feel a bit of a loss now that he's not writing." While I felt that gaining distance from all of the principal players was the healthiest thing I could do, I had embarked on my genealogical journey to find real family connections. My sister and father were deceased, and I really *wanted* a cousin. Belief is a fluid thing, but I had taken it all so seriously. When Leonard responded with sexual taunts the shock was penetrating. The disappointment and shame was a direct path back to how I felt about my father's sexual improprieties. It seemed that no man I sought a real connection with was ever going to deliver. It wasn't the first time I had tried to care for someone who abused me and left emotional scars. I had been on that road all my life—wanting someone to care for me in return, with no regard to how fucked up they were. I'd therefore developed what I had perceived was a sense of kinship with Leonard (or the person who was playing his part) despite his erratic nature and appetite for the dark underbelly of life. Like me, he'd been hurt by Sharon, and we'd managed to find a certain measure of sympathy and understanding for each other, whether he was LenDog or Leona. Bobby and I had talked endlessly about Leona, and after all was said and done, Bobby was correct: he had an endearing side that was hard to ignore.

Meanwhile, Nolan concentrated on school and work and didn't care to discuss the intricate web that had been woven around both of us. He'd contacted the FBI and he was ready for this to be over. He had no patience for the melodrama—who could blame him? So I continued to spend an inordinate amount of time emailing and talking with Bobby, who voraciously consumed the ongoing saga as if it were a drug.

For the most part, things in my life were quiet. It was chilly and gray, and the November fallen leaves piled up in my yard. I was relieved that my inbox continued to be free of email from Hal, Karen, Leona, and the rest. I therefore kept myself busy. I cleaned my apartment, brought in cactus plants from the yard, swept and raked leaves. I stayed busy at work as well. I felt pretty good, but, admittedly, I was also experiencing a certain amount of withdrawal due to the cessation of the emails. That didn't mean I was eager to hear from that "ole gang of mine," but the quiet was disorienting after months of being literally shocked out of my senses. The plug had been abruptly pulled on the choir of darkness, and I was left dangling with my raw and tangled nerves, waiting for the next shoe to drop. It was like detox, and the poison was not yet completely purged from my system.

In reality, I didn't think that readjustment was totally attainable until the FBI finally weighed in with something definitive. It was at this point that Bobby began to take cheap shots at the Bureau and Agent Waller, undercutting my sole hope that resolution to my dilemma was indeed possible.

"Anything from the FBI yet, Doll?" he asked.

"Nothing yet. Quiet as a cemetery."

"Do you think anything happened to him?"

"Happened? To who?"

"Yikes, this is like Abbott and Costello. Are you saying the FBI agent hasn't returned your phone call yet? I thought you were waiting since Monday for a callback. Hope he's okay. Maybe he's in a stew pot someplace rural ... LOL."

I was not amused by Bobby's glib suggestion that Waller was simmering in a cauldron. I was familiar with his gallows humor, but he'd pushed the wrong button with his comment. I was tired of his digs. I told Bobby to sit tight given that "the agent" was a busy guy.

Bobby launched a new guilt trip by relating how James was continually asking if Salt (my nickname) had heard anything about McCottry from "the FBI Guy." He added that, "It sounds like you've been dropped, dear. Case closed. I just figured by now you'd have had a courtesy call." I didn't feel as if I'd been dropped at all. I shot back with, "Give it time."

His follow-up email was equally insulting.

No big deal, but you seem to be the only one that thinks that the FBI is even working on it. I know James's secretary at work suggested it was a "dead log" since the agent's failed to return any of your calls too. Just sounds like case closed to everyone else. Oh well, like I said ... you did the right thing. Maybe he'll get back to ya next week or something ... you know ... when he's not so busy. Hey, perhaps he and Cyrese are down in Mexico, living it up on Lenny's dime, hahahaha imagine.

Glib had morphed into cruel, and I wasn't going to let his puerile nonsense go unanswered.

I called the agent once to inquire. If he doesn't call me back by tomorrow, then fine. But try to have some patience. Or at least try not to make me feel like a fool.

That was the crux of it: Bobby was trying to make me feel foolish for attempting to reclaim my sanity by enlisting the aid of law enforcement. I'd tried before and been ignored, but now I was being taken seriously. I was aware that Bobby didn't like cops, but why couldn't he display a little respect for my efforts to feel safe? I wasn't proud that I'd allowed myself to be drawn into this, and Bobby's hurtful replies were tantamount to rubbing salt in my wound. He was at it again, and he didn't let up.

Look I'm sorry but maybe you ought to look back at some of your old emails where you almost brag-bull about how wonderful the agent is, how handsome, and on top of the case he is, how interested, and only a matter of time, matter of time, time ... tick tock ... He seemed so into this, was going to "interview McCottry in person", hahahaha in person.

I think his superiors got wind of the story and pulled him off the case. They don't have $ for this kind of unsubstantiated claims, and this one's a dilly!

It got under Bobby's skin that I respected and trusted Agent Waller, and hence allusions to my being "brag-bull" over him, or that he happened to be handsome. The biggest slap in the face, however, was to call my complaints "unsubstantiated claims." Bobby had always reveled in discussing "the case" and had talked at length about how creepy the whole thing was, as well as how credible it was in its presentation. He'd been by my side the entire time, and now my story was "unsubstantiated?" It seemed that to Bobby, Agent Waller was intruding in his very own online mystery game that he could play whenever he felt like it—or turn it off when he and James needed to socialize. With harsh sentiments such as this, is it any wonder that we'd had a falling out the previous December?

I told him that I didn't understand why he was angry with me.

Hahahahaha, well I really could care less, it's kind of old at this point. I am just not sure why you don't seem a bit annoyed about getting 'the brush.'

I mean you guys took all this time to compile all your papers, then take time off of work and school, and explain everything to the man ... tick tock ...

Since then, nothing ... and now we're speculating that the entire story is FAKE just because this guy that doesn't have the courtesy to return your call said McC has always been "inside?" This is your reliable source of information?

Bobby was intimating that he thought the cyber scenarios to be genuine and believable and was also suggesting that Waller was taking too long to get back to me and, using his inappropriate sense of humor, stated that the agent was "stewing" upstate in a pot, an obvious allusion to The Tribe of Twelve. The gloves were now off. My lone confidante was ridiculing me, implying that the FBI was either inept or outright ignoring me. Further, that I was naïve in waiting for a reply—"tick tock"—nothing but a fool. In fact, the notion that I'd been hoaxed was itself being called into question. The absence of a speedy reply meant that speculation as to the bogus nature of the entire sordid game was unwarranted. Though he had begrudgingly agreed with me a few days earlier that matters pointed in the direction that all online exchanges had been a farce, it was obvious that Bobby still wanted, even *needed*, to believe in the corporeal existence of Leonard, Hal, Sharon, Karen, and their seedy cohorts— perhaps Leonard more than anyone else given his own fascination with dungeons and S&M.

I told Bobby that I was no longer being harassed, and that I did indeed regard the FBI as a reliable source of information. I added, "You *do* care because you call me every day."

Bobby's focus, however, remained on my previous email in which I alluded to his anger. His response was defensive in the extreme.

You're putting words or emotions onto me that don't exist.

Angry? Why should I be? I'm just so amazed at how trusting you are.

Man, a week ago you were on cloud 9 - feeling jubilant the case was in the FBI's well-manicured hands.

And today, you can't even get your phone inquiries returned.

You're just as happy as a clam to accept it too. I guess if the Nachmans popped up again, or someone started to bug ya, you'd be on the horn for some info. But now that it's peaceful, who cares, right?

I don't think you realize how much you talked this guy up - his interest and dedication, and now, nothing.

Anyhow - I won't ask ever again. I will tell James and the other people not to ask me any questions either, because then I ask you and this whole circle jerk starts all over again. "Who, what guy"?

I'm sure you'll keep me posted or fill me in if you ever hear from him again.

He ramped up his criticism of the FBI's reliability by adding in a separate email, "Aren't they still under investigation over the 9/11 debacle?" There was no way to reply to such an abrasive comment, so I reiterated that there was nothing more I could do but wait and hope. Bobby's terse reply was, "Okay, Saltz. I'm outta here."

That was fine with me—there were times I needed space from Bobby—but he continued to be relentless. He told me to, "Get off the persecution trip. I don't think you realize how ridiculous this whole story sounds to anyone. Fourteen days of silence from the law says a lot." Furthermore, he alleged that I'd painted Agent Waller as my "Savior" and that it was my "pot to boil in."

How strange that Bobby, who touted the entire email tapestry as eminently believable because of the "sincere sentiments" they expressed, was now calling the story "ridiculous." This was further confirmation that Bobby was enmeshed in the world of the Gardiners and the Nachmans and didn't want the Federal Bureau of Investigation encroaching on what, for him, lacking meaningful employment or engagement in anything other than his social calendar, was an interesting hobby. It was starting to seem that I was less his friend, than something that had kept him entertained, and he didn't want the show to be over.

As for Agent Waller being a potential savior of sorts, that was a fair assessment, but I didn't regard my trust in him as misplaced. I was the one running from my home and losing time at work, not Bobby. I'd been hated and hunted by one or more people whose identities I had believed were real, though I no longer regarded them as such. Even allowing for his difficult nature, I couldn't understand why Bobby was so unhappy with me all the time.

Bobby had said he was through me with—"outta here"—but he couldn't stop taunting me any more than he could let go of the idea that the senders of the many emails were probably not real people. He continued to email me reiterating that our relationship was over, although he now alleged that James was unhappy with me as well. James, he said, had been uncomfortable when I'd emailed twice the previous year to thank him for his friendship since, at the time, I thought Bobby and I might be over for good. He was, in Bobby's words, resentful and didn't want to be bothered anymore. "You go your way, and we'll go ours," Bobby wrote.

The previous year's dust-up was germane inasmuch as Bobby's portrayal of his partner's reaction didn't tally with my recollections. I'd felt that Bobby, as usual, had overstepped his boundaries. I'd grown fond of James, who was a hardworking, good-natured guy. It was impossible not to like him. In the two emails I'd sent to James, I wished him well and said goodbye. In a warmhearted response, James told me he was sorry Bobby and I were at odds and confessed that Bobby could indeed be difficult at times.

I suppose I could have left matters as they stood, but in all honesty, I, too, was enmeshed with both Bobby and the twisted tale that had latched itself to my neck like a digital vampire. I continued responding to his emails because I didn't have anybody else who knew just how far down the rabbit hole I'd fallen. For all of his cruelty, he knew the complete backstory and had been my support all throughout the ordeal. In fact, I had been so terrified at times that I had actually forwarded emails to Bobby without reading them, allowing *him* to sort through their content and tell me whether they were threatening or benign. I was prepared to once again put space between us if it came to that, but part of me hoped that it wouldn't. Without a response from Waller, Bobby was still all I had, so I told him that despite his "cutting into me" and genuinely hurting me, I hoped that we could mend the fence.

He certainly wasn't going to let that little gem pass without comment. Being the master manipulator that he was, he sensed my neediness. His lengthy reply was part apology, part patting himself on the back for being such a good friend, and part vindication for his own actions. He reeled me in all over again. He was sorry for angering me; he believed that I'd made some poor choices in my life (i.e., going out with a much younger boyfriend); he claimed his boiling pot references were simply a little "cannie" (cannibal) humor; he said that he and James had worried that my "troubles would somehow spill over into our quiet and private lives"; he emphasized that he was upset at how law enforcement had treated me; and he said that if I wanted to mend our broken fence, then he was willing to try.

Maybe the most interesting part of his email was the following: "We laugh and love our Great White Shark, his majestic form and cold, unfeeling demeanor, but I don't think it's anything to emulate. Being able to flip a switch on a friendship . . . is very dispassionate." Mimicking Lou Burr's idiom in order to retain his edge of sarcastic humor, he added, "Well, that's really cool, lady, LOL."

The mention of the Great White Shark referred to our mutual fascination with sharks—the coast of New York had been the scene of several shark attacks in the summer of 2001—and the Great White's fondness for attacking seals resulted us in nicknaming a baby seal "Salt" or "Saltz" (which was the source of my nickname).

The server was down at Rizzoli, and I wasn't in the best of moods, so I responded to him in a rather terse manner. I told him that I'd been hurt enough to cry, that the cannibal humor wasn't funny, and that his sarcasm had fallen flat. I appreciated the help and hospitality he and James had extended, and I'd wanted a "break" rather than complete severance of our friendship. All of this had been too much and I needed to heal, not have my friend mock me. Finally, I told him that, just as he was free to criticize me, I was not especially impressed with many of the things he himself did in his personal life.

I was tired of being everyone's punching bag.

CHAPTER THIRTY-TWO

A CONVERSATION WITH MCCOTTRY

What one man can invent another can discover.
—Arthur Conan Doyle, *The Return of Sherlock Holmes*

It turned out that Agent Waller hadn't spoken with McCottry yet, but he'd been working the case and contacted me with some startling information. My patience, it turned out, had served me well. No arrest records existed for Leonard or Sharon. There was no judge in Massachusetts corresponding to any court decision regarding Sharon, nor was there any attorney of record for Hal. He hadn't found any evidence that Cyrese Bork really existed, and no reports had been filed indicating that Mulgrave was dead, although Mulgrave was still getting summonses on his automobile. These reports were on a par with knowledge that McCottry had never left prison. Bobby had impugned the integrity and efficiency of Agent Waller and the FBI, and he'd been dead wrong. I was eager to see how Bobby would respond to news that hard facts about the case were again emerging.

I relayed to Bobby the latest update from Agent Waller, adding that, "Dead people don't drive, as far as I know. From the minute I heard that McCottry was never out, it all unraveled for me. As strange as it all is, the whole thing, or at least ninety percent of it, is very likely total BS. A ride. A joke. A play. "

Bobby, of course, was not about to eat the well-deserved portion of crow I'd served on his plate. He replied, "I am so glad I pushed you to call him back. It's more than just McCottry having been in jail the whole time. The whole f'n thing seems fake."

That was rich. Bobby was now taking credit for me involving law enforcement, even agreeing that everything had been a hoax. He'd ridiculed and criticized me, bruising my sense of self-worth and battering my shaky self-confidence. But this new posture, this "180," was almost as painful. His agreement that it was all fake, coupled with his self-aggrandizement for spurring me forward to find the truth, brought home that Bobby perhaps hadn't changed that much.

My mind was whirling. It was time for me to sit down and think—and then think again. Who had reached through the computer screen when I'd made an ordinary attempt to connect with family members? Somebody had put their meat hooks into me and left me to dangle over a precarious psychological void.

And then there was another question even more disturbing. Why would anyone go to such lengths to torture me? Who would hate me that much?

I continued to see LNachman1 signing on and off AOL's Instant Messenger, sometimes remaining online for as long as forty minutes. Furthermore, Sharon's old email from Hebrew College seemed genuine, and I suggested to Agent Waller that he take a closer look at it. Everything pointed to not just an off-the-cuff prank, but to a well-orchestrated cyber siege intended to terrorize me.

I was relieved that "this" unknown was leaving me alone, and it wouldn't have surprised me if he or she had closed down all their email accounts. At this point, however, I didn't feel like testing the waters. Instead, I began combing over months of old emails, looking for things that didn't add up. I didn't come up with any immediate answers, but at least I was now asking the right questions.

Who was responsible? Was it the man outside Nolan's place? And how did they find Nolan's last name and cell number? How did they know that I changed my clothes before I walked my dog? How did they know where I worked?

Carl's death, his sister Janis—it was all BS.

I didn't hesitate to toss these questions and conclusions to a chastened Bobby, who now sang a different tune. He asked if I thought that Hal was a "set-up" as well.

The answer was an unqualified "yes," and I reminded Bobby of specific events that were now smoke dissipating in the breeze. Hal had gone along with the story of McCottry's arrest to the hilt. His lawyer had told him that McCottry had been arrested. He'd also gone to New Jersey to help Leonard with his deposition on McCottry's disappearance.

Furthermore, if McCottry had never been out of prison, who wrote to Sharon claiming that the two had met the last time she was in New Jersey? Who put the spyware on Leonard's computer and knew what Leonard and I were talking about?

Judging from Bobby's enthusiasm, one would have thought he himself wore a gold shield on his belt. "And don't forget the woman who stopped to ask if you were 'Sue'? That scared us to death. I still feel you guys were being followed. The stories were fantastic, but the sentiment in the emails seemed so genuine."

"The truth will be stranger than we thought," I replied. Of that I was convinced.

***

The last weeks had been somewhat restorative. I was still tense, but I had hope, and that was the one tonic capable of lifting my spirits even though Agent Waller hadn't yet connected all the dots.

A ride. A joke. A play.

I was still tense, but I had hope, and that was the one tonic capable of lifting my spirits even though Agent Waller hadn't connected all the dots.

If it wasn't for hope, I might have lapsed into frayed nerves and compromised health again when Bobby located a new Yahoo profile for *thegoodswan*. It belonged to Leona. The monster that had stalked me was still hidden for the most part, but this new discovery equaled the monster's hand reaching from behind the curtain. It wasn't finished toying with me yet.

Bobby urged me to make contact. I was naturally hesitant, but with the FBI clearly on my side, I thought it might be a useful way to gain more information. It was a risk, but one that I thought could bear fruit. Leona quickly replied, "My good swan!!!"

Elated, he relayed that he was told that I was dead and he had been sick and sad from the news. Everyone had cried and missed me. Since I was clearly alive, he asked where had I gone?

I was forced to second guess myself. I was encountering more lies and craziness, which seemed to go with the territory. As I told Bobby, it literally gave me the shivers.

There was much to be learned from Agent Waller's update, but now apparently the mysterious force behind the cyber gas lighting had claimed I was dead.

Looking back, there were times when it wasn't possible to think about the entire story without naming its characters, despite the realization that they weren't real. The he/she or they masterminding it were still *persona non grata*. And since I was examining so many past emails to ferret out meaningful details, my mind still seized on the names of "the cast" as obvious points of reference.

Now, someone behind the curtain was wondering what had killed me.

Whoever was penning this grim tale had violated the integrity of the plot. Such slip-ups could only reinforce the fraudulent nature of the entire story.

I told Bobby that "they" were all loonier than a fruitcake. They had killed off their beloved cousin, and not even the wise and nurturing Hal, the man who'd always put out the family fires, had bothered to check on me. The truth, however, was probably far deadlier than speculations about "loony" characters. Whoever was responsible may or may not have been crazy, but he/she or they were most assuredly dangerous and completely fixated on me.

I didn't want the hoax taking over my life again. I wanted to leave the theater with my dignity intact.

I wasn't shaking anymore or wearing disguises, although when walking in my neighborhood I still memorized license plate numbers and kept an eye out for anything strange. As it was, Williamsburg was a magnet for unusual people to begin with. A nameless ghost was sitting at a computer keyboard somewhere, his fingers, invisible to my limited perspective, tapping out messages to alternately terrorize and seduce me. And he *had* seduced me with his childlike lyricism and feigned reassurance that I was his "good swan." He had figuratively tied my wrists and put me in his dungeon without ever even entering my home.

With the dust settling somewhat, thanks to Agent Waller, I was able to take a closer look at things as I continued to examine old emails. I noticed details that had been consistent throughout the saga. McCottry and Sharon, for example, had both typed the words "thank you" as one word: thankyou. In fact, as I studied the entirety of the emails, I saw that *all* my correspondents had committed the same typographical error, which was more than a little coincidental, bolstering my increasing conviction that a single hand might be responsible for most, if not all, of the emails. I also noted that Felix had used the word "addy" to refer to email addresses, this petite abbreviation being more of a "chick thing" than an idiom used by a convicted felon or macho rapist.

Bobby was noncommittal, saying, "Who knows?" He felt that the perpetrator might simply be a newbie on the internet, someone trying to use the web's new lingo. Ten years ago, when internet communication was not quite so evolved and standardized, people were indeed adopting new trends and abbreviations almost daily, but my gut still told me that such details pointed to a fraud.

Bobby no longer challenged my assumption. For the time being, he was on board, although I knew that he was capable of jumping off at any moment. He said, "You really got duped, all right. Any word from the pro?"

"No. I'll leave him a message when I get home from work. Too many people here listening in."

"I don't blame you," Bobby replied. "Keep it private. Snoops abound!"

CHAPTER THIRTY-THREE

POOR DEAD SWAN

The silver swan, who, living had no note,
When death approached unlocked her silent throat.
—Orlando Gibbons (1612)

Meanwhile, other kettles continued to boil. Agent Waller called to inform me that McCottry was being held in a civil confinement facility in Kearney, New Jersey. He explained that civil confinement was used for convicted felons who had served their prison sentences but were deemed to be too dangerous for release. The confinement was open-ended, with authorities having the latitude to keep a felon detained for as long as they could prove the inmate to be a potential danger to society. Although I was feeling safer in general with all the details I was learning, this bit of information was the exception: I was very frightened at Waller's news about McCottry. Even worse, Bobby looked up this form of detainment online and, much to our dismay, learned that the Kearney facility had a high escape rate, with the surrounding communities understandably up in arms over their presumed lack of safety.

Waller also told me that he'd spoken to McCottry's girlfriend, who lived in New York City and professed ignorance of any of the Nachmans or me, or their morbid milieu. It seemed odd that a hardened criminal like McCottry had a girlfriend, and I hated the fact that they were both hearing my name. I didn't want the noir tale getting deeper and darker since a pinpoint of light was finally emerging.

I thought about how so many trials and tribulations had resulted from what started as a little correspondence on *genealogy.com* at a moment when I was feeling vulnerable and seeking connection. Genealogical websites are promising venues for useful information and possible contact with loved ones. They're generally not known to be repositories for pain, misery, the threat of rape and cannibalism, and worse.

I went back to older emails to review the ordeals and found a brief video clip of Leona writhing in a chair. Greasy, stringy hair was pressed flat against his head. There was no evidence that he'd made any attempt to pretty himself up. It was Leona in a raw and carnal state, seemingly oblivious of the camera. I'd seen dozens of his still photos, but because I had rushed this off to Bobby for review because I couldn't bear to look it, this was the first time I was seeing him in a film. It was jarring and frightened me in a new, more visceral manner. He was no longer just jumbled lines of dada-esque syntax or an oddly contorted face in a still photo. Here, he was a real person, living and animated, luridly twisting his body. Even more unnerving was that all of the nylon, lace bras, and black chokers couldn't conceal the fact that Leona was a physically fit man. Watching the clip again and again, I searched for light in his eyes, something redeeming, even if it was only the joy of pleasure, but he was deadly serious as he squirmed, his legs crossed tightly as he sat in his chair. His upper lip curled in an anemic attempt at a smile, succeeding only at producing a tortured grimace.

Totally engulfed in his fantasy, his expression was blank as he fitfully performed his animalistic moves for the camera. Now, grunting and licking his lips in the forty-three second clip, a thick liquid dripped from his chin. Instantly, all of his sweet notes disintegrated in my mind as I stared at the strange, self-possessed fetishist. I felt a strong surge of terror rise in my throat, a sickening, all-too-familiar feeling. Leona was grotesque and conflicted in a world of no boundaries. Was this the individual, his personality fractured into a dozen personas, who liked to type "thankyou"?

I inhaled and decided to choke back the terror. This had to be fake. All of it. With the story falling apart, I reminded myself I no longer needed to be crippled by frayed nerves. I soon stopped shaking altogether and instead of fearfully casting fleeting glances at this bit of evidence, I committed myself to study the clip with renewed strength and a critical, discerning gaze.

When I finally removed my focus from the primitive, writhing spectacle clad in a sheer black cut-off body suit and tights, I noticed a small website logo watermarked in the lower right corner of the video: *AEBN.com*. A brief search revealed that the letters stood for the Adult Entertainment Broadcast Network, a porn website. After clicking through several pages of garden-variety sluts, trannies, and leather gang bangers, I discovered a collection of over a dozen films starring Leona. Titles included "A Shemale's Night Out," "Vennessa's Pantyhose Tease # 4," "Fetish Apocalypse," "Vennessa Goes Out # 2," and others. There was no mistaking it: this was the persona I had come to know as Leona. Who was it really? By this point, I had become very adept at searching for information on the internet and learned that Mistress Vennessa lived in Florida, not New Jersey. The individual on my screen had a thriving career as a stocking transgender fetishist, complete with a library of videos sold on porn sites. He had a booming cottage industry, as it were. I realized that Leona's wealth of internet materials was being farmed from the AEBN website. Consequently, these videos of "Leona" could be found be anyone on line. Bobby challenged my theory immediately. He pointed out that the stern, leggy shemale wearing the ever-present rose-colored granny glasses was too pale to be a Florida resident. Bobby himself had lived in Florida and said it was impossible to avoid the sun. Despite his assertion, the more I reflected on the video of Leona, or Vanessa, the less credence I gave to Bobby's reasoning. I knew for certain that I was staring at the video used to convince me of Leona's persona.

Agent Waller had more news that further unraveled the coil that had been wrapped around my neck. He had discovered that McCottry had indeed not left prison since 1989. McCottry and someone named Nick had raped the mentally disabled daughter of a woman he'd known, which was definitely not the story I'd been fed by Karen and others. There was no rape involving Leonard, Burr, or the Cat. Waller also told me that he had an agent in Massachusetts looking into the existence of Sharon Barnes.

With the story increasingly collapsing deeper into a black hole, Bobby's terse comment was simply, "OK great, thanks for the update." I suspected he couldn't bear that the sordid armchair mystery he seemed to love discussing wasn't even real.

"So I guess the whole thing really is BS," I had said. "Wow."

Bobby wasn't ready to let the narrative die. He wanted the story, like Lazarus, resurrected. He replied to my comment with the following:

Yeah, according to *Him*. [Referring to Agent Waller, italics mine]

The whole thing just doesn't make sense, especially this situation with this agent that needs to be tracked down every few weeks/months.

Like the judge - one minute there is no judge in the state - then the next she's very well known. One minute Mulgrave is alive and well, getting parking tickets, the next, well, it's "inconclusive."

Now he's got someone else working on Sharon in MA.

He was ripping into Waller again, denigrating him, and even implying that the agent was inept. His next email jabbed even harder at Agent Waller.

So where did you leave off? Is he visiting anyone else, or is it pretty much over, etc.

Just out of curiosity, does he offer any other explanation, or ask any other questions, or does he just tell you what he found out and then hangs up. I mean, do you two discuss other possibilities, or does he just go down a list, checking off names, and theories?

We talked about it a few days ago, I guess early this week when we expected the agent to get back to you after last week's big visit to the cat. None of it seems to make sense. Like why would a NY FBI agent go all the way over to NJ to interview LaChat, when all of that could be done over the phone or thru via authorities at his penn.

Then he goes mute for another week until you're pressed into calling him again

None of it seems real, especially this "FBI agent."

It was pure hubris on the part of my thorny confidante that Agent Waller wasn't conducting the investigation according to his—Bobby's—schedule. But the real gem in Bobby's email was his clear implication that Agent Waller himself wasn't real. Bobby was suggesting that Waller's methods seemed inept and unprofessional to the point that they were as unbelievable as the storyline that he was investigating. Once again, I didn't care what Bobby thought, nor did I take his bait. I trusted Waller and was going to hold onto the very solid leads that he was turning up, even if the emerging information aggravated Bobby. It was a slow process, but I was systematically cutting the threads leading from my life to the puppeteers. I did inform Bobby, however, that Waller was being a bit more diligent than he gave him credit for. Using a private email account rather than the *.gov* server, Waller had emailed Hal a very generic "Hey, haven't heard from you in a while" to see what he might get back.

Agent Waller did not receive any reply from his generic emails, nor had he heard from the Boston office, but I knew that patience would continue to pay off. Too many facts were coming to light, and I was growing more confident that the truth would be exposed.

Leonard wrote to me at my office, but I'd never given him my work email address. Not to him, Hal, or anyone else in their circle. I hadn't even told them where I worked. Had I gotten sloppy by emailing some of them in the past from my office? Were "they" clever enough to trace my IP address and wind up with the Rizzoli domain in their clutches? Anything was a possibility.

Bobby was still obsessing about the FBI. Referring to Agent Waller's email to Hal, he wrote, "What the hell did he send them, a recipe? He sounds a little suspicious too. Nothing makes sense, especially him mailing everybody little hello's from anonymous servers. This is his big investigation?"

He was not only trivializing Waller, but my own ordeal as well. I replied, "I've been stalked, threatened, followed, abused, and maligned. These freaks found out stuff about Nolan that no one could have known."

In January, I continued to dig for clues about the ultra-mysterious Vennessa. In the process, I began to notice other things. Having gone back to the New Jersey Department of Corrections profiles for McCottry and Burr, I discovered that their crimes had been committed and prosecuted in different counties. This was proof positive that there was no kidnap and rape case involving McCottry, Burr, and Leonard Nachman. The men weren't connected. Additionally, I checked Yahoo profiles for those who wrote to me about Kinkfest. All of the addresses had been created on the same day, that being the day the emails had been sent to my inbox. Exactly who was pretending to be Mistress Vennessa remained to be seen.

I tossed Bobby several links from the *AEBN.com* site on January 19. If one typed in "Vennessa's Video Productions" and clicked the third studio button, a slew of Leona vids appeared. He was a sex maven of the highest order. Bobby believed that the links solidified the fetish side of Leona and noted that some of the "playmates" in the pictures looked like Burr and his prison pals.

I was amazed at the vastness of this perverse empire and decided to click around to see if I could discover more. As I told Bobby, "[You] can't keep the old swan down for long." I went through old emails from Karen and company and, approaching the subject from my new, less fearful perspective, noticed some odd inconsistencies. She had, at first, told me that McCottry had been arrested on the spot for his crime. In a later email, she claimed that he was caught two years later. I also discovered that *sharB@hebrewcollege. edu* was from MailStart, a phony emailer. By scrolling all the way to the bottom of the email, I saw that it read: Sent using MailStart.com I felt as if I was getting closer to the truth as I continued my examination of old correspondence. Even if I wasn't piercing the veil as much as I thought, I was nevertheless distancing myself from the lies.

Somebody hadn't covered his or her tracks well enough to hold up on closer examination.

That was the crux of the matter. The emails had tapered off at one point, as if my monster had grown bored or was simply running out of steam. But if this was the case, why not just fade to black and end the show altogether? Did the person standing behind Leona have an addiction to digital voyeurism in addition to nylon and hosiery? Had he been trying to unsuccessfully wean himself from the hoax? If so, something was still irresistibly drawing him to my inbox.

I had no intention of letting up at this point. The tables had turned. The perpetrator was showing his holes and had left a trail of loose ends. No lie could be that perfect. I plowed through old profiles, mug shots, and web links, searching for further inconsistencies. At the New Jersey Department of Corrections website I found what appeared to be a file for Robert McCottry's brother, David McCottry.

Records indicated that he was arrested in November of 2004 for burglarizing a chemical factory. I recalled Sharon had asked McCottry if he could still procure chloroform when the plan was afoot to drug Nolan and me in order to traffic us to the Fall Slaughter held by the Tribe of Twelve.

"It's kind of a new twist finding da Cat's brother, and just incarcerated recently for a crime of unknown date," Bobby remarked. "I tell you, there's some truth to this story somewhere. Somewhere there is a key!"

"Guess he burgled a chem lab."

"It was a lab, yes. I am freaking. I tell you we haven't seen the end of this yet. I think it's bigger than we think. I mean, imagine if there is a sicko named Bork in California and a bitchy daughter taking money from a deranged housewife someplace, and a tranny brother. Seeing the reality part of this makes it frighteningly real. There's something to this story."

"I think if we keep digging we'll find more," I replied.

There *was* something to this story, but I didn't know what that something was. I no longer believed in the Nachmans or Gardiners, but Robert McCottry was real, and his brother had robbed a chemical factory. That seemed almost too coincidental. This time, Bobby had a point.

On January 26, at 10:00 a.m., I received another American Greetings e-card at work. The sender was *stinkingwhore@ hotmail.com*. I told Bobby that it appeared as if someone was up to his old tricks again but I hadn't clicked on the link to open it. We discussed how odd it was that somebody was still sending me garbage despite the fact that I had retained a low profile for many months. My only theory was that the monster demanded attention because it needed to be fed.

It's hard to say at this point. Months ago, I'd say definitely not. But now, it's like swinging in the dark. Some creepy, angry, perverted scum is doing it. Sharon/Len/Lou. Or an unknown. Other than actual snuff, it's as perverted as you can get. Last filthy e-card I got was early December. Somebody just can't let it go.

"Don't let it distract you, doll," Bobby advised. "I sense a dark evil. Something so bad it stinks."

Nolan started getting hang-up calls from anonymous numbers again; we weren't able to trace the calls. There was a pay service that was capable of doing so, but Nolan declined. He remained totally disgusted and fed up by the whole ordeal and was growing quieter and more withdrawn.

Agent Waller was a busy man, but he hadn't forgotten me. On February 8 he provided me with new information that would further erode the elaborate narrative that had been woven around my life. The entire Commonwealth/ Nachman vs. Barnes document was bogus. Assistant District Attorney Deborah Ahlstrom had never worked on such a case and was startled to see her name on the mock-up. Of the judges mentioned, one had been retired for many years, while the other, according to the ADA, would never have tried such a case. In fact, the wording and formatting of the header—Commonwealth/Nachman vs. Barnes— would not have been used. Waller explained that fabricating government documents was actually fairly common and that it would usually be relegated to the circular file, meaning that it would land in the garbage. But Waller was personally interested in my case and stated on more than one occasion that he found it quite baffling. He even admitted sitting up at night thinking about it. The case was unlike anything he'd ever encountered. He called again to ask about the Jennifer Whipkey case, which he was also going to check out.

Bobby seemed to be pumped up by the new developments. "OMG! Imagine you solve this murder or something. Gosh Saltz. It still is kind of exciting. It's all so amazing. So there is no Sharon Barnes, or was the case just faked?"

"He said if it was, God forbid, a murder case, he'd be able to knock on every door belonging to a Sharon Barnes in Massachusetts.

"That Whipkey murder spooks me," I said.

"He sounded like he knew inside information on it all. I find it off-putting. Some of these are real cases."

"Too creepy. Someone—he, she, they—has knowledge of courts, judges, assistant district attorneys in Massachusetts, sex crimes in New Jersey, cults in New York, and rapes, murders, and abductions. I've been pouring over my old emails, looking for the one where Hal describes the Whipkey murder. The agent gave me an email address to send him stuff if need be."

Bobby thought that looking into the Whipkey murder might entail risks.

Wow that's great. Hope you can get a lead. Then again, do you think you might just be spinning your wheels, and upsetting her family or getting investigators interests when all of this is looking like one big joke?

If The Cat is not a real player, and Sharon Barnes wasn't in court, I don't see why your information from "HAL" would do anyone any good. Everything so far he sent is bogus, or so it seems.

Hate to see you get involved by supplying info on the case, when it's probably more fantasy or sick minds at work, but you never know.

This person Leona looks like a mild mannered TS/TG. If he's not linked to the Cat and the others, I can't imagine he killed Whipkey either.

I didn't think looking into the Whipkey case was out of line, but I agreed with Bobby on other points.

I doubt the agent is contacting Whipkey's family directly. If he does anything at all, it will probably be through law enforcement.

I doubt Leona killed her, and why would Hal tell me of the connection? Ah well, just like all the other crimes in this case, just another way to scare me?

It's also hard to imagine ol' Leona with her long hair and stretch velvet picking up pizza parlor girls for dates on the road.

Whoever is behind this knows of these things. Cats, Burrs, Whipkeys, slaughters, other killings, real & not.

Too many puzzles for one mind.

The agent also told me that McCottry still calls him! Wants to talk about his own case!

He said he's not the nicest of people. Apparently he did rape a mentally impaired girl. And he knew the girl's mother. Gross.

For the reasons I had given Bobby, I didn't believe Leonard had killed Jennifer Whipkey. It was somewhat amusing that McCottry wanted to talk with Agent Waller about his own case. I suspect that once McCottry had the ear of a federal agent, he'd seen the opportunity to try and further his own dismal cause.

I was well aware that there was no Leonard or Leona. I was certain, however, that Vennessa was a fetishist in the Tampa, Florida area. The most disturbing aspect resulting from my many recent epiphanies was in trying to comprehend why someone, fetishist or not, would waste a year of his or her life harassing a female (s)he'd never met.

Bobby chose to analyze the old narrative as if the characters were real, despite his occasional growing admission that the characters were fake. "I sensed a real moral dilemma in him [Lenny] during those writings last year where he had trouble disassociating you from a sexual object and having to face the fact that you're his relative."

I had enough information now to frame a reply based on solid fact.

Karen's huge lies from day one about Burr and McCottry are the tip offs here. Hal's monumental lie in that faked court document is another enormous red light. I have separated myself from thinking they are real.

Bobby responded with, "Very good points," but then went on to say, "I think it would be so cool to sit down with Leona one day and just hash it all out and find out what is real (if any) and just actually see him alive and in person."

"I'll let you have the honors," I said, "since you're all going to be down there together."

I let all his verbiage pass. Bobby was a gossip, and despite his claims that people in DC were worried about me, it wasn't surprising that he would continue to resurrect people who had now become unreal to me. For him, it was like watching a soap opera, and given that he frequently alerted me to what was online, I let him have his opinions. Curiously, Bobby postulated that Leona might not be my relative. He often switched pronouns when he referred to Leonard and Leona. "If this is your real cousin, LNachman, then I'm interested in her. If it's not and it's just some tranny 'they' dug up to represent, then I don't really care much."

There was really no opinion I could render regarding his dissatisfaction. He was perfectly free to cease communicating since I was becoming a great deal sturdier and more independent now that the fog was lifting, leaving in its absence the realization of so many lies. Bobby needed a hobby in the worst way, although I didn't think collecting stamps would pacify his insatiable need for interjecting himself in other people's business.

He sent me a picture of Leona, who looked as startling as ever. Lenny's reflection in a bathroom mirror showed him in full dominatrix regalia: hair pulled back, choker fixed tightly in place, and tinted granny glasses perched on the tip of his nose. Grandmotherly bathroom wallpaper print recoiled in the background.

"That's a scary pic," I commented. "He never smiles. He does have a super body though. I'll give him that much."

"I've seen guys swallow cum before, and even though he does look great in a pair of hose, it ain't all that unique. If it's Lenny, it's really kind of interesting. I swear he looks like you very much."

I gave him a short reply that sidestepped his implied snark, "One day I would like to know the truth."

The next comment from Bobby was a bizarre non-sequitur: "What are you going to do when this all ends? I mean, will you find yourself hard-pressed for something to do?"

I was employed. Bobby wasn't, and I told him succinctly that, "I had a life before this."

My statement was true, but was this ever going to be over? I scarcely remembered what "normal" life felt like. What kind of day would I wake up to once the monster had been excised from my life?

Bobby said he'd only been kidding, but his next remarks were equally strange. Referring to Agent Waller, he said,

> There might even become some kind of attraction between you guys as time goes on and you continue to mail him pics or links to men wearing silky tights or cumming in their pantyhose.

> It would be subliminal and not conscious ... pretty gal mailing attractive man kink sites and perverted links.

> It would happen naturally and by proxy - all under the guise of trying to find an answer - and Sherlock trying to figure out the ladies mystery for her ... kind of Sexxxxy in a way. Keep me posted :)

Although Agent Waller was attractive, I was not romantically interested in him. In Bobby's mind, I suppose, there was the possibility that he would have something new to chat about once the hoax had been completely exposed and satisfactorily explained. Maybe he wanted to gin up a romance to gossip about, but I wasn't interested. It was as if Bobby was answering his previous question. In his mind, after it was all over, I would date Agent Waller, and that would be my life. Bobby was attempting to manipulate me yet again.

I wrote to Bobby. "Honey, it was the biggest charade of our lives."

"Are you telling me it's over?"

"I hope it's over."

"What's up with the agent?"

"He's out of town this week. Back Tuesday."

On February 25, I confided to Bobby, "I feel like such a duped dummy sometimes lately."

I had believed so many lies over the months. In retrospect, however, the entire plot grew slowly and organically. It's why the internet can be such a dangerous environment.

"Well, don't feel so bad. We were frightened out of our skins all the way down here in DC. It was such a sick and twisted tale. But it was so elaborate. It really was like a bad dream."

But it wasn't over yet. March was relatively uneventful, but on the last day of the month, I received another American Greetings e-card at work from *poordeadswan@yahoo.com*. I didn't click on this one either, but the Yahoo profile pic for the sender was a dead and muddy swan lying in a shallow concrete ditch. It was extremely disturbing to look at.

Things had indeed been quiet, but the monster wasn't letting go. In fact, he was poised for a new and more daring attack.

CHAPTER THIRTY-FOUR

SUBPOENA

Give a man enough rope and he will hang himself.
—Mid-17th century Proverb

As was the case during the previous fall, things once more grew silent. I resumed my life, although not from the point where I had left it eighteen months earlier. I had been working hard as a publicist while also trying to find out information about my ancestors—I was simply Jane Q. Public going about her business—but now I'd been deposited in a dark place with more than just the casual debris of defunct kink parties. I was living in the wake of a stampede of treachery and horror. Weary and emotionally injured, I wondered who could hate me so much. Who would want to inflict such an inordinate amount of degradation and horror upon me? I'd stopped quaking, but I was still looking over my shoulder, literally and psychologically, as well as tiptoeing to street corners, peering in all directions before proceeding. This was not the life I remembered.

In this renewed silence, I realized that I would never be able to use my real name for an email address ever again, even if my own personal monster was ultimately caught. How many other monsters might be waiting for me in a world with tens of millions of computers? I was keenly aware of how vulnerable technology made people, and I was resigned to living in some form of personal hiding forever—living incognito, as it were. I was resolved to never again make it easy for someone to turn my world upside down. But these were matters for future consideration. I knew equally well that the silence did not mean that I was necessarily free yet from my waking nightmare. My unknown stalker was surely still on my tail, still looking for an opportunity to drag me back to a world of fear and illusion.

I was extremely busy with Rizzoli's spring titles, and the looming fall list was sitting on my desk. That's the norm in publishing. You always handle three seasons simultaneously: the backlist, current titles, and upcoming titles. My weariness wasn't lessened by immersion in my job given that it was extremely tough to work at Rizzoli. There were unforgiving deadlines and incessant demands. My boss Katy Winter was an excellent publicist; she was tough and ran a tight ship. She'd nevertheless been patient in putting up with my ceaseless distractions that were clearly affecting my ability to focus. For that I was thankful, but in the midst of constant emails and phone calls, my concentration was further compromised by the blaring street noise outside from trucks, traffic, the beeping of impatient cabbies, and the more than occasional sounds of jackhammers pounding concrete into powder and rocks. This awful cacophony banged into my corner work cube for hours at a clip. I was severely worn out and given the demands of a job that paid the rent, I desperately hoped and prayed that the invisible monster's obsession with me would soon stop for good. There was noise in the street, and there was noise in my body, mind, and soul.

The accompanying email "noise" resumed on Wednesday, April 13, at 2:51 p.m., when a Yahoo greeting popped into my work inbox. It was from *poordeadswan@usa.net*. After the incredible number of emails I'd received for the past year and a half, my mental state was such that now I don't even recall what the card said. Another card, this one from "Suzy Fensten" via *USAGreetings.com*, arrived at my office inbox the very next day.

This was disconcerting but not at all unexpected. I knew the monster was still watching me with a lurid eye. On the following Tuesday, April 19, however, things exploded.

It was a particularly hectic day, with work stacked high on my desk. There were books on where to find extravagant cocktails in Manhattan, thick photo books dripping with lavish spreads on fabulous apartments, books on luxury cabins, and even books on naked rugby players. Meetings and reports were scheduled with clockwork precision, and my boss, being a stickler, sat on my elbow through it all. The pressure was on.

In the midst of this busy day, a golf book author strolled unannounced into my cubicle. He was a young, ambitious man, a well-connected fixture on the New York social scene, and married to a wealthy socialite much older than him. He wore leopard print pony skin penny loafers, which was what my eye caught first upon his entrance at 11:52 a.m. as I pounded away, nose to the grindstone, at my computer keyboard. I had work to do, but his Hamptons-tinged voice, possessing the energy of a motivational speaker, pierced the drone of the workplace, hearkening his arrival. That's when all hell broke loose.

Before I could completely turn around in my chair to address him, something dreadful cascaded down my computer screen. My heart was filled with panic as I watched a veritable waterfall of messages scrolling into my inbox as the golf book author prattled on. The column of messages was lengthening at an alarming rate.

Here's a copy of your eCard

Here's a copy of your eCard

Here's a copy of your eCard

Your eCard has been picked up

Here's a copy of your eCard

Your eCard has been picked up

Your eCard has been picked up

Here's a copy of your eCard

I couldn't count the messages—it was happening too fast. Recipients were obviously clicking on the eCards' links, and God only knew what was being displayed by the URL they were seeing. More cards continued to arrive, and the column grew longer. The monster was making up for lost time. The days of silence had been, as before, a hiatus from the business of inflicting horror.

The boyish author in my cubicle, unaware of the terror that was paralyzing me, babbled on with marketing ideas for his book as I mentally groped for some kind of clarity and focus. This was, of course, quite impossible to achieve, and my mind went blank. There were jackhammers on the street and jackhammers in my computer, pounding away at my sanity. I wanted to run away and vanish. And yet I had to talk with this unspeakably golf-obsessed author. It wasn't his fault. He was just another writer with big dreams and even bigger expectations—one of the many. I don't remember what I said to him, but it was paramount that I found a way to focus my attention on the emails running amok in my computer. The leopard print loafers would have to take a backseat while I tried to steady my nerves and assimilate the nature of the latest attack flying through the fiber optic cables of the internet. Unfortunately, there was no "Control, Alt, Delete" in my brain to erase the ugly mess in front of me.

I somehow managed to get through the impromptu author tango so that I could finally examine more carefully what was happening. A Yahoo eCard had been set up to appear as if it was sent from my work email address and was being delivered to a variety of Rizzoli employees, including my boss, another publicist, two editors, the production staff, two freelancers, sales personnel, and the president of the company. Phones were ringing, cabbies were honking, and my monster was screaming at me. In that moment, I despised my life. Drenched in shame, I reached for my mouse, clicked, and waited for the eCard to load. My heart sank as the cartoonish illustration of a donkey appeared on the screen. The animated head of the jackass rocked from side to side as the sound card played a carnival tune reminiscent of a cheap, obscene sideshow. The message enhanced my humiliation.

> I'm bored. I don't really like my job. My mind is on other things, like sex. If you want to get together later, email me. —Susan F.

The card notifications continued to pour in. The dam was breaking. Fortunately, my boss came to my desk to ask if I was alright. She informed me that she had sent out a company-wide email requesting employees to disregard the eCards, which pertained to a personal matter I was dealing with. I felt grateful that she had taken the initiative so quickly to diffuse the situation with sage, understated damage control. And yet damage had surely been done even though the notifications that the greeting cards were being picked up slowed and then ground to a halt. My boss's email had quelled the emergency, but I was still humiliated beyond words. Without a doubt, such salacious material had caused some raised eyebrows and random chatter around the office. Everyone was gracious about it, but I nevertheless felt as if I'd been picked up and body-slammed by an unseen hand. And it had been done by sending simple eCards. I had no idea how the monster had found the names and email addresses of my co-workers, but it had. I shouldn't have been surprised given that it had been doing whatever it wanted with impunity for over eighteen months.

I lowered my head onto my desk and cried. I was emotionally drained. I realized that my only course of action was to call Agent Waller and let him know what had happened. I pulled out his card, which had a handwritten direct extension on it, and dialed the number. His voicemail picked up, and I left a message explaining the eCard debacle, my words choking off into tears at the end. I hung up, took a deep breath, and hoped for the best. The FBI was all I had.

I pulled myself together—I still had to get through the rest of the day—and collected my thoughts. But the same questions lingered in my thoughts. Why was this happening? Who could be so cruel and sadistic? Why did they hate me so much?

My time for reflection was short-lived. A high speed stream of yahoo eCards newly deluged the computers at Rizzoli. These were different cards, all sent to even more people at my office. This batch was delivered to the staff in accounts receivable, the receptionist, two editors, and various sales reps. As before, there were so many that it was hard to keep up. I refused to open the ones addressed to me from *poordeadswan@yahoo.com* because I didn't want to give the sender the satisfaction of knowing I had seen it. But the sender was clever and somehow knew my thinking— and wanted and needed me to see its message. It demanded that my face be pushed into its insistent communication. I started getting cards addressed *to* me and *from* me. I therefore reasoned that I would be able to see the message without tipping off the sender, thinking maybe I could have a "private viewing." I clicked the link and saw the following: "You made me very happy today."

The truth was that sending me cards "from myself" had been an obvious ploy to trick me into thinking that I could click the link safely. The reality was that the emails sent "to me and from me" were going to the other employees via blind carbon copies—the "bcc" in emails. I'd fallen into the trap, and the greeting was an "in-your-face message" letting me know that the monster was quite pleased with terrifying me yet again. I'd been frightened out of my wits, and the terse six-word message was confirmation that he knew I'd read the card.

My boss suggested that I consult Rizzoli's IT specialist, Peter Walker, while I waited for Agent Waller to return my call. I explained the sordid story to Peter, who seemed quite intrigued by the situation. Such a scenario is a welcome challenge to IT personnel, not that Peter wasn't concerned about me, but it was more interesting than just routine server maintenance. He said that he would begin programming a "block system" for the company server, which would then target a specific domain, block it, and automatically delete it. I felt relieved to have his attention and expertise focused on my problem. I therefore gave him the website addresses, and he began creating the block.

Meanwhile, I emailed Bobby, relating everything that had happened: the eCards, my boss's response, my talk with Peter, and the tearful voicemail I left for Agent Waller. He emailed back, asking why I had cried. This would have been a strange question from anyone other than Bobby, who vacillated between being totally concerned about my welfare to expressing complete disdain for many of the actions I'd taken to protect myself. I chalked it up to yet another inappropriate response, knowing that my emotions that day were a normal reaction to eighteen months of psychological terror and warfare.

Thankfully, Agent Waller returned my call that afternoon. Relieved but desperate, I told him in a little more detail what was transpiring, and he reassured me that he would take care of it. He asked me about the various email addresses in order to ascertain where the cards had originated, and I told him that *poordeadswan@yahoo.com* was the chief offender.

After a few hours, the barrage of emails finally stopped. Peter had created a block known as a "banned content alert" and named the block "susanstalker." As soon as the block was in place, new eCards started to pour into the company's server from *kinkycards.com*, *USAGreetings.com*, *eGreetings.com*, and *blackgotham.com*, the latter being a strictly BDSM e-greeting site.

By 3:30 p.m. the block was working since, as I told Peter, I received an eCard with no message. Even though a notice had been sent that my greeting had been picked up, the greeting itself was a complete blank. The message had been obliterated. The content had indeed been banned.

Agent Waller had returned my call to inform me that subpoenas were being issued for *poordeadsawn@yahoo. com* and that it would take a week, maybe longer, to get any results. He also warned me not to get my hopes too high since the subpoena might only point to computers at a library or an internet café.

With the FBI ready to issue a warrant, my anticipation for discovering the truth was greater than ever, despite Agent Waller's caveat that I should temper my expectations with a little reality. Nevertheless, I believed we were one step closer, perhaps on the brink of a breakthrough. It was an exhilarating feeling.

Although my spirits were high with the realization that I might be drawing closer to identifying the perpetrator, the eCards kept crashing in. The block was so thorough, however, that it even deleted messages that I'd saved in my junk folder, the one to which I forwarded evidence of my ever-growing collection of emails to save for possible use in the investigation.

As fast as they could be zapped, new messages poured in. Peter had to create a block for each new domain being used by the sender. The next block was named "susanstalker1." Things were flying in every direction. At one point, I received greetings from Peter to me while he simultaneously received greetings from me. It was a blizzard of messages that continued to arrive throughout the day, targeting an ever-widening circle of people at my office. Fortunately, Peter's blocks worked and deleted the messages as fast as they poured in.

I reminded myself that subpoenas to Yahoo were going out as messages assaulted the Rizzoli servers. It made sense that the person who had conjured and pulled the strings for *poordeadswan* would be the primary focus. It was true that Agent Waller's hard work might lead to another slippery alley—evidence with teeth can run through one's fingers like sand—and "people" I'd dealt with for so long had indeed turned out to be mere shadows in someone's disordered mind. But one thing seemed certain. Even if an individual wasn't identified, I might at least learn the state where he or she resided. At present, I wasn't sure if the emails originated in New Jersey, Massachusetts, Florida, New York, or someplace else altogether. Knowing the perpetrator's location would at least give me partial satisfaction and possibly even ameliorate some of my worries.

With the barrage of eCards under control, thanks to Peter, I emailed Bobby with the good news about the subpoenas. I was especially eager to relate recent developments since he had given me such a hard time about the whole investigation. He replied immediately.

Oh? That's wonderful, but why are you doing this?

His answer was a non-sequitur. Annoyed, I reminded him of the obvious: I was doing this because it might turn up useful information that would lead to the person or persons responsible for harassing me. Perhaps I shouldn't have been surprised at his question given his previous ridicule of the FBI and Agent Waller, but I was nevertheless irritated.

Bobby remained confused as to my motives. In a demanding note, he asked who exactly was being subpoenaed and why. When I told him that *poordeadswan* was the target, he again asked, "Why?" I didn't understand the question and

I reminded him the perpetrator behind that email address was the source for much of my recent grief and I wanted the perp caught and hopefully punished. After my terse and rudimentary explanation, I let the matter go. Bobby could think what he wanted.

No matter what anyone said at this point, the subpoenas were being issued the following day. The monster had upped the ante, but the FBI was all in. I was one step closer to a resolution.

CHAPTER THIRTY-FIVE

SHOCK

To betray, you must first belong.
—Kim Philby, British intelligence officer and Soviet spy.

The subpoena for *poordeadswan@yahoo.com* was making its way through the legal system. I had no idea when I would hear any news about its progress from Agent Waller. It was Monday, May 2, and I had received no threatening or harassing emails since April 19, but I'd been through periods of relative inactivity before, and I wasn't going to be lulled into a false sense of security simply because the perpetrator was "lying low." It had become part of the pattern, and I took nothing for granted at this point.

After the multiple rounds of eCard attacks at Rizzoli, I thought it would be wise if Bobby avoided using my email address at work until the dust finally settled for good. I relented, however, when he asked if the coast was clear. While I wanted to keep the insane drama out of my inbox, I still relied on Bobby for support on a minute-to-minute basis. Even though at times he was less than supportive, he was all I had when it came to this and having a less than perfect person to talk to about it was better than having no one at all.

"Seems we're fine," I told him.

"Fine, dolly. Shall we write via this address now that the heat is off?"

My answer was "yes" since I didn't want to have to click over to personal accounts every time I needed to check my email.

Meanwhile, one of the many books on my work list was *Moonage Daydream: The Life and Times of Ziggy Stardust*, a stunning book with photographs of David Bowie and other rock and roll giants by rock photography legend Mick Rock. Being a longtime Bowie fan, I was excited to do the publicity for the book and meet the man who created such colossal icons as Freddie Mercury of Queen, Syd Barrett of Pink Floyd, and Debbie Harry of Blondie. I shot a note to Bobby to excitedly share my good news.

Just met with Mick Rock, big time rock photographer, Bowie, Iggy, Lou Reed, Stones, etc... we are doing a Bowie book soon. FUN, FUN, FUN! You would have loved him. Great older rock 'n' roll British salt!

Bobby seemed happy that I was working on a book with such a fantastic author. Our exchange was normal and healthy as opposed to the garbage that I'd been forced to read for so long.

While things had "gone silent" for a third time, my case nevertheless remained open and unsolved. I still needed to know exactly where and from whom the harassment had originated. Later that afternoon, I received a call from Agent Waller, who updated me on the progress of the subpoena. The news was encouraging. The subpoena had revealed the internet service providers for *poordeadswan@yahoo. com*. Remembering Waller's admonition that there were no guarantees, I again tempered my excitement about a possible bull's eye hit, but now he had specific information on the emails for the very first time: the sender was using AOL and Verizon accounts. Agent Waller didn't have any names or addresses yet, but the curtain hiding my tormentor had been pulled back, however slightly. The call served as validation that Waller's interest in the case hadn't waned, plus it also indicated that the sender was not invincible. The accounts were solid leads worth pursuing, and they would enable Agent Waller to take the next logical steps. I couldn't wait to tell Bobby, so I immediately relayed the news to him.

Heard back from the agent. He just called me. They found out that it's coming from an AOL and a Verizon account. Weird, eh? Still awaiting further information. He said that Yahoo and AOL only holds IPs for five days, so it wasn't the most useful, but he says he's subpoenaed AOL and Verizon for the billing information. So that'll be the key. He said he'd have to decide how best to proceed once they get an actual address. Sometimes it's just a 'knock and warn' ... which means the FBI knocks on your door and says, 'Look, we know it's you, so this is your warning to stop.' Or, it could be prosecutable, but that's up to the prosecutor. The FBI does the investigations but also makes recommendations on charges. I thanked him profusely and said that things have been very quiet here too, strangely enough. He said that he's very interested in getting to the bottom of this too.

So that's the scoop so far.

This distinct digital fingerprint wasn't necessarily a lot to go on, but it had been enough to identify the internet service providers of my stalker. The billing information held by these providers, therefore, was the key to going even farther. The next step was finding a real name that corresponded with the accounts. Caution was still in order since it was ostensibly easy for someone to use another person's computer without that person's knowledge, but I knew that being able to place a name and address to the two accounts could be potentially huge. It was possible that the fiend might be finally unmasked. Someone so masterful at manipulating my life for a year and a half could be identified by issuing an internet provider a subpoena. Waller himself had said that he would have to decide how to proceed once they'd gotten an actual address, but I remained hopeful.

Once they'd gotten an actual address.

I was too guarded in my thinking to believe that the nightmare was finally over, but Waller was as trustworthy as they came, and it certainly seemed as if he was closing in. The investigation was moving in the right direction.

"Wow!" Bobby proclaimed. "That is a bunch of news. Sounds good so far. It's amazing what they can find out. Keep me posted. Hopefully, it's all over anyhow."

While a U.S. District Attorney could bring charges at the recommendation of the FBI, I was concerned that any given prosecutor might *not* choose to do so, assuming there were any applicable charges to begin with. After all, it was such an unusual crime, one that sounded completely insane and, on so many different levels, entirely unbelievable. What had happened at my office had been the legal tripwire, enough to take action by means of a subpoena. The stalker had overstepped a legal boundary in what had, up until this point, been a carefully choreographed cyber ballet. The law had been tiptoed around—until now.

But there was yet another issue that could presumably present a hurdle in obtaining charges. Even if one or more laws had been broken, how would they stack up in federal court, in terms of priority, against terrorists, bank robbers, organized crime, and hundreds of other heinous actions that grabbed headlines every day? My case was about me and my terrible digital horror tale, a play of shadows animated with characters sealed in tight black hose, choked by ball gags, and restrained by leather and chains. It had been a virtual shanghai into an underground world where people are raped, murdered, kidnapped, and sold off to cannibal slave cults. And my evidence? I had a labyrinth of emails that wound around and wove through innumerable depraved characters, some fictional, some not. When I put it all together and considered the big picture, it actually looked hopeless. The only thing that overrode my worries and gave me hope was that the FBI could indeed recommend charges, and I knew that Agent Waller still wanted very much to solve the case. He had put a great deal of time and energy into it and wanted to see it through. It was more than him merely wanting to "get it off his desk."

***

Thursday, May 5 was a fairly ordinary day. I had a book signing with one of my authors, Thurston Moore, founding member of the band Sonic Youth, scheduled for after work at the Union Square Virgin Megastore. His new book was *Mix Tape: The Art of Cassette Culture*, a mixed media book with artistic notes, collages, and doodles, and a list of the music he had recorded. Throughout the day I exchanged some chatty emails with Bobby. While I was uncertain about how legal charges might play out, I was feeling better, and it was good to be able to laugh a little at my predicament. He also wrote of his new computer woes after finding a 'hidden trojan' and needed McAfee to help, after working on it all day to protect his data 'and such.' It had apparently turned on his PC after it disabled the firewall and anti-virus programs. He had heard that Broadband DSL services were under attack and suggested that I do a thorough scan when I get home.

Virtually everyone has had to cope with malware and internet security in the computer age, and having McAfee deal with a trojan was not all that unusual. Nevertheless, I thought Bobby's dilemma was strange. Even in my own worldwide web odyssey, my computer had never turned itself off and then on again. But I was now very aware that almost anything was possible.

I was so busy that I hadn't taken the time to scan my computer, and it was clear that my PC wasn't the problem. I was war-weary and had been waiting for nearly nine months for the feds to track down my stalker. They appeared to be getting close, so I wasn't really concerned about computer viruses or machines that behaved like those in a Stephen King novel. I was in the process of exorcising a much more serious virus from my dark and dangerous world. Bobby's PC troubles grew more and more convoluted, however, and he gave me chapter and verse on every gremlin attacking his machine.

A few weeks ago my PC popped on in the middle of the night and the modem was blinking like nuts … I thought I was dreaming … so hopped up and tried to turn it off but it wouldn't shut down, so I unplugged the sucker, hahahaha. Killed it quick. Then it happened again during the day last week, and when I was working offline I went to sign on to AOL to check e's and it said I was already on, and that I couldn't sign on with the same account??? So I went to reboot and noticed my Firewall and Virus Scan was disabled ... Anyhow – long story short, I think I have it fixed. But my settings and Buddy List stuff were changed ... I had everyone blocked, and there were real emails I never sent in my outbox ... two were from an unknown sender ... quaint? The McAfee folks say that some trojans can't be eradicated with a simple scan, they need to be done by hand, step by step ... This one made itself look like a normal Windows file ... can you imagine?? I'm so annoyed with all of this right now ... I have to get all of my personal pics and private stuff off the PC to be sure that it's ME on it for a few days ... fun isn't it?

"Weird!" I wrote back. "What the hell was it?"

Probably Spam. I also get them in my Spam folder, but this appeared as if I sent it, LOL! Remember I mentioned a while ago about email spoofing when we were talking about all this crap, and I mentioned spoofing, where you get an undeliverable email on one of your accounts saying – "Sorry we tried to deliver but couldn't" – and I check the email and I see that it is a spoof. Just someone using my accounts as the Reply and From aren't really on the account, they spoof it somehow with technology to make it look like it was from the account. Well a while back I signed on and no more than a minute later I got a Reply e-mail – User Unknown. To my horror, I checked my outbox and there was a real one in the sent folder. The perpetrator or whomever forgot to delete it, meaning my account had actually been compromised and used to send junk, probably more spam and porn and viruses. The whole thing has me disgusted, I feel like throwing the PC out the window. I didn't even go to my sites today or read the news. I've been too busy securing my set up. A day wasted.

Blinking modems, disabled firewalls, trojans, unknown senders, spam, spoofing—I wondered if Bobby was now being targeted by my tormenters. I thought it interesting that someone was making it look as if Bobby was sending out emails, including spam to himself from his own IP address. Spoofing was (and still is) quite real. People can use someone's email address to impersonate them by sending out mail from remote servers located almost anywhere in the world. While I didn't doubt Bobby was having trouble, I confess to feeling a small amount of schadenfreude, knowing that he was having to contend with so many problems. He was now living in my world instead of living vicariously through my many retellings of my experiences. Or of having his main concern be so trivial as to worry about getting a present of "tobaccy smokes" for someone's birthday. From my perspective, it seemed the majority of his days were "wasted," to use his own term, not just the one or two necessary to solve his computer glitches.

The lengthy account of his computer woes wasn't finished, however. He seemed insistent on relating every last detail of his hardware problems.

Oh yes, of course sign off, but is your PC on, or in standby mode or off when you leave it? Apparently there is still a lot of communication done through the phone line to the router or modem, even when the PC is off. I thought it was *The Exorcist* when it powered up on its own around 3:00 a.m. a few weeks ago. And when it wouldn't respond or shut down, I had to pull the plug ... hahahahaha! Funny how something so lovely and fun can instantly turn into a dark and foreboding object!

I told him that I sometimes turned off my PC, while other times I merely disconnected from the internet by pulling the jack from the computer. I admitted that the scenario he described was scary, almost like a horror movie. But he still wasn't finished his tale of magic machines.

HAHAHAHA yes it was, and imagine it not responding to your prompts to shut down? When I pulled the plug and unplugged the phone line I felt like I was killing a monster. Oh, the monitor was blinking too. I first heard the start-up – but tried to sleep more and then I woke up to crazy flashing as the monitor heated up too, Surreal, nightmarish. Anyhow, I think I have it all fixed. I had to change EVERY password I own and then do some more configuring. Drained.

I, myself, had been drained for eighteen months. Was I supposed to feel sympathy for a man who had turned on me with such vitriolic emails just a few months earlier? I had bigger fish to fry than Bobby's overheated monitor and blinking modem. He had solved his problems with McAfee and a disconnected phone jack. I had had to enlist the assistance of the Federal Bureau of Investigation.

At six o'clock in the evening, I headed to the Virgin Megastore for Thurston Moore's book signing. Rizzoli's office was only eight blocks away, so I walked down to Union Square. The walk was enjoyable as always, especially on this warm May evening, but as usual I was distracted by my back story, which continually extended itself into the present, never seeming to end.

At the book signing, life was normal. It was a day like any other in New York City. A musician (and just-published author) was promoting his new book at a busy music store, shepherded by his harried and beleaguered publicist. Ordinary music fans were eager to have Thurston Moore sign copies of his new book, as well as other items they'd brought, such as old audio cassettes, posters, and album covers.

Publicists are always harried, but most were not living in two worlds at once. In one world, star struck audiophiles thrust handfuls of rock and roll ephemera at a venerated music pioneer who signed everything with a blue sharpie marker while remembering—or pretending to remember—any number of them, as they breathlessly enumerated countless random back stage encounters. Uneasily, I hovered alongside, while simultaneously mentally occupying my other world, checking my memory files on Hal, Karen, Leona, Lou Burr, Carl Mulgrave, Sharon, and Felix da Cat. My overlapping realities were far more surrealistic than Bobby's blinking computers, which at the end of the day, amounted to mere hardware problems.

Once the book signing ended, I rushed home, eager to see Mini Me. The L train was crowded but it was a short ride to Bedford Avenue.

Arriving back at my building, I heard the phone ringing inside my apartment as I stepped into the building's outer hallway. I turned the key with a quick jerk, said hello to Mini Me, and dashed off a pat on his forehead as I reached for the phone, which had not stopped ringing. The caller ID displayed Agent Waller's number, so I grabbed the receiver on the last ring before the call had a chance to go into voicemail. This could be it—the truth reveal, after living in the dark for so long.

Or it could be nothing. Maybe just another update with information about procedural matters.

"Hello?" I said.

"Hi, Susan. Brandon Waller here. We got a hit on the subpoena."

"You did?"

They'd finally gotten a bite. Was this finally over? I was elated but braced myself for disappointment in case it was a dead end.

"Do you know anyone in DC?" Waller asked.

"DC? Yes."

The question didn't seem completely odd at first. DC was a big city, but I did know two people there: Bobby and James. It couldn't be them, of course.

"What's their name?" he asked.

"Bobby Ironside."

I had unexpectedly been returned to the surreal world I'd shaken off on my ride home. I had never mentioned Bobby even once in any of my personal conversations or contacts with Agent Waller, nor did Bobby's name appear anywhere in my written report. I'd tried to keep him out of the fray so as to avoid my roiling hell from spilling over into his life. Even though Bobby sashayed his way around the web all day, he was a very private and guarded person.

"What's his address?" Waller asked.

I was surprised that Agent Waller pursued his line of questioning after I gave him Bobby's full name since I was sure that he had nothing to do with my case. It just wasn't possible. AOL Instant Messenger could not have two people signed on at once. Bobby and I had frequently IM'd, and he'd seen Leonard pop on and off AOL numerous times while we were chatting. Besides, Bobby was my friend. As irritating as he could be, he was on my side.

All of these thoughts rushed through my mind in a split second. There had to be a logical reason for Waller's questions. My mind, shuffling through possible explanations, reasoned that the subpoena had somehow included data from Bobby's IP address since we traded emails and downloads with such regularity. And Bobby was now claiming that someone was using his email and IP addresses, which was fairly within the realm of possibility. But there was no time to sort out my frenzied thoughts since Agent Waller was now firing off his next questions.

"What's his address?"

I knew it well and gave it to him.

"What's the apartment number?"

I rattled off the number quickly.

Suddenly, it hit me. Waller wasn't mistaken. He wanted every little detail. The FBI was being very thorough because it now had its man. The seams in my reality began to strain and split as Waller asked his questions. I answered them like an automaton since I knew the information by rote.

"What's the phone number?"

When I provided the number, I knew the case had reached the point of no return. There would be no more "This can't be happening." It already was. Thoughts slowly hit me like the first fat raindrops thrown from thunderclouds. It was Bobby. *Bobby.* The truth stung and slapped me like slow, cold drops. *It had been Bobby all along.* How could that be? Questions pushed their way into my mind jostling for position with a growing and noisy crowd of memories and emails. Steadily, one realization followed another until collectively, they formed a hard rain of painful, stabbing recollections and bits of conversations, all smashing and colliding with one another—thousands of them. My trips to DC, the humiliating wild goose chases at the 94th Precinct in Brooklyn, fleeing my apartment again and again, Greystone Psychiatric Hospital, Leonard, Leona, Cyrese Cyndell, and Ray Hooch—the acts in my play had been endless. As these thoughts poured through my brain, Agent Waller pressed for more information without missing a beat. My mind was tumbling in every direction.

"How do you know him?" Waller asked.

Agent Waller knew nothing about Bobby, so I explained that he was a friend I'd met in Williamsburg in 1987 and that we had remained good friends until we parted ways in 1990. I further detailed that, after a decade, Bobby had contacted me online at my job at Oxford University Press, at which time we became friends again. Waller then asked where Bobby was originally from and if I knew any of his past residences. I told him that he was originally from Long Island but had moved to Florida and then to DC. Other than that, I didn't know his residential history. Waller also wanted to know if he had been involved in any criminal activity in the past. I didn't know of any convictions, although the question gave me pause. Was Bobby associated with illegal activities beyond his former penchant for frequenting seedy underground sex clubs? I didn't know, but apparently there were many things I didn't know about Bobby.

"I need to meet with you in person," Waller stated. "Can we meet in your neighborhood in about forty-five minutes? I am bringing another FBI agent if that's okay. He wants to ask you a few questions."

"Yes."

"Is there a coffee shop where we can talk? Some place quiet?"

There weren't any quiet places nearby, certainly none where two FBI agents and I wouldn't stand out like a sore thumb. I couldn't imagine going to the local hipster coffee shop, the L Café, but there was a bar on my corner run by a fish-eyed Mafioso from New Jersey. There was never anyone there, so it would be perfect.

"There's a restaurant on my corner that never has anyone in it. We can go there and sit in the back and order a coffee."

The thought of another FBI agent becoming involved made the matter all the more grave in my mind. I'd always known that Agent Waller was taking my case seriously, but his many questions about Bobby, coupled with the request for a meeting that very evening with another agent, conveyed that the Bureau attached a certain importance and urgency to the matter.

"Do you have a recent picture of Bobby?" Waller asked.

"Yes, I do."

"Please print it out and bring it with you. It's a color photo, right?"

"Yes, it's in color and it's recent. Are you coming from the FBI building downtown?"

"Yes. We'll see you shortly."

I had a photograph that I'd taken of Bobby in front of the Washington Monument during my trip the previous summer to visit him and James. In the picture, Bobby was standing with the monument directly behind him, the iconic column appearing to shoot out of the top of his head like a spike. Perhaps the symbolism was appropriate. Bobby, it appeared, was being impaled by federal law enforcement.

I couldn't think clearly after the phone call. I fumbled with my computer keyboard, my hands slightly shaking, my palms flush with sweat. *It's Bobby* I kept repeating in my mind. I was overwhelmed with thoughts, but I didn't have time to waste. The two FBI agents were on their way, and I needed to be ready and composed even though I felt like I was coming unglued. I reached for the mouse and clicked nervously through my folders of photographs. "DC pics" was the title of the folder. The images splashed one by one back to those happy, hot summer days on James's boat on the Potomac. James at the wheel. His white cutoff T-shirt gleaming in the sun. Bobby holding his chest from behind, the wind pushing their smiles at me even wider. You would never know what was lurking beneath the surface. There it was—the photo I'd taken of Bobby at the towering obelisk. My heart was gripped with fear as I opened and studied it. It was such an ordinary picture of what looked like an ordinary person, someone who would never occasion a sideways glance. He looked like a regular clean-cut guy, certainly not a monster. I hit "print," and as the gears in the printer whirred and clacked, I was bashed with waves of thoughts, feelings, and recollections.

Above all, I wondered how he could do this to me. This onslaught was uncontrollable, with fear claiming much of my emotions. Bobby, who had always been short-tempered and intimidating in his own way—that side of him was well known to me—had now become incredibly menacing. Bobby Ironside was the monster, not some stranger, and his masks had been a simple keyboard and a computer monitor.

I questioned how someone could so easily be two people at once—indeed, not just two people, but twenty. It was unimaginable and confounding, which is exactly why Bobby had been so successful. Despite the many months of mental leaps and emotional forays, my imagination had not seized on the possibility that a close friend would terrorize me in attempts to threaten my mental and emotional well-being, at times causing me to fear for my very life.

I would have time in the future to reflect on the limits to which he had gone, but first, I needed to tend to other issues. Bobby didn't know it yet, but he was about to go headlong into an ultimate confrontation with federal law enforcement.

***

The forty-five minutes flew by. I grabbed Bobby's photo under my arm, stepped outside to the corner, and nervously waited on the sidewalk in front of the bar. The sun was going down behind the Con Edison clock against the Manhattan skyline, and the early spring wind blew hard off the river, still cool enough to put a chill through a body. Bobby's photo flapped from its position under my arm with each new blast of wind. I peeked into the window, and just as ever, the bar was empty. I was about to walk in with two government suits, and I knew they wouldn't go unnoticed. You know the feds when you see them.

Agent Waller arrived and introduced me to the other agent, Agent Good. I shook his hand and led them in. I didn't want to sit at the bar and have the barkeep overhear us, so I suggested we take a table in the back room where we would be assured privacy. The place was quiet as a morgue.

The dimly lit room had a few booths along a marvelous mural that depicted the long history of the old Brooklyn waterfront. We sat in a large red booth in the center. I was shaking. The raw shock of what Agent Waller had told me over the phone still overwhelmed me as I digested the news that Bobby was behind the whole thing.

The thin Italian waiter walked over to the booth, and we ordered three coffees. Agent Waller asked for the photograph, and I handed him the printout. He took out a red marker and drew an arrow at Bobby's head as he informed me that Agent Good would be asking me a few questions pertaining to the murder of Jennifer Whipkey. Bringing up this real-life murder added even more magnitude to the situation, more pressure to bear on where this case might be going. Prior to this situation, I didn't know anything about the murder and had never even heard of the place where it happened.

Waller began asking more questions about Bobby. He wanted to know everything about him: where we met; what he did for a living; and whether or not he was involved in any crimes in the past. I spilled everything I knew. I wasn't feeling the slightest bit protective of Bobby anymore. Why would I shield someone who had displayed such blatant disregard for my well-being, had even shown me unreserved hatred, to the point that he seemed to have been slowly trying to destroy me, mentally, emotionally, and ultimately even physically?

As for what he did for a living, I told them that other than a short stint at Trash and Vaudeville, a punk clothing store on St. Marks Place in the East Village, I wasn't aware that he held many steady jobs. I said that he was a hustler, and the agents asked me to explain exactly what I meant by the term. I explained straightforwardly that he hustled men by any means he could. Among his victims was a prominent priest from Long Island. Bobby blackmailed him for money, rent, and whatever the priest would give him in exchange for keeping quiet about all the sex and cavorting in the rectory of the church in the upper class Long Island town where Bobby had been a school boy. According to Bobby, it had involved dog collars and chain leashes, with priests walking boys around the floor on their hands and knees. I detailed the ring bolts screwed into the wooden beams along the ceiling in Bobby's apartment—and his sporadic visitors—in the building where we first met on South 4th and Driggs in the mid-1980s. I also told them about the steamer trunk of child pornography that the priest had given Bobby before he retired to Hawaii. The transfer had been made in 1987, right before it became a federal offense to not only be involved in the transfer of such material but to simply possess it. This point interested the agents greatly, and they asked what had happened to the trunk and its contents. I answered that I didn't know what Bobby had done with it, only that I had advised him to burn it.

The waiter, clearly curious, stared at us from the arched doorway leading to the back room where we were seated.

The agents seemed stunned at hearing about the trunk of kiddie porn and the stories of sexual abuse at the hands of prominent Long Island priests. They suggested that Bobby was perhaps so traumatized by his early childhood experiences that he had evolved into a psychopath. I stated plainly that I did not in any way see him as a victim. The way Bobby had explained it to me years before made it clear that he enjoyed all of it, and was even able to manipulate and exploit the situation. Years later, he wound up running the entire sordid show when he turned the affair around by holding it over the priest by means of extortion.

Agent Good, who had been sitting quietly for some time while intently listening to my tale, now jumped in and hit me with a blunt question about the Whipkey case: What did I know about a truck driver in New Jersey? The inquiry came out of left field and struck me as abstract even though I had already run down a list of Bobby's activities that was getting long and dirty. I replied that I had no knowledge of *any* truck driver in *any* state. I felt unnerved even though I had nothing to hide.

The topic then turned to James. Waller wanted to know who he was and what his relationship was with Bobby. I told them that James worked very hard and paid all the bills while Bobby stayed at home and managed the domestic side of their lives. When I told them that James worked for a large DC consulting firm whose clients included the Department of Homeland Security, the two agents looked at each other, eyes flashing, their pencils dutifully jotting down this tidbit of information.

Next, they asked if Bobby had ever held a job in DC I replied that I only knew of one job, and it lasted all of one night, which was cleaning stalls in a sex club. Surprisingly, the agents pressed me about the sex clubs. I figured these places were mainstream knowledge, but they persisted. What were the sex clubs about? Who went to them? I could only give them the most generic of answers. The clubs were places where gay men met, mainly for sex. Waller and Good asked if Bobby and James frequented such clubs, and although I posited that they probably didn't, I really had no clue as to what went on between them behind closed doors. As far as I knew, they were a pretty conservative couple, even factoring in Bobby's past. "After all," I said without irony, "they're Republicans." It was the only time during the meeting when anyone laughed.

Despite my calm demeanor during the questioning, I was shaking deep down inside the entire time. I didn't like feeling that they regarded me as a guide for the criminal dark underbelly. It seemed I was giving them more than they had bargained for.

I then dove into the subject of Bobby's vast correspondence with serial killers. He had shown me actual letters, handwritten by murderers, letters outlining how they stalked their victims. The details of the letters were extremely disturbing, providing information regarding the type of people they preyed on, what characteristics they looked for in their victims, and, once chosen, the manner in which they moved in on them and snuffed out their lives.

The agents explained that there was more investigating to do and that they weren't sure yet how they were going to proceed. Waller reiterated that he really wanted to nail Bobby good. Both agents were stunned at the idea that a friend could do this to me. Agent Good, who was at first hard and brusque with me, had softened a bit. From his expression, it was clear that he realized that he had been listening to a first-hand account of an elaborately schemed gas lighting treatment—a systematic psychological and emotional torture delivered by the hands of an old "friend."

I added that it appeared Bobby was already concocting an elaborate story to serve as a means to exonerate himself. I related how, that very afternoon, Bobby had sent me an email about his computer being hacked, as well as its mysterious turning on and off in the night. It was fairly obvious that Bobby was now frightened at the increased involvement of the FBI and was therefore posturing to blame someone else for his "pranks," or to possibly say that viruses and compromised accounts had allowed information to be sent out under the aegis of his email address. The story of blinking modems, flashing screens, and unknown senders now had a clearer context.

The agents told me to continue my contact with Bobby and to behave normally in order to not tip him off that they had pinpointed the source of my cyber harassment. I was still shaking, and Agent Waller acknowledged that I was obviously in a state of shock. And I was. No doubt I had a one-hundred-yard stare in my eyes, while a continuous loop of the last year and a half played in my mind.

The waiter brought the check, and Agent Waller paid. The two federal agents had come away with much more than they had anticipated, and I thanked both of them. Agent Waller said that he would be in touch, and Agent Good shook my hand again, only this time it was to wish me good luck.

Time had, in a sense, stopped. The case wasn't over—there was much more to come—but at last I had my answer. It was Bobby. There was no more wondering who, what, and where, although I had yet to comprehend the how and the why. I was relieved and grateful that one phase of the nightmare was over, even though I would come to learn that a nightmare's aftermath can last a very long time.

I went home and sat on the couch. I'd left the TV on for Mini Me. The station was set to the History Channel, which was broadcasting a marathon of back-to-back programs about the controlled demolition of buildings. Lost in thought, time slipped by. Not moving, I stared straight ahead, my thoughts surfing wildly through memories, events, conversations, and lies. So many lies. The buildings on the TV screen exploded and fell again and again. Unaware of how long I had been sitting there, I watched hours of hotels, bridges, and stadiums collapsing, of building after building being dynamited and reduced to a pile of rubble. The footage seemed to fit my reality, which was crashing down around me, the play I had been a part of finally imploding. Everything was coming apart.

And yet I would have to act normally, although I had no idea how I was going to manage such a feat. I hadn't known at the time, but my updates about the FBI noose tightening around the perpetrator had been tipping Bobby off with each new email. Each chatty update, complete with details and speculation, inadvertently sent directly to my own personal monster.

It's Bobby.

Another building crashed to the ground, smoke and dust billowing out in a destructive cloud of debris. The memories tumbled about and flooded me.

Memories of "Leonard":

Thank you, my good cousin swan, for the nice pictures of you.

I would have to act normally. Maintain contact. Business as usual.

Memories of Bobby:

What's up with the agent? Are you telling me this is over?

Email after email, like building after building.

You have a very soft voice, Susan.

It was Bobby all along—Bobby, who had shot my nervous system full of terror, adrenaline, and threats of death.

Posted By: Susan Fensten Date: Oct. 22, 2003

My father's father was Morris Feinstein. From what little I know, he was born either on the Lower East Side of Manhattan or in Brooklyn around the turn of the century. His family, I was told, originally came from Austria, but I can't be sure.

He had 2 or 3 daughters, remarried and had two sons. Larry and Kenneth. He changed his name to Fensten before he had his 2 sons. Any information would be greatly appreciated. Thanking you, Susan Fensten

I had set out to find information about people in my past. I had succeeded, but not about the people I had intended.

"Act normal," the agents had said.

That was going to be hard.

CHAPTER THIRTY-SIX

THE EMPIRE IS BLUE

*We have to distrust each other. It's our
only defense against betrayal.*
—Tennessee Williams

I had the next day off from work, which was fortunate. It was Friday, May 6, and aside from desperately needing a rest, I was unable to think about anything other than the news given to me by Agent Waller, as well as the whole of my meeting with him and Agent Good. I was still absorbing the entire scope of the awful truth. Numb and in a state of shock, my mind continued to drift through a gallery of recollections from the past eighteen months.

Given the vast number of characters Bobby had created, seasoned with real-life criminals and an open murder case, these suffocating memories persisted, packed tightly with the denizens of Bobby's dark, perverse imagination. He had systematically stitched in subplots as needed to the theater he had created, and with his characters now expired and removed from the stage, my thoughts peeled away layers of dead tissue as if I was conducting an involuntary autopsy. Each character was presented in my mind for dissection and analysis. Each had been wrought from the many facets of Bobby's serpentine mind. He had populated his creation with a veritable armada of perverse phantasms from his wealth of unholy ugliness. His inventions flagrantly and purposely outlandish, Bobby had outdone himself time after time as he fashioned the personalities, histories, writing styles, motives, and agendas for each of his characters. Although they had vanished from reality seemingly in the blink of an eye, in the time it took for the investigation to reveal the truth, they still silently screamed at me, and I feared they always would. They had left impressions impossible for me to shake. Like neon signs flashing along dark, vacant New Jersey highways, the ghostly images of Kinkfest, cannibal courtship invitations from Lou Burr, and McCottry's hissing love letters burned in my mind with an eerie phosphorescence.

What was especially hard to comprehend was that Bobby, the architect of this monstrosity, had perched himself alongside me throughout the entire ordeal, consistently positioning himself well within my reach. He was far more dangerous than any of his creations in part, because virtually all of his characters issued from parts of himself and his unrestrained imagination, thus making up his whole. Karen, for example, reflected the domestic side that he lived out with James. Leona and many of his other decadent personas mirrored his tastes for S&M and sex clubs. Lou Burr and Robert McCottry, on the other hand, were clearly extensions of Bobby's fascination with violent offenders.

Perhaps the hardest burden to bear was that I thought he'd been my friend, a role he certainly played, and a fact that had also shocked and confounded Agent Waller. Bobby had performed the dual roles of nurturing pal concurrent with ruthless sadist with alarming ease and alacrity. One arm comforted me while the other busily stirred players and laid out plots. Like a capricious and evil god, with each wrenching turn of his computer-generated mandala, he twisted my fate back and forth. I recalled sleeping on Bobby's couch in DC, after fleeing my home in search of refuge, and pictured him in his robe on the other side of the living room wall, orchestrating my horror merely feet away from my tired, depleted body. Had it given him extra satisfaction to know I was so close yet so ignorant of his schemes? Clearly, it had. It was easy to envision his computer screen glowing late into the night like the eye of a cyclops, bathing his face in a bluish-white light while he danced his characters with fiendish fervor. And in the morning, he'd been an attentive minder who'd asked me if I'd like to use the very same computer to check my email.

It was his dispassionate, sadistic tendencies that had made me literally shiver for so many months, and I suspect that the sadist in Bobby was what had enabled him to perpetrate such pain on someone he called "friend." He'd been a maestro standing on the podium in the hushed moment before signaling the orchestra to play, only the maestro's baton he wielded was more like a long and meticulously crafted steel pin, one he slid into my mind, sinews, and bone as he orchestrated the many movements of his symphony, alternating his grim melodies between a deafening crescendo or softer strains. At times, the maestro had enforced complete silence, the barrage of emails suddenly ceasing, although even the silences had played on my nerves for the sake of his pleasure. Bobby steadfastly toiled as he watched me writhe in fear and pain as if I was his pet, a specimen, an unfortunate possession—a pitiful, blind captive unable to see her imprisoner, or to perceive when or where the next sharp plunge was coming. As I twisted and dangled after each slow and deliberate insertion, Bobby had stepped back to observe the result of his leisure. My emotions and suffering must have been like a treasure trove as he marveled at his ability to completely monopolize a human being's resources. Fear, longing, sadness, and a primal desperation that glistened across my face—curious things to a sadist—must have alternately amused and perplexed him, his little jewel and prize, his "Saltz."

I'd always known he had a dark side, and yet what I now perceived through his actions was more than mere darkness. It was a void, an empty place where a human soul should be. I was aware that he was skilled at cruelty, but I never thought that he would turn on me—and in *such* a way. How wrong I had been. Piercing though my anger was a searing humiliation. How could I *not* have known?

The greatest part of his manipulation (and another aspect of his sadism) was that he would then resume his role as friend, offering me comfort and safe harbor against the threats he himself had created. He was the peevishness of Leonard, the hatred of Sharon, the indignation of Hal, and the threats of known criminals. He indulged his streak of cruelty so as to fluidly morph from these creations into a nurturing mother hen or an armchair sleuth, the latter being evidenced by his collection of handwritten letters from criminals, a curious and morbid passion he had long pursued. He reveled in all of these roles, including that of friend, staged at my expense.

I told Nolan the news, and he wasn't at all surprised. He'd long suspected Bobby although he'd never met him. Nolan had kept his views largely to himself and hadn't pressed the issue, undoubtedly because the one or two times he'd brought it up, I had quickly dismissed the notion. Even though Nolan had mentioned he was suspicious earlier on, the reality of the truth fully setting in was shocking. It seemed impossible to me for so many reasons, or so I had foolishly believed, for many – what seemed to me – valid reasons. I could see Leonard using AOL Instant Messenger at the same time while Bobby and I chatted on the same service; he'd been my trusted friend, our long separation notwithstanding; the hoax had been sustained and elaborate beyond comprehension; and there had not been the slightest bit of evidence to indicate it was him. Bobby Ironside? No, it hadn't seemed possible. Perhaps Nolan had been far enough removed from the madness to see that Bobby's access to me made him the most likely suspect.

Too shaken to check my email the night before, I waited until later that morning. I dreaded looking at my account. When I finally signed on, I saw that Bobby had sent a few more emails regarding his tortuous computer plight since we had left off writing the previous afternoon. He forwarded me an email that notified him that he'd been subscribed to a list of USMC Forces in Vietnam. He added that he had also been getting a lot of weird spam.

I was a bundle of nerves as the morning zipped by, but I could feel Bobby looking for me, waiting for me. He was obviously worried. Until the day before, he knew more about my case than I did, but things had been completely turned around. Fear that the FBI was possibly closing in on him had to be eating him alive and driving him crazy. After all, a significant number of days had passed since I'd given him the last update on Agent Waller's progress.

He emailed me at 10:44 a.m.

"Where are ya? Taking a shower in your hose? Get crackin'. It's your day off. Sign on and gasssssss. Xx."

Attached to this brief invitation was an animated GIF cartoon of a whip-crackin', fishnet stocking-clad dominatrix. Somehow, I had to act normally and reply. Bobby knew me well, and any subtle changes in my tone or pattern would be instantly detected. Given his current mental state, ignoring him would set off blaring alarm bells in his mind. Bobby had made me nervous innumerable times in the past, and I was stalling. He could be intimidating, and now knowing what he was fully capable of scared me even more. Although Leona, Lou Burr, and Felix da Cat had all dissolved, it wasn't over yet. I was about to go into battle with a full sociopath, and I didn't want to deal with him despite my desire for justice. I was about to become his worst nightmare, and it was going to drive him mad. How would he react?

In the meantime, I had to at least keep up the appearance of normalcy. Agent Waller hadn't given me any clue as to what he might be planning, much less when something would actually transpire. But the clock was definitely running, and I didn't want to jeopardize whatever the FBI was planning by stalling, thereby tipping Bobby off. Around noon, therefore, I responded to one of his emails in which he had again referenced his PC powering up on its own at three in the morning and how he'd pulled the plug.

Man that would really get me. Seriously, how on earth can someone turn on your computer? That is too spooky!!!

I've got some errands to do, pet store, groceries etc. Will be back a little later.

*Hope you're having a nice morn, it's gray and cold
again here. Xx*

My reply was terse, acknowledging his trouble while at the same time begging off in the name of doing errands that precluded me "gassing" with him at any length. I hoped the brief mention of the weather and the "Xx" would be informal enough to match the forced brevity of my style. His lengthier response, which reinforced his computer miseries and the actions he continued taking to purge his allegedly compromised system, validated that he was scared, as he continued to elaborately craft his cover story.

> The Tech supports told me with a virus or trojan in hiding they can access your PC remotely - use your accounts, order stuff online - send out porno and spam - the usual. All clear now thank god - cleaned everything out after catching trojan and deleted all of McAfee Security and then download-ed a new copy and reinstalled it- did a total scan - Ohhhhhhhhh almost an hour, and all clear. Gray and cold here too, really awful. I had the windows open most of the morning, but now it's too cold. Talk later, enjoy your errands :)) xx

All of his excuses were moot because no one was remotely accessing his PC and sending out spam. Quite to the contrary, it had been Bobby who, without use of any trojans or viruses, had infiltrated my own computer and my mind with a low-tech method called email.

We didn't talk later, and I left his news unanswered.

***

Late Saturday morning, as prescribed by Agent Waller, I forced myself to email Bobby an obligatory greeting to keep the lines of communication open. It was idle chatter, mostly about the weather, and how it rained so much that I had decided to forgo Thurston Moore's book party. I knew it was a safer course than remaining silent.

Bobby replied ten minutes later with his own report of a routine weekend in DC; starting off with ordering squid and double-cooked pork from their favorite Chinese place, watching Oceans 12, and finishing with Meet The Fockers and Air Jaws—the documentary about leaping Great White Sharks. He asked if I was still thinking about taking a nice long weekend down in the nation's capital.

He seemed to be at ease, displaying his usual chatty self. Talk of double-cooked pork, The Fockers, and our ever-popular great white sharks made my head swim. I instinctively knew that he was looking for more from me, but I didn't write back.

He wrote again at seven that evening, attaching an animated chameleon eating a fly.

> Just wondering if all is well and if you're going to be online at all this weekend? Have a nice day out. Catch ya later. Xx.

His phrase "just wondering if all is well" was a sure indication that my silences were gnawing at him. I knew I would have to eventually throw him a bone, but the impulse to sign on, chat, or talk on the phone with him was long gone.

Sunday was suddenly upon me. The weekend was flying by, and I felt increased pressure to contact Bobby. I'd been evasive, and he was expecting—practically demanding—some reciprocity, so I decided, however hard it may be, it was a good idea to call him. It might just be enough to placate him until the FBI moved to the next phase of their investigation, whatever that might be. Calling was the last thing I wanted to do, but Bobby was sensing my distance. The mere thought of speaking to him and pretending everything was okay squeezed my stomach into a knot. It wasn't going to be easy for me to fake it.

I just wanted to forget him, to have him locked up and never see his face or hear his voice again, but he sent me a mid-afternoon email. I forced myself to call, my heart racing and my mouth dry as I dialed the number. The phone rang twice and I braced myself for his answer, each ring seeming to take forever.

"Hello," said a voice on the other end of the line.

It was James. His upbeat voice took me by surprise as a rush of relief washed over me that it wasn't Bobby. Tension loosened its grip on me for a second as I exhaled. James was a good guy, and I liked him a lot. And there he was, blissfully oblivious that their lives together were permeated by Bobby's immeasurable lies. I had to suppress my impulse to tell him to run, to get out of the house and save himself. But even if I could tell him, where would I begin? The feds were closing in, and I didn't want to endanger him, but I was frightened for James. I suspected Bobby, being on high alert could have been standing right next to him and might even be able to hear what I was saying. It was all I could do to stop myself from whispering to him to just leave and that I would explain later.

"James!" My voice quivered, almost a muffled warning in itself.

Happy to hear from me, James said that he and Bobby had just been talking about me when the phone rang. He wanted to know if I was all right and if there was any news from the FBI, another indication that Bobby was worried and speculating as to what the feds might be up to. I assured James I was okay, with nothing new to report. He also asked if I was planning on going down to DC for a visit. I told him I wasn't sure about any visit, and he passed the phone to Bobby. My muscles tensed again.

"Hello, doll!"

Bobby's upbeat, stage door tone piped through the telephone lines. I tried for a calm, easy demeanor, but I wasn't calm on the inside. It was a brief conversation, and I reiterated that I couldn't make any travel plans at present. The conversation then touched again on the FBI's progress, and I repeated that I was still waiting for news. Not surprisingly, Bobby brought up his computer woes, although I managed not to give myself away as he fed me lies in an attempt to distance himself from everything that had happened. I listened calmly and ended the conversation on a stable note. It seemed to do the trick and temporarily served to keep Bobby at bay as I patiently waited for justice to creak forward.

***

Agent Waller called me at my office on Monday morning, May 9, and asked me if I could go to FBI headquarters after work that day to discuss the case, although he didn't offer any details about what the Bureau was doing behind the scenes. I was in the dark but nevertheless confident that something was in the works. I looked forward to taking any necessary action and participating to the fullest extent in moving the investigation forward.

It wasn't until 11:00 a.m., that I replied to an email Bobby had sent the day before.

How are ya? Bright and sunny here, not quite warm yet. Can't wait until the summer sun. Talk later. Xx

My brief response about the weather, a growing topic in our superficial exchanges, was all I could muster. I tossed in the "Xx" at the end to at least make the email appear friendly. His response was one of the more curious that he'd sent in recent weeks.

All well here, except for an odd email. Yeah Summer sure is taking its sweet time about arriving, but I'm looking forward to it also. I wonder what this strange email means. What investigation, what dime? Must be some stupid spam or a joke. Can this be related...?

Bobby attached the "odd email" that he was sent on Sunday at 11: 37 p.m. from "Justin Time" at Justintime13181@yahoo.com. The subject line read "USPS Abuse." The contents were as follows:

National Drug Intelligence Center

8201 Greensboro Drive, Suite 1001

McLean, VA 22102

Postal Inspectors play a key role in helping wage the nation's war on illegal drugs. In fact, their work to identify and prosecute drug mailers and illegal traffickers is well-known and respected. Drop the investigation or we drop the dime.

Identifiable Information Collected:

Tracking Numbers

Email containing information

Handwriting on packages

Sworn Testimony CRIMINAL INVESTIGATIONS
CENTER

ATTN: MAIL FRAUD

222 S. RIVERSIDE PLAZA, STE 1250

CHICAGO, IL 60606

A couple of minutes later, Bobby sent me the link to the *justintime13181* Yahoo profile. He was clearly concerned.

> This seems to be a real person or maybe a set up? I am a little nervous regarding the verbiage used in that email I got last night. Should I respond, do you think or just delete it? If our email was hacked or compromised, I wonder if anyone has anything on us?

I wondered if the FBI was sending him emails to jar him a little and knock him off his game. He was rattled. It felt good to watch him swing in the shadows and feel the walls closing in. I took my time replying and purposely responded in a detached manner to convey that I was not all that concerned. "I looked at the profile, and I don't see what you mean. Who is it? What kind of email did you get?" My obfuscation rattled him further.

"I sent it to you," he wrote. "I'd rather talk on the phone."

I could tell he was feeling the pressure. He wanted to take our conversation offline, which meant he was tasting panic.

"I don't know," I wrote. "Seems weird. Chicago? Virginia? I haven't gotten anything strange lately, thank God!"

"Good, but after my account was compromised, I wonder if anyone read mail between us, or can my problems be related to the freaks that are bothering you?"

The allusion to the "freaks" who had bothered me was clearly Bobby's inadequate attempt at deflection, in an effort to distance himself from the drama that he himself had created.

That is strange. I've deleted you from my Outlook at work, so I don't think anyone could have gotten your email address. Maybe it's spam. Or a wrong address. Weird. But then again, we've seen some pretty strange things. I can't take another round of garbage from whoever was bothering me. My nerves are still shot. Just thinking about it makes me nervous again.

My cavalier approach to his dilemma—maybe it's spam or a wrong address—obviously irritated Bobby. He wanted the same give-and-take we'd had when I was on the receiving end of strange emails, but I wasn't going to give him the satisfaction. I had no intention of jumping up and calling him. I had better and more important things to do, like meeting with Agent Waller.

After work I took the subway downtown to the FBI building at Federal Plaza. As before, I passed through multiple security checks in the building lobby before gaining access. The doors of the elevator closed before it heaved upward. I reflected on how different things were since the last time I'd been there. Seven months earlier, when I'd gone to the building with Nolan, I was desperate. Now I had a shot at justice, for which I was grateful.

I was happy to see Agent Waller again, and he asked me how I was. I told him that I was still stunned at the news but was sobering up to it quickly. He asked about the nature of any ongoing contact with Bobby, and I related how I'd spoken to him briefly over the weekend and had been keeping a marginal distance while still maintaining ties. He then requested that, over the course of the week, I print out all continuing emails to and from Bobby, complete with full headers that displayed the detailed IP address, and fax them to his office.

Agent Waller's next action was unexpected. He pulled out a pen, placed it on top of a yellow legal pad, and slid them across the desk. He asked me to draw a detailed map of James's apartment. He wanted to know what the lobby of James's building looked like, where the elevators were located, and if there was a doorman. He also wanted directions to the apartment once the elevator arrived at the 7th floor.

Having been there many times, I knew it very well and began sketching. Waller wanted to know the location of every door, window, closet, and bathroom, and asked if any weapons were kept in the apartment. I told that that no, to the best of my knowledge, there weren't. I drew the entrance, the kitchen, the broom closet, Bobby's room, his bathroom, and James's room and bath. I also drew the terrace outside the living room, as well as the kitchen, with its marble countertop and stools. I even indicated where Bobby kept his file cabinet with the serial killer letters and his collection of CDs. Agent Waller found it strange that they had separate bedrooms since they were a couple. I explained that James had back problems and that Bobby was a light sleeper and a night person.

I knew that the FBI was going in, but when it would happen and in what manner was not something I was privy to. But another line had been crossed. Definitive action of some kind was going to be taken.

***

On Tuesday, May 10, I emailed Bobby from work to once again keep the lines of communication open since I had cut way back. It was a routine email about my work and the weather.

> *Hello- Gorgeous day here. Sunny and bright. I think the sun is back finally. So good for the eyes. Man, I got so tired of all that grey.*
>
> *Not much is new, just another day. Got tons of work to do. The only thing I am excited about is this new Mick Rock book. I just got the proof and the pics of Bowie are AMAZING. Such a cool time. It's the whole Ziggy Startdust tour in the US/UK. After all the architecture and design books, this one is at least fun.*
>
> *Tired today. Gotta get rolling.*
>
> *Hope your morning is fine.*

Bobby's reply indicated that he had received more strange emails similar to the one allegedly from the National Drug Intelligence Center.

> Hello~ It's still gorgeous here. Slept with my windows open all night – peaceful except for the bloody sirens. Are there really that many emergencies in a 24 hour period? I doubt it. That Mick Rock book sounds like a lot of fun. I'm glad that

you have a project there that keeps you happy. More spam here – now I've gotten two on mail and bank fraud and loads of PayPal – asking that I re-submit my details – hahaha, yeah right. Nothing else new to report. What a great dinner last night – Italian hot sausage and pepper and onions, a real delight! Hope the rest of your day is just as glorious... xx

It's common to receive spoof messages claiming to be from PayPal, but email about mail or bank fraud isn't garden variety spam or phishing. It occurred to me that either Bobby was sending these messages to himself and using them to fake me out, or that the FBI might be throwing Bobby some curveballs to see how he would react or possibly to see if they could actually make him respond. Having drawn the layout of his apartment, I knew they were after him. Agent Waller was playing it close to the vest as always. He was on my side, but he wasn't going to take the chance that I might slip up and tip Bobby off. I felt that the case was moving inexorably to closure, but I didn't know how it would play out.

I dutifully continued to maintain contact with Bobby, although the dialogue was growing more and more superficial on my end. There was no more "gassing." At three o'clock, I emailed Bobby and told him that I'd been pounding on my keyboard to turn out press releases. I mentioned that it was hot, that I'd gone out for lunch, and that I was tired. By this point, he surely must have known I wasn't being forthcoming with him. Indeed, I thought there were probably sirens going off in his head given my mundane chatter.

I emailed him the next morning, May 11, thinking I might be able to send him a few innocent lines about waiting to hear back from Agent Waller.

Ironically, I found myself telling Bobby precisely what he had formerly told me (and what I thought might placate him), which was that the FBI was getting nowhere. The implication was that I was beginning to believe I had been wasting my time with the feds. Showing discouragement, I thought, was a prudent way to keep Bobby on the hook until the FBI reeled him in. Even these brief exchanges were wearing on me, and I didn't know how long I could continue. As for Bobby, he didn't let up. I suspect he needed to keep in touch, hoping I might accidentally drop a crumb as to what was going on with the FBI.

> Hello Doll, I was just about to write you. I know what you mean about nervous. I've had my own share of sick stomachs last week finding out our security was breached. It's a violation and both James and I felt intruded upon, totally disgusting. So far so good. My virus stuff and firewall programs are all new and re-installed, drivers updated, accounts changed, etc. Somehow it sure opened me up to a boatload of spam too, what junk! Well, as long as you're not being bothered at work or home, I'd say it's a blessing. Let's hope it's over now finally and everyone can go their "merry" way.

> Started out as gray and cool this morning, and we left the living room windows open all night. My, wasn't it a chilly morn! But now the sun's out and it looks like it should be a really top drawer day!! I can write to you at Rizz if you're more comfortable, no problem. Whatever works … but have found the last weeks work a bit depressing. Ohhhhhhhhhhh… Gas soon….xx

It was the height of hypocrisy that Bobby was preaching to me about the indignity of being violated, of how he and James had been "intruded upon." Doling out his righteous indignation was, of course, part of his ongoing attempt to concoct a cover story. And he no doubt felt it "depressing" that he had to cover his tracks in a desperate bid to somehow forestall the feds because of the very real prospect of being arrested and going to prison. With his additional lies, he had appallingly and deceptively co-opted James into helping him by convincing him to change all of their internet accounts. Bobby had no trouble lying to anyone, not even his own life partner.

I replied to his email later that morning:

Yeah. I hope it's over too. I just can't take it anymore. I can't take the idea of these people following me around for the rest of my life. It's just too draining.

Oh well. Back to work. I think it's better not to use my office email. It still worries me quite frankly ever since that last round of crap I got. It's better that you are safe too. Sounds like you've had a problem there. Sucks, doesn't it?

I'll be back with you later. Busy as ever here. Boy, do I need a vacation! XX

I was buying more time with Bobby, repeating what I had told him many times, which was that I was tired and didn't want "these people" following me anymore. But I couldn't resist, in veiled terms, to get in my own digs at Bobby by referring to his computer problems. Such aggravations did indeed "suck," although he wasn't being terrorized by imaginary families, as I had been. His time at the keyboard was being spent covering his digital tracks, and if it took him time, I wasn't a bit concerned. He had brought it all on himself. Furthermore, my asking him not to email me at Rizzoli because "it's better that you are safe" was pure sarcasm on my part since Bobby was anything but safe at the moment.

At 4:15 that afternoon, Bobby sent me a note with "The Empire's Blue" in the subject line. As per Agent Waller's instructions, I printed out my exchanges with Bobby and faxed them to FBI headquarters. When I got home, Waller himself called and said he needed to come out to Brooklyn and briefly meet with me.

"The Empire's Blue" was a coded message to me from Bobby, something known only between us. The body of the email read, "You sure everything is okay? You don't seem like you lately." Attached was a small photo of the Empire State Building with a blue tint applied. A few years earlier, I'd had an online friend who sent me short, odd notes with his photos attached. He would take pictures of the city and send them to me, accompanied by enigmatic and detached taglines. One such email contained a shot of the Empire State Building with the cryptic message "the Empire is blue." Bobby and I used to joke about it. This latest email from Bobby, which used the same catch-phrase, meant that he had recognized that I was being short with him, that my emails were clipped and uninvolved, almost robotic. Though I had tried to maintain the status quo, I was clearly slipping. Bobby knew me too well and was picking up on my distant tone and homing in on it. Or maybe Bobby's paranoia was getting the best of him. Either way, he was looking for some reassurance that everything was okay and that he wasn't in the trouble that he was starting to suspect he might be.

I made no reply, and when Agent Waller arrived, Mini Me was by my side at the door. I told him that my dog, though he looked threatening, was really a sweetheart.

"Don't worry," Waller said. "I'm a big fan of dogs. And besides . . . ," he gestured to a hidden holster inside his suit jacket, "I've got pepper spray."

I didn't see any pepper spray when his jacket opened, but I did get a glimpse of the handle of his gun, which was a pretty serious looking weapon. I'd forgotten that these well-dressed and pressed government agents were also well-armed.

Agent Waller made it short and quick. He'd come to my apartment to teach me how to record a telephone conversation. He'd brought a simple Sony recorder with a wire connected to suction cups that attached to any part of the earpiece of the phone handset. We went through a couple of trial runs to make sure I could record conversations with Bobby correctly. He added that the Bureau might do something to try and make Bobby call me. I asked what motivation might be used, but he said he didn't know yet.

The thought of speaking to Bobby again made me nervous, especially in light of the fact that we were ensnared in a real life game of cat and mouse. I knew how the Sony worked, but under the circumstances, I wasn't sure whether or not I could pull off a successful recording should Bobby be prompted to call me. Agent Waller returned to his office, and I was left waiting to see what would happen.

I had to steer Bobby away from panicking given his email titled "The Empire's Blue," but communicating with him had grown incredibly difficult. I replied to his most recent email at eight o'clock that night. "I'm okay. Sorry. Just been busy at work and too tired to be ONLINE after work. Sorry to be a dullard. XX."

Writing the word "online" in caps was a reference to our inside joke about Sharon Barnes' previous railing against

Karen meeting strangers online. It was my way of showing Bobby that, despite my detached manner, I was still me.

Around noon on Thursday, May 12, I forced myself to send another note to keep things alive between us.

How are you? Hope you're having a good afternoon. Another sunny day here. I'm good. Busy crazy here at work. Sorry to be so quiet, I've just been so dead tired this week. Could barely get up on time this morning. I'm also not in the greatest mood since I haven't heard back from the agent yet and I feel I am back to square zero once again. Feeling worried about what might happen next if it all starts up again like it did the last time. I just dread it. Anyway, so tired of it all and don't want to bore you or be a downer, but I guess I'm a little depressed. Hope you're good.

I thought it good to reiterate that I believed the FBI might have dropped the ball, as well as accentuating my fear that the entire saga might begin again, this being merely the latest lull in the string of perverse emails. Also, suggesting I was depressed might further allay any of Bobby's suspicions that had precipitated his coded "Empire message" to me. My strategy must have worked, for Bobby sent me a reply that was starkly different in tone from anything that he'd recently written.

Hi ~ It's good to hear from you. It's a gross day here, gray and overcast, but warm. :0) That's okay about being quiet. The whole thing is very depressing, but I think it's over. If you can, let it go and just keep working and living and loving. I doubt you'll ever hear from any of them again. Anyhow, quiet time is good. I just wondered about us because I asked you to ring me when you had a chance a few days ago, and have also mentioned coming down for a little vacation several times without any response in return. I just figured something was wrong. I am really glad that you are busy at work, that's a good sign, and of course that nothing new has happened regarding the freaks. I think we're in for a nice peaceful summer. Let's really enjoy this one and try to focus on the good things in our lives, the people, places, and pets that make us happy. When the war planes soared over head yesterday – I, along with thousands of other people here thought we were under attack. It brought up all the emotions of 9/11 for a few minutes anyway. As I had a cigarette on the roof and watched them secure our air space, I noticed I was shaking involuntarily. A by-product of living in this world in 2005. Point being – 9/11 changed me and yesterday was a good reminder of the real possibility of something else like it happening again. All the more reason to live a full and well-rounded life while you can. I supposed things like yesterday keep one on their mettle. You're a wonderful woman with so much to offer. I hope you find someone in the near future to share that with, meaning someone truly deserving and appropriate on all accounts. In the meantime it sounds like everything is relatively peaceful, and you're busy working and life continues as usual, which in itself is a blessing. Hey, we'll be 43 this summer, can you buy it? Oh man, getting closer to 50 every hour, hahaha! Anyhow, if you ever want to talk about anything you know I'll be here. Love ya

The email revealed that Bobby had sobered quite a bit, probably as a result of his fear of incarceration. It was not his usual banter filled with humor, abbreviations, grammatical errors, and "Bobby-speak." He had wished me well and sang my praises, although he was almost certainly trying to bring his cover story to a close with a mature, almost philosophical quality while at the same time trying to con me once again into thinking he cared about me. In Bobby's mind, any future reader would have to concede that he loved me dearly and had only my best interests at heart. A short time earlier, I myself might have believed such sentiments. Regrettably, it was just more of Mr. Ironside's masterful control and manipulation. But I was now the one in control of information, and Bobby was out in the cold. Act One of a new play was about to commence, and I, with the help of the FBI, was about to bring up the curtain.

I sent him one more email to hopefully "hold him in place." Keeping in touch with him had been agony, and he had definitely noticed the changes in the quality of my replies, but I had succeeded in my larger goal: to keep him engaged and at his computer while the FBI quietly prepared to take action. In fact he had to stay engaged, to do otherwise would just be a sign of guilt. I could envision how terrified he was, my imagination enhanced by how he had been terrifying me for years.

> *I sure hope it's over. I wish I could believe it. It was quiet for months, then BAM! Out of the blue it started again. I'm just feeling out of sorts and distracted. Always waiting for the next shoe to drop. Hope you're right and it's done. But there is no way to really be sure. Of course I always appreciated the invite down to DC, but right now since I'm behind because of taxes I don't think I can afford it honestly. Which is depressing in itself. I think I need to get out for a walk and get some*

lunch. Jet skiing towards 50~! Oh Lord! I can't fathom it!

You're a wonderful woman with so much to offer.

Did he really believe that? I couldn't buy into it any longer, but what *did* he believe?

Who was the real Bobby? How long was he going to drag this out? Would he put his handiwork away for a few weeks or months and then, if the heat died down, fire up the whole kit and caboodle again? If the FBI merely issued a warning, it was not out of the realm of possibility, but Waller wanted to nail him badly, and I wasn't fully sure that Bobby could restrain himself from reanimating his macabre play if that happened. One thing was certain, however: Bobby hated me, and he had turned torturing me not only into his full-time job, but into a fine art.

I printed out the last few email exchanges and faxed them to Agent Waller.

CHAPTER THIRTY-SEVEN

RAIDED BY THE FEDS

The Sound of Surprise
—Whitney Balliett, title of a book on jazz (1959)

The L train, headed for Manhattan, barreled into the tunnel on Friday, May 13. It thundered into the underground darkness, a wild rush of loud air compressed around me as the roaring grew louder. Descending deeper under the East River, the car rocked back and forth. It was the end of the week, things were getting tense, and there was no information from the FBI about what their next step might be—and no indication of what to expect.

It was a little after nine o'clock when I stepped off the elevator at work. Rosemary, the receptionist, locked eyes with mine as I approached her desk. Normally she ignored me with barely a glance, but this time she had a severe look on her face, her stare trained on me like a laser. She said someone had been calling the main number nonstop and asking for me since the offices had opened that morning. The calls had come in rapid-fire, about two hundred in all. The caller, adamant about wanting to speak with me, hadn't been satisfied with leaving a message, nor had he been placated with assurances that I would be in the office shortly. He had dialed Rizzoli over and over like a maniac. It had gotten so bad that Rosemary reported it to the president of the company, who then rang up the caller and ordered him to cease. Otherwise, he had said, his next phone call would be to his lawyers.

Rosemary said he wouldn't leave his name but she had his number. I looked down at her telephone switchboard. Stuck to it was a bright yellow Post-it note with Bobby's number written on it. She picked it up, handed it to me, and indignantly asked if I knew who he was. Taking it in my hand, I said that I did and then continued toward the publicity department. Not immediately connecting this with any action the FBI might have taken, I braced myself for yet another salvo of Bobby's insanity. Heading through the corridors as I got closer to my work area, I could hear my boss, Katy on the telephone. The conversation sounded like a struggle.

"Susan's not here," Katy said, her impatience tempered with civility. "Can I take a message?"

I knew it was Bobby. Knowing that he was on the other end of the conversation caused a chill to run through me. Even through the phone line, the forcefulness of his presence made it seem like he was standing in front of us in the office. I waited outside of Katy's cube entrance and listened as she tried to wrestle herself from his grip.

Katy looked at me while struggling to peel him from her line, not giving away that I was standing right next to her. She held her ground.

"I'm sorry, but Susan isn't here right now, and yes, I will give her the message that you called. There's nothing more I can do except let her know that you called. Yes . . . yes . . . okay. I will . . ."

She still couldn't get him off the phone. I could tell by her tone that he had been at her for some time now. He was relentless, and it was obvious that he was in a state of sheer panic. Katy finally hung up, likely while Bobby was in mid-sentence. She had to, since he was unyielding.

I stepped over to my desk and looked down at my phone. Its blinking lights indicated that I had several voicemail messages. As soon as Katy had put her phone down, mine began to ring, Bobby's number flashing ominously across the LED panel. I had no intentions of picking it up. Each ring wailed desperately like a siren until it was swallowed into voicemail. I did not want to talk to Bobby, who was on a rampage through Rizzoli's phone lines—and he wasn't giving up. I knew something big must have happened.

Over the cube wall, I asked Katy what was going on. She came around to my desk, looking annoyed. She said he'd been calling incessantly for over an hour, and she wanted to know who it was. I told her that he was the person that the FBI had identified as my stalker and that he was also my best friend.

She shot me an unsettled look as if to say, "This person is your *friend*?"

Her expression of exasperation, shock, and disbelief compounded what I was already feeling. Seeing these emotions displayed by someone else was at the same time both a minor relief and quite humiliating. I had felt alone and afraid for such a long time, wondering what I could have done to deserve such cruel treatment. That Katy could mirror my horror validated that I was a normal human being who was reacting with understandable pain and anguish. And yet I felt terrible that once again my ordeal had spilled into the office. I had no idea that Bobby's phone assault would be coming and still didn't know what had taken place that morning. The only explanation I could offer Katy was to say that the FBI was on the case and, though I didn't have the facts yet, it was evident that push had finally come to shove. I needed to get in touch with Agent Waller immediately to find out what happened. Her expression grew all the more grave at the mention of the FBI.

My phone continued to ring. I felt as if Bobby's two hands were reaching for me, incandescent with rage. I waited for it to stop and then picked up and dialed Agent Waller's office number. No answer. I left a message that I was at work, that Bobby had been calling the office frantically all morning and that I needed to know what had happened.

I paced around the office waiting to hear back, my stomach in knots, thinking of the possibilities and wondering what had sent Bobby into full tilt.

Approximately fifteen minutes later, which seemed like a lifetime, Agent Waller returned my call. He said that he'd gotten my message and that he was in Washington, DC, and had tried to reach me at home earlier that morning. I asked him if I could call him right back from a line where I would have more privacy. He agreed, and I quickly trotted down the halls, turned into one of the small conference rooms, closed the door, and quickly dialed his number. I couldn't wait to hear what had taken place.

Agent Waller picked up immediately. He relayed to me that before dawn he and fourteen SWAT team officers had served a search and seizure warrant to Bobby and James at their condo. He said that he first presented the warrant to security in the lobby and was waived through without any resistance. They then poured into the elevator, which swept them up to the seventh floor, just as I had laid it out. When

Agent Waller knocked on the door, James answered in his bathrobe. After that, Waller and the SWAT team fanned out through the apartment, seizing Bobby and James's computers, laptops, and the contents of Bobby's file cabinet, the latter containing his personal writing and collection of letters from serial killers. This was not conducted under an arrest warrant, but rather a search and seizure warrant to gain access to the apartment in order to gather evidence in the investigation. Bobby and James were physically separated and questioned at the condo. Agent Waller took Bobby up to the roof of the building for preliminary questioning, after which they were asked to go to FBI headquarters at 935 Pennsylvania Avenue for further questioning. They both agreed voluntarily to do this. Waller said he would call me later after he had spoken with them.

Agent Waller asked me if I had spoken to Bobby and if I had been able to record any conversations with him. It never occurred to me to bring the recorder to work. I told him that I hadn't spoken with Bobby and that I didn't have the tape recorder with me. If I had known they were going to move on his apartment so soon, I would have carried the recorder, as intimidated as I was, and would have tried to be prepared.

The meaning of Waller's earlier comment now dawned on me—that they were going to "do something" to get Bobby to call me. The "something" had turned out to be the dramatic early morning raid on the condo. The FBI had left me out of the loop as a way to prevent leaks, particularly in such an odd case as this one, in which the victim and the perpetrator were close friends. There was no chance that I was going to spill the beans to Bobby, even accidentally, and I wished that I had been offered some kind of clue, however small or enigmatic. It would have been nice to know about their actions ahead of time.

I was stunned as I thought of how the morning's events might have unfolded. I envisioned the entire operation. I saw the building's lobby entrance, with its soaring marble walls, crowded with fourteen federal officers, all silent, wearing bulletproof vests and riot helmets, guns drawn. You hear a sharp knock at the door before dawn, no doorman buzzing to request permission for the impromptu visitors. Not fully awake, you open the door, and a badge is flashed in your face, a dozen armed federal agents in the hallway with "FBI" written on their jackets and vests. They state who they are and what their purpose is, push right past you into your home, and rifle through everything, taking what they want. The whole time, there is absolutely nothing you can do about it.

The mental picture was overwhelming, and I could only hazard a guess as to the depth and breadth of Bobby and James's shock at the unannounced arrival before sunrise.

It would have shaken anyone to his core.

This is what had greeted Bobby on Friday morning. Bobby may have been half-expecting it, but to a control freak like him, it must have been the worst moment of his life. He could not have anticipated the feeling of total helplessness and powerlessness he was about to experience upon opening the front door.

He probably thought he could hide everything from James, but there was no hiding *anything* from that moment on. His attempts to purge his hard drive and cancel email accounts notwithstanding, how was he going to explain it or spin it now?

The phone calls at my office from Bobby ceased completely. A short while later, Agent Waller called. He said that he had talked to Bobby and had a few questions for me. He asked if my father had died in a psychiatric hospital, if I did drugs, and if I knew anything about a movie called *The Audition*.

From the questions Agent Waller asked, it was clear that Bobby had tried to paint things to look like I was crazy, a drug fiend, and into ultra-violent movies. I told Waller that my father died of lung cancer at the Cobble Hill Nursing Home in Brooklyn, that my worst vice was smoking pot, and that I had heard of the movie *The Audition*. I had told Bobby about the film but had never actually seen it. Thinking himself invincible, Bobby was already projecting the workings of his twisted mind onto me.

I was a total wreck and unable to focus on work. I explained to Katy what had happened and that I needed to go home. Drained and shaken, I headed back to Brooklyn. The caller ID on my home phone showed that Agent Waller and Bobby had both called me repeatedly that morning, but I had gotten into the habit of turning off the phone's ringer. So wracked from the ordeal, even the sound of phone ringing was too much, no matter who was calling. The entire morning blitz had blown right past me while I prepared for work shortly before nine o'clock. I crawled onto the couch and pulled the blanket over my head.

Now that he was caught, Bobby wasn't going to go down without a fight. From the sound of it, things were about to get even uglier. Lying to Agent Waller's face was just the beginning. Lying to me was one thing, but trying to fool the feds was another, a fact that further unnerved me. This was one scary individual, someone with no conscience whatsoever. He must have been furious that he was busted. Bobby was also the sort of friend to whom I had confessed some secrets. He knew things about me that most people did not, and I could only imagine what else Bobby was telling Waller, true or false. He was preparing another attempt to destroy me.

As much as I wanted to see justice prevail, the implications of unfolding events didn't escape me. The thought of pressing federal charges against my friend of many years was not entirely pleasing. The bizarre thing was that I almost felt sorry for him. I couldn't imagine being in that much trouble. After all, we *were* close friends and had shared a bond for many years. The truth, however, was that he really was no friend of mine. But why had Bobby done it? He *knew* the FBI was involved. Most of all, why had he continued? He could have stopped at any time after the FBI became involved. It was almost as if he had become addicted to the rush of torturing me.

As for me, that resounding collective silence after my first contact with Agent Waller should have been a red flag that he was the mastermind of my terror-filled ordeal. He was the only person other than Nolan who knew that the feds were engaged in the case. Why hadn't I figured this out?

And what about James? Unlike Bobby and me, he wasn't even remotely aware of the impending storm. Prior to the FBI involvement, Bobby and I were locked in a vortex in which unstoppable events were about to take their own course. Bobby was aware long before me of what was really happening. When Yahoo was served with the subpoena, he hastily began his cover plan. The blade was coming down and Bobby knew it. But James had no idea whatsoever, not even when he changed all of their internet accounts at

Bobby's urging just days before the SWAT team knocked on their door. James must have been bewildered and confused. He lived with Bobby, supported him, and took care of his every need and whim, lavishing him with expensive gifts and first-class trips, providing for everything from capping his teeth to medical care for treating his psoriasis. James had lived through a year and a half of a masterwork of deceit, and now his life was being torn apart. He'd been completely blindsided. I felt awful for him and hoped that the storm wouldn't affect him too negatively. I would have done anything to spare James any disruption, but there was no way around it. James was innocent in every sense and just as much a victim as I was.

The next few days felt not much different than the last eighteen months—complete mental strain—the one exception being relief in knowing that the bulk of the horror was over for good. There would be no lingering mystery as to the author behind my private hell. The worst was behind me, but I was still on the edge, and Bobby was a cornered rat. If he hated me before, he must *really* hate me now. How dare his little pet fight back? How dare I choose to protect myself? It must have been unimaginable to him. I had already tasted his evil, but in his defensive survival mode, Bobby was going to be just as low down and dirty—perhaps even more so. He scared me, only this time in a different way. I now had a real fight on my hands. The mask and the gloves were off. What was truly underneath all along, now exposed, was going to be even uglier.

It was now Tuesday. Submerged in thoughts as I got ready for work, I paced around the kitchen, wondering what was going to happen next. I tried to be steady, but I was lost in thinking about raids, judges, warrants, James, and

Bobby and his noir tragedy that had turned my life upside down. Standing by the door that opens to the hallway, something caught the corner of my eye. An envelope had been slid under the crack in the door and now lay at my feet. It startled me, and then I recognized the childlike handwriting on the front. It was Bobby's. It was a little too early for the postman, and my brief surprise turned to terror. Bobby might have brought it himself by hand and pushed it under my door. After all, DC was no more than a quick train ride to New York. Could he be waiting right outside my flimsy tenement door? Bobby was impulsive, and given his takedown by federal agents twenty-four hours earlier, what would stop him from hopping an early Amtrak train to confront me? My heart pounded. Was he really standing there? My old friend fear shook me, as I stared at the door, not daring to move or breathe. I turned my gaze downward for a closer look at the delivery. The express mail envelope certainly bore Bobby's handwriting on the label, with the return address being Dupont Circle, but it was postmarked by the U.S. Postal Service. My fears now allayed that Bobby was not standing outside my apartment door, I breathed, reached down, and picked it up.

Touching the physical letter made me feel sick. This was far more than pixels on a screen. He hadn't called me at home, which was good, nor had he emailed. He'd dashed off this letter the same day as the raid and managed to get it into the mail overnight, which indicated that he was in a state of desperate calculation—someone who, instead of coming clean, was going to try to manipulate the situation at every opportunity.

Inside was a white envelope.

Please keep this confidential

Dear Saltz,

First I want to sincerely apologize for my frantic calls to your office last Friday. Please believe me, I wasn't trying to bother you or get you in trouble, I was desperate to reach you and not thinking clearly.

Second, and most importantly – I am so very sorry for my foolish participation in this awful scenario. I should never have gotten involved or tried to contact the creeps. I got involved when I should have stayed away and now I am suffering the consequences for my actions.

So many times I wanted to say something to you or include you but I was too afraid. Saltz, I don't know what is wrong with me. I hurt two people that I love and I am finding it hard to live with myself because of it.

What happened here last Friday was a nightmare, and is unbearable to remember. I ruined my life and hurt James's. His job and home life have been affected by this and there is no way to turn it around. The dye is cast.

Today is our anniversary and I have to find a new place to live, with no money and no job or even a future to look forward to. They took the book I was writing and all the pictures of my family, pets, and life up until this point. All my work over the last year is gone. But my deepest regret is hurting you and adding any pain you already had concerning this story. I had thought in my delusional mind that maybe we could look back and laugh about a few things in the future, but I see how wrong I was.

Salt, you've been a good friend to me over the years and I have really enjoyed the times we've had. If there is anything I can do to rectify the situation or make it up to you somehow, or answer any questions you have – please let me know.

There is nothing I want more than to make this right.

If you wanted, I could even take the train up one morning and meet you someplace and we could talk, maybe have lunch, sit in the park. But I wouldn't blame you if you never wanted to see me again. But if you do, please let me know soon and I will meet you anywhere. I would really like to see you and explain – one of the reasons I was hoping you could come to DC next month.

I don't know what to do at this point my old friend. I don't think I can live with myself after hurting you and James; I feel too ugly.

And I am afraid to die, I don't want to die Salt, I want to live but I can't find the strength to go on for too much longer like this.

Yes, I am crying as I write this.

I am trying to think of a way to get to see my mother one more time. I can't bear the idea of hurting her by killing myself, but I don't know what else to do.

I keep thinking that if there was some way out of this I would jump at the chance, but I don't see any light at the end of my tunnel.

I am at my end Saltz. I feel so miserable and low that I can't even look at myself in the mirror to shave. I hate myself.

Please friend, if there is anything I can do to fix this, give me the chance.

In the spirit of all our good times please consider this as time is running out. I would do anything possible to make it up to you, anything.

You can call me or write me or email me anytime. I would welcome the opportunity to rectify this in any way you saw fit. Please let us meet and talk.

I don't know what else to say right now except I am sorry, and please forgive me.

Help me please...

Love always,

Bobby

I should never have gotten involved or tried to contact the creeps.

Gotten involved? Trying to weave another tale at this point was sheer audacity. It was almost as if he was living in an alternate reality. There was no end to Bobby's arrogance. Did he really think that I was going to believe this? He was the draftsman of this horror production, not a hapless bystander swept away by impulse—and if so, impulse to do what? Even if he did "contact the creeps," which of course was babble, in what way exactly could that that be done? That alone made no sense. He *was* "the creeps." It was a painful lie, pathetic at this stage in the game. He was caught dead to rights. According to the information that Yahoo provided to the FBI, Bobby was identified as the creator of *poordeadswan*. There was no way to spin that or make it appear that he hadn't been able to resist the draw to "get involved" or insert himself into a drama of his own making.

The idea of having lunch with him in the park was like imagining sitting on a bench with Frankenstein's monster, tossing daisies into a lake. I did not want him anywhere near me, and I hoped that he wasn't going to just show up breathlessly in Brooklyn or at my office. Everything about this letter was self-serving and false. Did he really envision me down in DC on James's boat on The Potomac, grilling shrimp, and passing me a drink while saying, "Oh, by the way, Saltz, I've been meaning to tell you . . . " But which story would he have presented—that he "wrote to the creeps" or that he *was* the creeps? I guess he hadn't worked out his current lie so well. This was understandable considering that he was staring at a possible indictment or two from the feds. As for his feigned threats of doing himself in, they fell flat to my ears. He was pulling violin strings from the bottom of the barrel.

I called Agent Waller that Tuesday to let him know about the letter. He said he wanted to see it. I offered to bring it downtown, but he told me he was heading my way at the end of the week and would pick it up then. In the meantime, I faxed him a copy that day so he could see the contents sooner. He also told me that Bobby had faxed him a twenty-five-page letter about me that morning. That was a bit of a shock, but I guess I shouldn't have been surprised. He probably began composing it in his head while he was typing up his S.O.S. letter to me. One can say a lot in twenty-five pages, but I couldn't imagine that he would have had enough for even twelve. A few impromptu lies at FBI headquarters in DC had now turned into a short book. Agent Waller said he had started reading it and that it already appeared to be false.

It was true that Bobby knew a lot about me, and I didn't relish having personal secrets presented along with the kind of unimaginable fiction he resorted to.

CHAPTER THIRTY-EIGHT

INTERROGATIONS

For murder, though it have no tongue, will speak,
With most miraculous organ.
—William Shakespeare, *Hamlet*

Several weeks passed, and in preparation for my case Agent Waller asked me to print out all of the emails between Bobby and me over the course of the last year and a half. Everything had to be printed with complete IP information displayed. He also wanted to see the emails in which Bobby specifically talked about the FBI and the investigation, requesting that I highlight those passages. This was going to be quite a task. There were at least a thousand pages of emails to wade through.

Fortunately, I had saved almost all of the correspondence with the exception of a few I lost due to the closing down of certain email accounts and those emails that had been automatically deleted by Peter Walker's hyper-effective spam zapper at Rizzoli. Being chased by fiends had kept me in the habit of collecting evidence in case anything further happened. It was therefore easy to hit SELECT ALL in the columns of emails so that my extensive conversations with Bobby were netted along with the countless emails from Karen, Sharon, Leona, and Hal. Our exchanges included our cyber detective work, day-to-day chit-chat, musings on what the Nachmans were up to, and several desperate and futile plans for my escape. From humiliating accounts of my trips to the Brooklyn 90th Precinct to Bobby's suggestions on how to find an apartment in DC—it was all there, along with our fights over the FBI investigation and ultimately our last emails forever.

Because of Yahoo's email format, printing out the messages with headers included was going to make the mission much harder since each page had to be hand-formatted to avoid losing information that Agent Waller needed. It had to be done one page at a time.

It was the night of Friday, June 17, and I set aside the weekend to get this done. Given the volume of evidence, it looked like I was going to be glued to my chair until Monday morning. I set up and began printing each page one by one. Stopping to read some of them at random was like pausing the DVD of a movie in which I had been unwittingly cast. The scenes I saw brought back the surreal nature of Bobby's montage of horror.

> Me: *Mulgrave did say they were awaiting DNA on that red stuff [blood].*
>
> *Oh well, maybe it's all a big joke.*
>
> Bobby: Could be...but I doubt it at this point. As for the dna - wouldn't that be a NJ Crime thing? I mean if the Cat is in NJ Custody and the crime is a NJ Crime. I'm just putting 1+1 together. Who knows....?

Bobby had played detective with fervor, encouraging me not to assume anything was a joke. Ironically, he had indeed been "putting things together" while at his computer, but in a manner I had not suspected. It was a storyline worthy of a hardboiled detective flick, only there had only been Bobby Ironside. He was an author writing a novel or screenplay, with me in the dual role as audience and victim. He had created stories within stories, moving from pulp noir crime fiction to the elegance of a Dashiell Hammett plot twist.

Had I actually gone to the police long before Nolan solicited aid from the FBI? Yes. Was it any wonder that the detective thought I was crazy? It was clear how Bobby egged me on, even to the point of suggesting I might be able to help solve the Jennifer Whipkey case. Bobby truly had no boundaries. He extrapolated possibilities on the fly based on each new move I made, or each new idea or theory I shared with him. Watching entire dialogues between two or more people had made the imaginary seem so plausible. The Nachmans communicated with each other, and I was forwarded their correspondence on many occasions, especially by Leonard or Hal. In the midst of these very believable exchanges, I was labeled by Sharon as a "no good rotten bitch" seeking Lenny's money or attempting to destroy Hal's marriage. Sharon had been one of Bobby's most masterful creations, a fiendishly cruel woman who was his vehicle for so much of the sheer madness this invented family was sending my way.

And there was Lenny's evolving persona that waded into S&M and the infamous Kinkfest, which would occupy so much of the plot, generating fear as the "dark undertone." One that Bobby knew personally, which was introduced and sustained for months on end.

There it was, all in black and white; a systematic psychological wood chipper engineered by a master of sadism. By disorienting me and isolating me with constant threats, I found myself flailing in every direction. It ripped away my sense of privacy and safety, simultaneously alternating brief reprieves with punishment for no apparent reason. This textbook blueprint served to break down my psyche, ultimately making me more malleable. As highly crafted as it was fervently executed, it created an intricate psychological process which also established a toxic bond, an order between the perpetrator and victim. It would be a long many years before I could even begin to fully understand it all.

I continued to print the emails one by one, unable to refrain from looking occasionally at what had now become back story. It was about 7:30 p.m. on Friday, and I was well into printing the opening acts. It was a mosaic of cunning cruelty, a patchwork of plots and lies designed solely for his amusement. During the process, the phone rang. It was Agent Waller, who needed to ask me a few questions. He had a few more bits of information and was still checking off odds and ends.

Agent Waller said that Hebrew University had never heard of Sharon Barnes. He had also learned that her email address was fake. He then moved on to Leonard Nachman. We both agreed that this was, in fact, a real person who lived in West Milford, New Jersey, someone with a fairly common name. Bobby had borrowed names, so to speak, like Carl Mulgrave and his sister Janis, and brought them to life in his psycho-drama. Furthermore, Agent Waller said that Robert McCottry still called him, wanting to talk about his case and other matters. He explained that convicts did this frequently. Once they get your number, he said, they never stopped calling.

He then asked me the oddest question. He wanted to know if I had any reason at all to believe that the original Karen Gardiner might be real. Unless Agent Waller knew something I didn't, there was never any real Karen Gardiner. Even Agent Waller, who was more than familiar with the case, had trouble wrapping his head around the concoction of real and created characters. It was understandable that, from an outside perspective, Bobby's plot looked so real that some of it *had* to true. There was no question in my mind that Karen was solely Bobby's creation. Any real life Karen Gardiner would not have deviated into the kind of topics invented by Bobby—but it was a puzzling case, and from this standpoint I could appreciate the question. I assured Agent Waller that it was impossible for there to have been a real Karen Gardiner or for *anyone* to have hijacked the situation other than Bobby.

Bobby had fashioned this hoax purposely and made it flagrantly outlandish in order to make it incomprehensible to the point of overkill. There could be no other explanation since every character was completely intertwined with the other so that any of them could pop in or out of the story seamlessly. Everything fit perfectly. Without one piece, the whole thing would have collapsed at any given time.

Waller asked me if I would hold on the line while he called Leonard Nachman. Every unknown or loose end had to be verified and tied up. I said, "Sure. I'm just sitting here printing." He clicked off while I continued to print emails. I imagined the real Leonard Nachman to be just an ordinary guy home from work on a Friday night, maybe having a drink, watching TV, relaxing—maybe even doing something odd, bizarre, or illegal—and the phone rings. It's the FBI, and they've got questions.

Waller's call took a bit more time than I thought would be needed to exclude the real Leonard Nachman from any involvement—asking a couple of questions and verifying his identity— he was on with Nachman for about twenty minutes. When Agent Waller came back on, I asked how it went. He said that Nachman sounded very surprised.

Waller then explained that there was a lot of paperwork to fill out and that it would take some time to assemble the case. He asked me to please bring the entire set of emails to his downtown office on Monday evening after work. It took three solid days to print out everything, sitting in one place from morning until late at night, allowing myself only short breaks.

Bobby and I had renewed our friendship in September of 2001 after ten years. I distanced myself from him a second time for about six months because of his arrogant, meddlesome nature. He contacted me as himself right before Christmas in 2003, which means that he had been in my life since October without my knowing it. During our last falling out period, Bobby must have searched for me on the internet, discovered my earnest quest for my father's relatives, and in his twisted mind had hit pay dirt. Was it all payback because I had distanced myself a second time from his intrusive personality? Perhaps. The pieces of his diabolical puzzle must have formed quickly in his mind, and Karen, Sharon, and Leonard had been born. These characters multiplied and spread like wildfire in his imagination. Returning to page one in this terrible odyssey was staggering to behold as the printer noisily clicked out the pages of Bobby's script.

I thought back to what I remembered about Bobby's life. As close as we were I could sense zones in his sphere that were dark and secretive. During our movie afternoons and nights, I noticed the eyehooks screwed into the exposed beams in the ceiling, just as I noticed the mysterious men that came and went. How he paid his bills was his own business, not mine.

Bobby gradually drifted into the expanding world of S&M, which was very popular in New York City in the late eighties. I accompanied him to The Vault, one of these eerie dens one night, and I left after a single drink. This lifestyle was not something I was interested in. By the early 1990s his romance with the S&M underworld began to exert a corrosive effect on his character. His normally sharp humor took on an extra bite. Stories of his decadent adventures started to take on a macabre edge.

How foolish of me to put all of that aside and believe he had changed.

The result of my "lost weekend" was an incredible 1,200 pages. I dropped them off at Agent Waller's office after work on Monday. He said he was still preparing the case to present to the prosecutor. He then asked me if I was ready to do this and if I was willing to go the distance in pressing charges and prosecuting. Without hesitation I said, "Yes."

Before I was introduced to the prosecutor, Agent Waller brought me into the office of another special agent. Agent True was like the other FBI agents I had met—clean cut and highly motivated. He said he had heard a little about my case. We talked about it for a while, and I got the feeling that I was being checked over by another pair of eyes to be sure I was on the up and up, but I didn't mind. I had nothing to hide. Afterward, I met with Marshall A. Camp, Assistant United States Attorney, U.S. Department of Justice, United States Attorney's Office for the Southern District of New York.

After meeting with the prosecutor, Agent Waller said two homicide detectives working on the Whipkey case from Thorofare, New Jersey, wanted to speak with me. Clearly, I had no connection to the murder, but this was an unsolved case and the detectives assigned to it were anxious to follow up on any lead they came across as a matter of course. The murder had gone unsolved for years, and they wanted very much to close the case and bring some relief to the victim's family. Waller told me that Bobby's emails contained information about the crime that had not been released. The detectives had already travelled to DC to speak with Bobby and wanted to speak with me as well. I said that I would be happy to help, although I really didn't have any clues to offer.

I really wondered how Bobby could have been in possession of unreleased details about a brutal murder case. In all likelihood, Bobby, who was an aficionado of true crime and murder cases, had tunneled deeply into some of Google's very early crime group forums, which allowed open and anonymous memberships. An early form of social media, the groups were crude and unrefined by today's standards, with crime groups in particular consisting of hardened true crime junkies who clung to the underbelly of criminal cases like barnacles to the underside of a rusting tanker. It was feasible that he exchanged information with cops, private investigators, or even criminals themselves.

***

A week after I dropped off the emails with Waller I went to FBI headquarters and met with two homicide detectives handling the Whipkey murder case. Although I was on friendly terms with Waller and other agents and detectives and had always felt at ease discussing my case, this was serious business. These guys were topnotch professionals, and I was grateful to be given the opportunity to seek justice. My familiarity with Agent Waller notwithstanding, I was nervous about meeting the homicide detectives investigating the Whipkey case. It had been a ferocious killing. I had absolutely nothing to offer them, and I hated the idea of wasting their time. These were the cops who had to look the deceased's family in the eye and report that they still had nothing. They had followed up on yet another lead that went nowhere. It was an unenviable position and a largely thankless job for them.

Waller reiterated that they had to follow up on all leads and that I should not feel nervous as I answered their questions and to tell them what, if anything, I knew. The thought of these dedicated cops chasing all the way to DC to speak with Bobby and me was stunning. They really wanted to solve the case. Throughout my nightmare I had seen a lot of bad things, but I had also personally seen good, honest, hard-working people who devoted themselves to justice for victims. It was humbling.

Agent Waller introduced me to the two detectives and took a chair in the room. One of the investigators handed me his card.

INVESTIGATOR MICHAEL RUFFALO,
BUREAU OF DETECTIVES,
TOWNSHIP OF WEST DEPTFORD
POLICE DEPARTMENT

West Deptford. Seeing the name again, this time spelled out in blue engraving on an investigator's business card, brought it all back. It made this horrifying slice of the nightmare all the more real and heartrending. Jennifer Whipkey's murder was no longer something remote, a violent crime viewed at a distance, but rather was one of the many constituents of Bobby's sick imagination. Jennifer Whipkey was now a real human being, mutilated in a fury and left posed in the New Jersey sunlight. The case was about an entire family: a mother, friends, and Jennifer's own little girl who had been orphaned by a sadistic lunatic on the loose. Without hesitation, Bobby had dared to intrude on their tragedy and grief.

And there I was, the subject of interrogation by law enforcement officers desperate to crack a case with very little evidence. There was no time to drift into frightened thoughts and impressions before the detectives started right in. They thanked me for coming in and got right down to business. They began asking me ordinary things, such as where I lived, what I did for a living, and what my relationship was with Bobby. Their interrogation then veered into questions about my social life and whether or not I went out a lot, frequented bars and clubs, and the like. I could already tell that they had gotten an earful of Bobby's lies, and through their questions I could hear what he had told them. I said that I was not part of the bar scene. In fact, it was quite the opposite. I was a real homebody, rarely went out at all, and didn't care for the taste of alcohol. I went to work in the morning and came right home every night to be with my dog. The detectives' expressions didn't change. I had nothing for them. They weren't outright accusing me of withholding information or any actual involvement in the murder, but they were looking at me as any homicide detective would—as someone who might be guilty or knew someone who was.

They asked me how I had heard about the case since it wasn't a very well-known crime. I told them the story: I had searched for my family online, met people who I thought were relatives, and was led into a dark world of mental illness, S&M, and crime. I explained that it was the "Hal Gardiner" character who first told me about the Whipkey murder in an email. In it, Hal said that his brother-in-law "Leonard," during his travels back and forth to Philadelphia, had met Jennifer Whipkey at the pizza restaurant where she worked. Leonard was said to have talked a great deal about Jennifer to Hal and "Karen," his wife. He was very excited about this new girl, but suddenly all talk of the romance ended. Hal was convinced that Leonard had something to do with it and informed me that he even went so far as to speak with the police about it. According to Bobby's script, Leonard, of course, was cleared.

The two investigators, though aware that this was a hoax, reflexively said they were never contacted by anyone named Hal Gardiner and had never heard of Leonard Nachman, who was not even on the list of possible suspects. They asked if I still had this email, and I replied that I had given the sole existing copy to Agent Waller, along with the stacks of other emails. It was the copy I had printed out to bring to the 90th Precinct. The original email (in electronic form) was automatically deleted when I temporarily abandoned that particular email account. The room was silent as everyone looked at each other. I reminded Agent Waller that I was one hundred percent sure he had it since I no longer did. All eyes were on Waller. He got up and left the room to look for it. The minutes dragged as we waited. I was nervous that he wouldn't be able to find it in all those piles and piles of paper. After what seemed a very long time, he came back with the email in hand, looking relieved. He gave it to the two New Jersey detectives, who quietly read it for several minutes. They asked if they could have a copy.

After reading Hal's email detailing Leonard's involvement in the murder, there was a momentary silence. Detective Ruffalo looked at Agent Waller, one cop to another, as if he had run up against a dead end. I could see his frustration.

"What about this guy Bobby?" Ruffalo asked.

Agent Waller shook his head and said that Bobby was a pretty wily character. He explained that after being questioned at FBI headquarters the previous month, Bobby had stood up to leave, taken his Styrofoam cup from the table, and said, "I'm not letting you have my DNA."

***

In late June received a letter about the case from the U.S. Department of Justice. I had been referred to the FBI's Victim Assistance Program. I was also assigned a VIN, a victim identification number, and given access to an FBI website where information was available about the case, court dates, and the status of the defendant.

Agent Waller explained that it was going to take a while—several months at least—to prepare the evidence for the case. There was a lot of material to sift through in addition to a lengthy process the case had to undergo in the channels of federal law enforcement. Bobby's computer and laptop had to be sent to Quantico for forensic analysis. My case was in line behind countless others.

The vexing problem, however, was that no laws had been violated by Bobby. There *weren't* any laws prohibiting what he had done. It was inarguably an awful thing to do and showed him to be a horrible person, but was it criminal? Bobby had maneuvered around any existing laws by steering clear of issuing direct death threats by email or telephone. The FBI was attempting to bring charges against him, therefore, for supplying false and misleading statements in the twenty-five page letter he had sent the Bureau on May 30.

After so much time spent in fear, I wasn't giving up.

***

In December, Agent Waller asked that I come down to his office to go over a few things about the case as it moved toward prosecution. It had been a while since our last meeting, and I reflected on how much had happened since Nolan first made contact with the FBI. Waller advised me that not all cases that they investigate are prosecuted. In fact, most are not. Filing charges was at the discretion of the U.S. Assistant District Attorney, and there could be many reasons why he would choose not to do so. My case was unusual in that most federal cases do not involve one individual as the victim. Most are about banks, financial institutions, or corporations.

On a positive note, Agent Waller said that the analysis of data on Bobby's hard drive was back from Quantico. He said they found everything they were looking for—and more. Although Bobby probably assumed he had permanently deleted all of the data on his hard drive, the computer experts at the FBI lab were able to retrieve it fairly easily. Just because something is deleted doesn't mean it's gone forever. Bobby went through the trouble of convincing James to change all of their internet accounts, delete files from his computer, and update drivers, but it had all been done for nothing since the IP "fingerprint" inarguably pointed to the perpetrator. If Bobby had been smart, he would have dropped his entire computer into the Potomac River, and yet even that wouldn't have been the end of it. There was still plenty of evidence. All roads led to *poordeadswan*.

The FBI lab had recovered other things from Bobby's hard drive not related to my case, items that were nevertheless of interest to the FBI. Casting his eyes downward and shaking his head, he said, "Some of it is of a highly disturbing nature." The look in his eyes spoke volumes. He didn't specify what they were, but I knew Bobby had a taste for the macabre.

He also wanted me to meet with other FBI staff to determine how I would do in a courtroom should the defendant plead not guilty. If the case went to trial, I needed to be aware of what the defense would do in court. Defense attorneys can be real bastards, and it was likely I would be raked over the coals. It would therefore be a difficult prep. He asked, "Are you sure?" I confirmed I was.

We walked into a large conference room with several people seated at a long table. Assistant U.S. Attorney Marshall Camp was among them. I was seated at the head, but it felt more like the foot. Agent Waller pulled up a chair behind me on the right. He explained that they were going to ask me some questions, adding that he wasn't required to be there or participate in the session, but he wanted to attend. I was glad he was present. The prosecutor introduced everyone in the room then the session began with a round of basic questions: tell us about your case; how did it begin? Who are Hal, Karen, and Leonard?

I spelled out the twisted story slowly and painstakingly as I had many times before. Prosecutor Camp instructed me to take my time and not feel rushed. Intermittently during my telling of the story, different kinds of questions were lobbed at me. Some were ordinary, seeking clarification for the characters and sequence of events. Others were obviously meant to test me, rattle me, or throw me off track completely as they questioned and re-questioned me on things I had already explained. Although I was in friendly company and these people were clearly there to help me, I felt I was getting impatient, defensive, and brittle. They asked dozens of personal questions about my habits, my lifestyle, and drug usage. I shifted in my seat uncomfortably, knowing that I had to come clean, but admitting it to a room full of federal law enforcement officers wasn't easy. They waited silently, sternly. I said that I smoked pot. A look went around the room. Pot? That's it? It was met with a collective shrug and eye roll, like "big deal." Relieved, I said that was it. They didn't care. It wasn't ideal, but they were used to seeing much worse.

My story was long and twisted, and it took a long time to get it all out. Two hours must have gone by, and when I was done, there was silence, everyone taking it in and looking at me. Looks went around the room, but no one said anything. Marshall Camp thanked me for coming and asked the attendees to remain and discuss it. Agent Waller said he was going to join them for the meeting and asked me to please wait until he was done. I was directed to another room and waited the better part of an hour for them to conclude. When Waller came back, he looked serious. He remarked at how insane the story was now that he had heard again in its entirety. He thought it was amazing how I remembered everything. He said that I didn't do so well when it came to dealing with questions designed to rattle me, but otherwise my recounting of the events held up well.

CHAPTER THIRTY-NINE

ARRAIGNMENT

On the stage he was natural, simple, affecting;
'Twas only that when he was off he was acting.
—Oliver Goldsmith

Bobby was charged with providing false statements to the FBI during the course of an investigation. It was the letter that Bobby had faxed to them that hung him. There were no charges to bring against him for harassment, stalking, or threats, as serious as these might have been. Agent Waller was nevertheless determined to bring whatever he could against Bobby and make it stick.

A little over a year had passed since the FBI raid at James's DC condo and I had moved on with my life. Nolan and I had parted ways, and I got a new job at teNeues Publishing, a German illustrated book publisher whose New York offices were located in a loft building in the Flatiron District just a few blocks from Rizzoli. The first day I walked into teNeues and saw my new office, I knew it was a full break from the past. I had an office of my own, industrial and stylish, with a nice clean desk, a phone, and a brand new unviolated computer.

Leaving my old job provided an invigorating change of scenery and a cautious sense of freedom. I had a new job, a new office, and a new email address that, like most in employment use, had a straightforward combination of my first and last name. I had previously been unable to stop looking over my shoulder—Bobby's assaults had made that unavoidable—and each time I opened my work email the fearful expectation of watching a global e-siege explode in my face was ever-present. I dared to hope that these days were behind me even though Bobby's ultimate fate was yet to be decided.

Agent Waller informed me that Bobby was going to plead guilty. There would be no trial, only two court appearances, one for his arraignment hearing and one for sentencing, both of which I was entitled to attend if I chose to. Waller said that pleading guilty was generally looked upon favorably by a judge because it saved government money and precious court time. Pleading guilty also meant that the defendant agreed to waive certain rights and placed him at the mercy of the presiding judge.

The plea hearing was fast approaching. Agent Waller assured me that I would have no contact with Bobby at the courthouse. He said they would bring him into the federal building through a different entrance than the one used by the general public. I thanked Agent Waller for what could have been the hundredth time for everything he'd done for me. I told him that if he hadn't cracked this case, it would still be going on. Bobby's "torture hobby" could be fired up at will just for the hell of it. It might have continued in perpetuity.

On August 25, 2006, I put on my best skirt, blouse, and shoes. Nolan met me in Brooklyn, and we drove downtown early to the arraignment hearing and grabbed a couple of donuts and coffees at Dunkin Donuts. Nolan chose to be there since Bobby had made his life hell, too. He wanted to see the man who had caused us so much grief that it had propelled him to seek help from the FBI. We were also to meet a friend of mine, Bill Harris, who wanted to join us in order to show support. I was nervous, and though I felt somewhat prepared, I really didn't know what to expect. The courtroom where the guilty plea was to be offered was located in a brand new federal justice building at 1 St. Andrews Plaza among the stately limestone and granite columns of Federal Plaza and Foley Square.

As we approached the building on the winding street, the bright summer sunlight illuminated two figures smoking cigarettes, figures I quickly recognized as Bobby and James, the last people I expected or wanted to see. Bobby was wearing an ill-fitting chartreuse suit that flapped like a sail as he expelled a plume of smoke while he stubbed out his cigarette. James looked his normal self, but I was surprised and somewhat dismayed to see them still together. I had hoped James would have moved on. I wondered how he could stay in the relationship given the level of cruelty, lies, and betrayal. Agent Waller's rock-solid assurance that I wouldn't have to make contact with Bobby evaporated in the morning sunlight. I wasn't angry, just unpleasantly surprised. But there they were. I was a bit startled at seeing his garish figure. I hadn't seen or contacted him in over a year, but the memories of his cruelty came flooding back, together with the churning, sick feeling in my stomach that had gnawed at me for over a year and a half.

Looking in our direction, they saw that it was me. Bobby actually waved, which I thought was strange, and I had no intentions of returning the gesture. I pointed them out to Nolan and Bill and said, "I'm getting out of here" as I turned around in place and headed in the opposite direction and kept going. I didn't want to be anywhere near them. As soon as I gained enough distance to lose sight of them, I stopped, waiting for Nolan and Bill, who caught up with me. We waited a little while until just before the hearing was scheduled to start before entering the building. Security was tight at the entrance. Bobby and James were gone, but I ran into Agent Waller and the prosecutor. I told them that my timing was lousy and that I had bumped into the perp. Agent Waller apologized and said he had done everything he could to prevent that from happening, but apparently something had gone awry with his efforts and I understood. After all, he couldn't possibly control everything.

The marble lobby was impressive. The courtroom was on a high floor overlooking downtown. The view was breathtaking as we waited for the courtroom doors to open. It was all so surreal. Bobby had gone to such great lengths to scare his "beloved Saltz" with an intricate web of imaginary characters and real-life criminals and cases, and this was how it had culminated. We were now waiting to enter a federal courtroom.

Marshall Camp and Agent Waller waited with us. I was told that basic procedure was that the defendant would be brought in before the judge accompanied by his defense, and enter his plea, which in this case was a plea of guilty. After the plea, he would provide an allocution, which is a formal statement to the court in an effort to hopefully minimize any sentence to be imposed. Marshall Camp also told me that a New York State senator charged with embezzlement was being arraigned before the same judge that morning, so there would be a good number of reporters in attendance in what would otherwise ordinarily be a fairly empty room.

The announcement was made that the courtroom doors would be opened, hearings would begin, and the gallery was ready to be seated. We approached, and the mahogany doors glided open without a sound. It was like watching the gates of the Emerald City open. The atmosphere immediately intensified, as if the air itself was transformed as we entered the courtroom. From the carpeting and lighting fixtures to the commanding wood paneling and acoustics, the entire design of the room projected a sense of power. The room was beautiful, official, and otherworldly. I was in awe. It was part of the United States federal government, of course, but the decor was brilliantly effective in communicating the message that this is where justice and the possibility of punishment were meted. I would never want to be a defendant making a trip to federal court. It was overwhelming.

Agent Waller joined Marshall Camp in the front before the judge's bench. Nolan, Bill, and I took seats in the very back. The left side of the gallery was filled three rows deep with about two dozen disheveled, seasoned reporters who rarely looked up from their notepads. They were the very image of cynicism, and who could blame them given all the things they had seen. They looked like they were regulars on the courtroom beat. Each probably had worn down his own spot on the wooden benches.

The judge entered, and we all rose with a rolling sound.

Bobby was brought in, his lawyers behind him. He seemed to stumble, as if he was drugged, acting, or perhaps even having a psychological break in the midst of the legal event being held in his honor.

Bobby's case was then officially called.

MR. CAMP: Good morning, Your Honor. Marshall Camp for the government. With me at counsel table is Special Agent

Brandon Waller of the FBI.

While the prosecutor spoke, Bobby stood before the judge with his hands behind his back, locked in two tightly balled fists. Before I could think, he cocked his right hand and forcefully extended his middle finger. His rage and defiance were shocking. He was directly and angrily telling me "Fuck you," and he knew I saw it. I couldn't believe his lawyers didn't see it, or maybe they did but ignored it. It was intended for me and me alone. No matter that we were in this majestic and imposing courtroom, no matter the presence of the FBI, or the possibility of serving jail time—Bobby was not only not sorry, but actively demonstrating zero regard for the judge as well as for his own fate and well-being. Nothing could suffocate his bold insolence, openly displayed to intimidate me. He had needed to grasp whatever thin shred of control at his momentary disposal to make sure I knew he was furious with me, and that he didn't care about me or the stately surroundings where he was being arraigned.

James had apparently hired two lawyers for Bobby since the crime scene was technically in New York although James's residence, where Bobby lived and had orchestrated his madness, was in Washington, DC.

His contempt was obvious but his demeanor was alarming. I figured the accused would be on his tippy toes, standing at attention and not missing a beat with "Yes, Your Honor" or "No, Your Honor."

THE COURT: Sir, you can be seated if you wish. Do you understand, sir, that any statements you give here could be used against you in a prosecution for perjury?

THE DEFENDANT: Yes.

THE COURT: Tell me your full name.

THE DEFENDANT: Robert Ironside.

THE COURT: What is your age?

THE DEFENDANT: 44.

THE COURT: Are you a citizen of the United States?

THE DEFENDANT: Yes, sir.

THE COURT: Are you able to read and write in English?

THE DEFENDANT: Yes.

THE COURT: What is the extent of your formal education?

THE DEFENDANT: Ninth grade.

Several reporters in the room looked up from their notepads. Ears perked up as the details of Bobby's background were addressed. I knew that Bobby had dropped out of high school and had not attended college, but I hadn't known the specifics.

THE COURT: How old were you when you left school, sir?

THE DEFENDANT: I guess I was around 16½, close to 17.

THE COURT: Are you now or have you recently been under the care of a doctor or psychiatrist for any reason?

THE DEFENDANT: Yes, sir.

This was a revealing bit of information. Had Bobby been so stressed when he'd finally been caught and his perverted schemes exposed that he'd needed to consult a psychiatrist? It seemed more likely that his attorneys had advised him to seek mental health care to send a message to the court that he was aware that his actions had been improper and that he needed treatment.

THE COURT: Does the condition for which you are being treated affect your ability to see, hear, or make decisions or understand things?

THE DEFENDANT: No, sir.

THE COURT: Have you ever been hospitalized in the past for mental illness?

THE DEFENDANT: Yes, sir.

THE COURT: When was that?

THE DEFENDANT: Within the last year.

THE COURT: What was the diagnosis?

THE DEFENDANT: Chronic depression, post-traumatic stress disorder, anxiety, agoraphobia. I believe that was it.

I guess Bobby should have read the warning on the label that said, "Caution: The FBI has been known to cause anxiety, depression, and PTSD." I wondered if his hospitalization was also part of his legal strategy—he might have voluntarily checked himself into a facility for observation—or if he was really blown apart by being exposed and charged with a serious crime. *Agoraphobia*? I laughed to myself despite his chilling performance. Surely he was acting. Flipping me the bird did not speak of successful psychiatric treatment or recognition of what he had done.

The questions about his current state of sobriety were undoubtedly part of standard operating procedure by the court, but I wondered if anyone in the courtroom was picking up on the unhinged mannerisms that radiated from Bobby. The judge was clearly annoyed. Bobby swayed with a swagger, and his tone, his body language, and his attitude were working against him, but he seemed unconcerned. It was as if he still lived by his own rules and no one else's, not even those of the U.S. Department of Justice. Certainly his attorneys must have advised him on how to behave in court. Maybe they did and maybe they didn't, but his behavior flew in the face of common sense and courtesy.

> THE COURT: Have you had a chance to discuss the charge and how you wish to plead with your attorney?
>
> THE DEFENDANT: Yes, sir.
>
> THE COURT: Are you satisfied with your attorney's representation of you?
>
> THE DEFENDANT: Very.
>
> THE COURT: Have you had a full opportunity to discuss this case with him?
>
> THE DEFENDANT: Yes, I have.
>
> THE COURT: Are you ready to enter a plea?
>
> THE DEFENDANT: Yes, sir.

THE COURT: Sir, Count One of the information charges that on May 30th of 2005 you made a false statement or made an omission that caused a statement to be materially false, specifically, that you faxed a letter to the FBI in Manhattan that made false and misleading statements and material omissions regarding your knowledge and responsibility for electronic mail messages and communications that had been sent by you to other individuals.

The hammer had officially dropped. He was charged with providing false and misleading information to the FBI in his twenty-five page letter to Agent Waller. If he had never faxed the letter, he wouldn't have been standing in court. He was a man, however, who could not control his impulses, so great is his need to manipulate the outcome of a situation. He could not refrain from lying. He had written to me asking for forgiveness while simultaneously throwing me under the bus in the letter to Agent Waller. What he might have said in the letter—or omitted, as the charge indicated—was not known to me. Agent Waller was in possession of over a thousand emails that I had provided him. Perhaps Bobby had made statements that flagrantly contradicted what Waller had read. I could have requested to read the letter but I didn't. I've never read it and do not intend to. For eighteen months I had read his emails, including those harshly critical of me for seeking help from law enforcement, and I didn't need yet another sampling of his fictionalized account of reality.

THE COURT: Do you understand that you have a right to plead not guilty to this charge and the right to a jury trial if you wish?

THE DEFENDANT: I do.

THE COURT: Do you understand that if you plead guilty and go to trial, you would be presumed innocent, and the burden would be on the government to prove your guilt beyond a reasonable doubt?

THE DEFENDANT: Yes, sir.

THE COURT: Do you understand that at a trial you would be entitled to be represented by an attorney at all stages, and if you could not afford one, the Court would appoint you an attorney for free?

THE DEFENDANT: Yes.

THE COURT: Do you understand that at a trial you would be entitled to cross-examine any witnesses called by the government against you?

THE DEFENDANT: Oh, yes.

His last words were said with a great deal of emphasis. They oozed slowly out of his mouth like bitter lava. This was Bobby's signature arrogance. He relished the idea of flaying me in court instead of accepting responsibility for what he had done to me for so long.

THE COURT: Do you understand that no matter what sentencing range the sentencing judge believes is called for by the guidelines, that range is just one of many factors that the judge will consider in determining sentence and that you may be sentenced to a term of imprisonment that is below or above the range, anywhere up to the maximum sentence of imprisonment of five years? Do you understand that, sir?

THE DEFENDANT: Yes, sir.

The possibility of five years in prison must have hit Bobby like a wrecking ball. Although Bobby's lawyers had obviously discussed sentencing guidelines with the prosecutor, the court had informed him that the actual sentencing judge could impose new guidelines and, in essence, impose whatever sentence he wanted, which included up to five years in prison. In a sense, the rug had been pulled from beneath Bobby's precarious stance. He now had a different reason to swagger and sway.

This was going well by any account. Bobby was guilty and completely at the mercy of a federal judge and there was absolutely nothing he could do about it.

THE COURT: Is your plea voluntarily, that is, made of your own free will?
THE DEFENDANT: Yes, sir, it is.

THE COURT: Did you in fact commit the offense that is charged in Count One of the information?

THE DEFENDANT: I did.

THE COURT: Sir, before I ask you to tell me what you did, I am going to ask the government to summarize the elements of the offense and, if they wish, to tell me the evidence they would offer in support.

MR. CAMP: Thank you, Your Honor. Section 1001 of Title 18, the offense charged in Count One of the Indictment, has five elements:

First, that on or about the date specified in the indictment, the defendant falsified, concealed, or covered up a material fact;

Second, that the fact falsified, concealed, or covered up was material;

Third, that the defendant did so by trick, scheme, or device;

The handful of reporters that had gone back to their notepads were suddenly paying attention again. A few heads went up, followed by a few more.

> Fourth, that he acted willingly and knowingly; and

> Fifth, that the falsification, scheme, method, or cover-up was with respect to a matter within the jurisdiction of the government of the United States.

> At trial the government would offer, among other things, documentary evidence and testimony showing that from November 2003 through December 2004, Bobby Ironside, the defendant, sent hundreds of electronic mail messages and other communications, including a large volume of harassing and abusive communications, to an individual with whom he was acquainted; that Ironside sent these communications through numerous email accounts using aliases such as Karen Gardiner, Hal Gardiner, Sharon Barnes, Leonard Nachman, Robert McCottry, Carl Mulgrave, and Leona Kink.

The entire assembly of reporters craned their necks, fully at attention. This was far juicier than a state senator from the Bronx charged with embezzlement. This was a special treat, a view into something very disordered, demented, and completely out of the ordinary.

It was incredibly satisfying to hear Marshall Camp run down the list of characters in Bobby's magnum opus of terror and cruel deceit. While he wasn't being charged with how he had orchestrated these characters to torment me, their names had been read into the official record. This was justice in and of itself. A bright light shined on Bobby's madness as Camp read the five elements of his offense.

THE COURT: Sir, can you tell me what it is that you did that forms the basis of your plea.

THE DEFENDANT: Could you repeat it, sir? I'm sorry.

THE COURT: Can you tell me in your words what it is that you did that causes you to plead guilty.

THE DEFENDANT: Basically, I sent a fax to the FBI with misleading information, and when they came to question me I wasn't truthful with them.

THE COURT: Did the fax itself contain any false statements or material that was, based on omissions, materially false?

THE DEFENDANT: Actually, it was a mixed bag.

A mixed bag? His answer was so blatantly disrespectful. While pleading guilty, he was almost at the brink of recanting his admission of guilt.

THE COURT: What do you mean?

THE DEFENDANT: Well, there was a lot of truth in it and some falsehoods.

THE COURT: There were false statements contained in it?

THE DEFENDANT: Yes, sir.

THE COURT: And this was sent to the FBI?

THE DEFENDANT: Yes.

THE COURT: And this related to an investigation the FBI was doing?

THE DEFENDANT: Yes, sir.

THE COURT: This was on May 3, 2005?

THE DEFENDANT: I believe so.

THE COURT: Sent to their office in Manhattan?

THE DEFENDANT: Brandon Waller.

THE COURT: It was sent to their office in Manhattan, or don't you know where it was sent?

THE DEFENDANT: I don't remember.

The judge's tone of voice clearly indicated that he was displeased with Bobby's flippancy.

THE COURT: Let's have a disposition sheet. Sir, I had not been informed this was your initial appearance in court. Accordingly, I am going to tell you some things that are required by our Federal Rules of Criminal Procedure that may not make sense given what we just did, but I don't want to take any chances.

Let me tell you that you are not required to make any statements, that anything that you do say can be used against you, that you have the right to be represented by counsel during all court proceedings, including this one. If you could not afford an attorney, we would appoint one to represent you. I think we have gone through the information and what is there. What's left is now the setting of the bail condition. What is the proposal?

MR. CAMP: I have spoken with defense counsel. We have agreed, I believe, on a joint proposal of a $15,000 personal recognizance bond.

The $15,000 bond would come right out of James's pocket since Bobby didn't have a dime. Between the two defense lawyers, this had to have cost James thousands of dollars, not to mention the trip to New York to face charges, the hospitalization, medication, and Bobby's ongoing psychiatric treatment. James stood with his head lowered the entire time. I could only imagine the humiliation and devastation he was enduring.

Bobby was now a convicted federal felon. He had no priors, and I expected that he would receive a fine and probation when he appeared for sentencing even though the government had left the door open for stiffer penalties. I am sure Bobby thought the same thing, or he never would have pleaded guilty.

He was led out of the room with James right behind him, looking severely dejected. Nolan, Bill, and I filed out the main door. Given Bobby's demeanor, it was clear that he was not subdued but, in fact, enraged and belligerent. What a ride back to DC that was going to be for him and James. I was sad for James to be dragged into this hellish experience, and now he had to fork over a substantial sum of money for Bobby's bond. I didn't understand how he could stick so steadfastly to a cruel and craven liar, but that was out of my hands. I had been through enough, and to add insult to injury, Bobby had given me the finger in federal court, which said it all.

It wasn't over.

CHAPTER FORTY

SENTENCING

The psychopath is the furnace that gives no heat.
—Derek Raymond, *The Hidden Files* (1992)

I was notified in September that the December 4, 2006, sentencing date was moved to February 8, 2007. The few extra months only prolonged the strain of waiting. Like the entire ordeal, the end always seemed just out of reach.

I wasn't looking forward to seeing Bobby in court again although perhaps approaching a federal sentencing hearing would cause him to behave a bit better—I hoped, but I knew better. As much as I dreaded it, there was no way I was going to miss it. I didn't feel triumphal, but I did feel vindicated. Sweet justice!

There were a few options available to a victim for the sentencing hearing. I had the right to attend and speak to the court if I chose. I was also given the opportunity to submit a victim impact statement, which is a formal written statement, to the judge about how the crimes had affected my life and what sort of sentencing I was hoping for. In the interest of full disclosure, my victim impact statement was also available to the defense to read. I was apprehensive about speaking so I declined. Nolan was also given an opportunity to write a victim impact statement which he readily took advantage of. As much as I dreaded it, there was no way I was going to miss the sentencing. Once again, Nolan and Bill came to show support.

Before the hearing began, Agent Waller and Marshall Camp escorted me into a private waiting room to the left of the court room doors. It was a small, private room, sealed off from the presence of others. The prosecutor, Agent Waller, and I conferred for a few minutes before being led into the courtroom. They said that if I wanted to, I still had the opportunity to address the judge, but I really did not want to. I felt the impact statement had said enough. In it, I had written that I was hoping the judge would give Bobby two years in prison to think about what he had done to me. He stole almost two years of my life. For what? To torment me for his own amusement. I asked Camp and Waller what kind of sentence they were expecting. They said that considering all things, i.e. Bobby had no priors, had entered a guilty plea to a non-violent first offense, and given the prison overcrowding and the cost of housing inmates, they felt he would be sentenced to probation and maybe a fine, but that would be it. Time in prison seemed like a long shot and though it was my hope that he would spend time behind bars, I was reconciled to whatever outcome there would be. After all, I had received justice in a world where there is very little of it to go around. I was grateful for the conviction, as it affirmed to me that the court agreed it was no laughing matter. I could finally believe he wouldn't be bothering me again. However, I was a little worried that the venerable judge might not fully appreciate the gravity of the rebounding repercussions of internet stalking and harassment, and how greatly it can wreak havoc in someone's life.

The judge entered the room and everyone rose to their feet. He was indeed an older gentleman, appearing every bit the seasoned jurist who had experienced a long and storied legal career.

No television drama adequately compares to actually being in court and being part of the process—and in my case, being the victim. The very character of the room crackles with intensity. No moment is wasted. Everything matters. The players have everything at stake. I hung on every word.

> THE COURT: Does the U.S. Attorney's office have anything to say in this case?
>
> MR. CAMP: Good afternoon, Your Honor, Marshall Camp on behalf of the United States. Do you want my position on sentencing?
>
> THE COURT: If you have something to say, you are entitled to speak.
>
> MR. CAMP: The presentence report does a pretty good job of laying forth the circumstances of this offense, although it is, as false statements, crime of -- crime, the circumstances are somewhat unusual. The false statements were made in connection with an investigation into a nearly year-long period of e-mailing and electronic communication that had effectively terrorized the victim. I believe the victim is in the courtroom.
>
> THE COURT: She wants him sent away forever, which is probably in my power to do.
>
> MR. CAMP: I am not certain of that, but I know she was extremely affected by the course of conduct. I just wanted to make that clear, that it is the government's position that this was on the scale of false statements, the offense is more serious than, perhaps, the ordinary type offense. Beyond that,

the government is not taking a specific position on sentencing other than the guidelines range of zero to six months.

THE COURT: That's what you agreed to?

MR. CAMP: That's right.

THE COURT: As a reasonable sentence?

MR. CAMP: Yes, under 3553(e).

THE COURT: I will hear from counsel.

MR. KEY: My client is 44 years old. He's before the Court today for sentencing, having accepted responsibility for his actions in this case. Your Honor, he is sorry that his actions caused anguish to the victim. Unfortunately in this case there is nothing that he can do to make up for that at this time. The thing he can do is make sure that it doesn't occur again. And I think that he has done that, Your Honor. For the first time in his life, after a fairly disturbing childhood that included sexual abuse and being basically on his own since the age of 17, for the first time he is in a mutually-supportive relationship with his partner James Water, who is here in the front row, Your Honor. This has had an incredible effect on my client as well. He has had a lifetime of severe depression, panic disorder, Your Honor, he has also suffered from agoraphobia, the fear of being in public places, or outside.

I knew Bobby well and I had never heard him discuss severe depression, panic disorder, or agoraphobia. Not ever. I had been to DC a few times and on each visit we were out and about all over town. Bobby and James had also taken trips together to Hawaii and Florida that bore out no fear of being in public places or of being outside. Bobby had also maintained a very active social life that showed no indication of agoraphobia. This was nothing but a predictable play for sympathy.

> MR. KEY: Your Honor, as a result of this, and the stress that this caused, in addition to that that he already had, he immediately went into a four and a half month inpatient program with the Psychiatric Institute of Washington, where they addressed all those issues, including his use of drugs, since that time. He has been drug free since that time. Your Honor, Dr. Matson released him after four and a half months, and he is continuing on an outpatient basis. And Dr. Matson ... the report makes it clear that Mr. Ironside is a changed man, in that he has dealt with many of these issues; he is a changed man in that he is remorseful, he stopped using drugs, and he is now in a better place where he can be a normal member of society.

> In particular, the doctor doesn't think that he is a threat to anyone. And that he is unlikely to repeat any of this behavior. Your Honor, he has continued to see Dr. Matson and also Dr. Merzing in addition to that. He felt that the group treatment that he was receiving was beneficial, so he signed up for another outpatient facility, Whitman Walker Clinic. And from October last year to this January he has continued with weekly group sessions. In addition to those with his doctor, Your Honor, also starting in July of '06, he felt comfortable enough with the treatment, that he was able to go out in public, and he wanted to know what he could do to give back to society. And since July '06 he has been working three or four days a week at Capital Hospice, in doing what they need help in, terminally ill patients and their families. He did tell them of his pending case, he was required to disclose that. And they still decided to use his services, Your Honor.

Your Honor, he has done everything that I think he can do at this point to make up for it. You don't just have to take the word of Dr. Matson that he is not going to repeat this behavior, that he is not a threat to anyone. The fact is that he has not had any contact with Susan Fensten for two years now. And there is no indication that he ever will.

Dr. Matson wanted me to explain to you that he would like Robert to continue in therapy with him, he is hoping that he could get to the point where he could actually start working for the first time in an awfully long time, Your Honor.

He is here with his partner today who stayed with him. It is very difficult for his partner. Mr. Water was very displeased with his behavior, and they almost broke up. But he is here today asking the Court for understanding.

I am asking the Court to place him on a period of probation, certainly to require no contact whatsoever with Ms. Fensten, and any other conditions that the Court deems appropriate.

THE COURT: Well, the one factor that you don't deal within your presentation is punishment.

MR. KEY: Your Honor, I understand that. I think there actually has been punishment, he basically was in a facility for four and a half months. He has been basically in fear ever since this occurred because of his panic disorder.

Bobby was in fear alright: in fear of being a convicted felon and facing sentencing, and the very real possibility of going to prison. His lawyer continued by offering that his client had already paid his debt to society.

MR. KEY: Your Honor, he has, in my opinion, been punished. I don't think that a period of incarceration would be appropriate in this case. Although I understand that Ms. Fensten was scared, and I understand -- and there is no excuse for the behavior or the e-mails that he sent, no one was actually injured. She was never in any actual danger. And it has been over two years that there has been any contact. So there is no reason to think -- I would ask the Court to sentence him to a period of probation and suspend that and hang it over his head for the entire period of probation, so he knows if there is any problem whatsoever, he knows the consequences.

Never in any actual danger. That ticked me off. I *was* in fear for my life and not only mine, but for Nolan as well. How was I supposed to know that I was never really in any danger? I knew the attorney was just doing his job, but what a dirty job it was. It was tough to listen to him minimize my experience.

THE COURT: Does the victim want to be heard?

MR. CAMP: My understanding is that she does not. She is nervous about speaking in the courtroom. But her sentiments are heard in the presentence report.

THE COURT: I will hear from your client.

THE DEFENDANT: Good afternoon Your Honor. Well, several years ago I made some terrible mistakes that I regret now and that I am remorseful for. My greatest source of angst was not being able to do anything about it. Not being able to make amends for the wrongs that I did.

So the first thing I did was try to work on myself. As Mr. Key stated, I won't repeat what he said, but I immediately stopped using drugs, checked myself into a psychiatric facility. And since that time have built myself back up to a redeemable person that I feel that I am. I do volunteer my time with the sick and dying all week, which has helped me a lot. I am sorry for what I have done. I don't know how I can take any of it back, but again it's been a few years now.

Bobby delivered these words in a monotone so wooden I wondered if he was on some kind of medication or just bereft of a soul. In a flattened tone, "I'm-not-here" sort of delivery, it was as if he was trying to diminish his actions by distancing them from the immediate issue.

THE DEFENDANT: I have no ill feelings towards anyone in this courtroom, or Ms. Fensten. I have no plans to contact her ever again in the future. It was a mistake, something that started as a prank and went way too far.

THE COURT: A prank in what way?

THE DEFENDANT: Ms. Fensten and I pulled pranks together, and at one point I decided to pull one on her, and it went way too far. And I take full responsibility for my actions.

Here again was a deflecting tactic. Shifting blame to the victim is common when one simply has no defense. He really should be admitting guilt and apologizing.

We played pranks together? Hardly. The pranks that Bobby was talking about involved goofing around on a message board we had both visited and a profile on a dating site that we created to test a man who had contacted me. Both were short-lived, about a couple of weeks at the very most. Neither of these pranks ever left their respective websites and none of it ever involved elaborate backstories, much less threats and harassment.

> THE COURT: It is a rather extraordinary pattern of behavior. It existed for some period of time. It wasn't just a one-shot deal.

The judge was not letting Bobby off so easy.
> THE DEFENDANT: I wouldn't have been able to do it without her.

The atmosphere in the court room came to a dead silence. The normal soft clamor of a court session, papers rustling, low whispers, and shuffling movement in and out of the room came to a complete standstill. One could almost hear the proverbial pin drop.

> THE COURT: That's an odd thing. What do you mean you wouldn't have been able to do it without her?

The judge was clearly irritated and his demeanor shifted. I could almost hear Bobby's defense attorney's head exploding.

> THE DEFENDANT: She was a correspondent. We communicated via e-mail, and I would never have been able to continue if I never received another e-mail in response. So it was a correspondence more than it was harassment.

A "correspondence"? He was making it out to be a page from Karen's kerfuffle with the recipe club—a mere minor infraction. Just the normal things that friends do online. I couldn't believe what I was hearing. But I probably shouldn't have been surprised. Bobby was a skilled manipulator, or so he thought.

THE COURT: And you made all these false statements to the government too.

THE DEFENDANT: Yes, and that was a big mistake. I should have been honest with the agents when they came. And I admit to my wrongdoing.

The judge still wouldn't let Bobby's peculiar previous answer go so easily.

THE COURT: Your answer intrigues me. I can't understand it, what you are saying. How you couldn't have done it unless she answered the telephone -- it was on the internet.

THE DEFENDANT: Yes, sir.

THE COURT: Suppose it was the telephone, you call somebody up on the telephone and they don't hang up, and you say, well, if they had not hung up I wouldn't be here.

THE DEFENDANT: It is my fault, Your Honor, I take full responsibility for anything that happened. I don't put any blame on Miss Fensten.

THE COURT: In a sense you were.

THE DEFENDANT: You mentioned that it went so far and you were intrigued by that. The only reason it was able to go as far as it did was because I had a willing participant. It's a long story, Your Honor, and I wish I could you.

At this point, I was furious. A murmur went through the room. I imagined that the defense attorneys were apoplectic with their rogue client. James must have been beside himself.

Agent Waller saw that I was upset. He came over and asked if I wanted to address the court. He said that the judge did say that he wanted to hear from me. I was encouraged by that. My heart pounded. Still slightly hesitant, I asked, "Should I?" Agent Waller nodded and I raised my hand high. The judge looked up and took notice of my signal while continuing to grill Bobby.

> THE COURT: Willing participant goes very far removed from what I have been reading from her. You notice I have given her the opportunity to speak, she doesn't appear to be a willing participant.
>
> THE DEFENDANT: I read that report as well, Your Honor.
>
> THE COURT: Who is a willing participant in threats?
>
> THE DEFENDANT: She is not.
>
> THE COURT: But you sort of suggested that she is.
>
> THE DEFENDANT: No, what I meant was that was how it was able to go as long and as far as it did.
>
> THE COURT: Because she kept answering the telephone.
>
> THE DEFENDANT: There was no telephone communication.
>
> THE COURT: I understand that. I will let her speak further and then I will give you an opportunity to speak.

Bobby side-pedaled fast and resumed his threadbare play of false contrition.

> THE DEFENDANT: Your Honor, basically I take full responsibility for everything that happened. I

am sorry for what happened. It was a few years ago, I -- nothing has happened since, nothing will ever happen like it again. And in the meantime, I have made changes in my life. I am not the same person in the paperwork before you.

Again he repeated that it was a few years ago. He also seemed painfully unaware that his claims of being a new and better person were falling flat each time he accused me of be a co-conspirator in my own torture.

THE COURT: No, but rehabilitation is only one aspect of the sentencing process, making you a new person is only one part of it. There are consequences that are attached to acts and punishments that are meted out for offenses -- the offense.

The sentencing factors in 3553 are not only rehabilitation, but they also concern specific and general deterrence, and punishment. These are all things I have to consider in fashioning an appropriate sentence. You are not facing 60 years here, you are facing six months maximum, which the government has agreed upon as an appropriate sentence, and I am not going to exceed what the parties have agreed upon. But I don't think we can leave that out of the equation, is what I am saying.

THE DEFENDANT: I understand that, sir.

THE COURT: Anything else you want to say?

THE DEFENDANT: Just that I am sorry. And I thank you for letting me speak.

THE COURT: All right, I will hear from Ms. Fensten if she wants to be heard. Pretend you are in your living room and talking to me directly.

I was anxious but anger had overridden the fear. I was not about to let Bobby get away with this. I rose in my seat, straightened my blazer, and strode up to the podium before the judge. I couldn't believe I was actually standing there. It was surreal and overwhelming. Bobby sat less than four feet to my left. My palms throbbed with sweat. I felt I was about to burst. I hadn't planned what I was going to say, but it all came forth from a well in my chest.

> MS. FENSTEN: Thank you for giving me the opportunity to speak. I didn't plan on it, because I wasn't really sure what to expect today.
>
> But in response to being a willing participant, I just want to make it clear that I was never a willing participant, and I don't even see how that relates to my situation in the threats that I received.
>
> And I also want to make the courtroom aware that the defendant was fully aware that I was seeking law enforcement aid through local police. And I had actually tried the FBI at one other time, but I wasn't given an opportunity to speak to anybody. When I finally did, the defendant was fully aware that I was in contact with federal law enforcement and was trying to save myself.
>
> The defendant stopped harassing me for about three weeks. And then started again. And then stopped again. Fully aware that the FBI was investigating my complaints. And then continued. And continued to send threats to my office, which was completely unwelcome or uninvited, and was sending death threats over the phone to my boyfriend at the time, Nolan Grey, who is in the courtroom here today. So I want to make that understood, that nobody was a willing participant.

THE COURT: You may have been a willing participant at the start but at —

MS. FENSTEN: -- I was never a willing participant, sir, with all respect, I was tricked into believing that I had relatives in a genealogy site online. The defendant acted as my closest confident and my friend, my adviser, and my sort of rock that I leaned upon.

THE COURT: How did this whole thing start? Maybe that's what I am missing.

MS. FENSTEN: I put a message up on a genealogy website looking for information about my father's family, who I never met. It was an innocent message, and I never expected to get any kind of responses. There are thousands of people doing family trees on the internet all the time. And the defendant found that message sometime, probably by Googling me.

The message still exists, same website, same date. He pretended to be several people in pretending to lure me into this sort of strange scenario where it just became worse and worse, where there was presence of mental illness in these characters and the number of actual convicted sex offenders in New Jersey that were supposedly writing to me and knew where I lived. So there was a long concocted story with an immense amount of detail and time and effort put into it.

THE COURT: It is not somebody you knew? Did you meet him personally?

MS. FENSTEN: No, I never met any one person, it was all internet correspondence. And it sort of gravitated into telephone calls and threats over the telephone. And through e-mail.

THE COURT: What was this talk about a prank?

MS. FENSTEN: I don't think -- I don't know about, if it was a prank. I think he thought it was funny, in the beginning, to trick me and fool me. It went over a period of two years or more.

THE COURT: You are saying it was never a prank to you?

MS. FENSTEN: I didn't know I was having a prank played on me. I believed every word that I was hearing and seeing as fact.

THE COURT: All right, well, I think that -- is there anything you want to say in response?

THE DEFENDANT: I better not, Your Honor.

THE COURT: All right, well, you can sit down.

THE DEFENDANT: I am just so sorry about everything. And I think that Ms. Fensten and I know exactly what happened, and I know, but I will be quiet.

THE COURT: I could always have a hearing if you want me to have a hearing.

The hearing question was directed at Bobby's lawyer who had jumped up and tried to gain control of his client and the situation, which was looking like it was about to spin out of control.

MR. KEY: We don't need a hearing, your Honor.

THE COURT: You don't want a hearing?

Bobby's lawyer shook his head "No."

I stepped down and walked back to my seat in the last row. Agent Waller said that I did great but all I kept hearing were Bobby's last words, *And I think that Ms. Fensten and I know exactly what happened, and I know, but I will be quiet.* The impudence was extraordinary. Implicating the victim at a sentencing hearing demonstrated that Bobby was tone deaf when it came to critical self-reflection and penitence. His contempt of the charge he was facing was reckless to the point of self-destruction. He was like a kamikaze pilot ready to commit legal suicide to prove a point. This was not the time for him to try and prove points, but he couldn't resist. His guilty plea had forfeited most of his rights under the law and he was now in front of a federal judge at sentencing. This was a time that any sane person would be contrite, declaring guilt and remorse, and begging for mercy. Everything Bobby did was about to backfire in a most unexpected way.

> THE COURT: All right. I read the presentence report. I have seen all the extenuating circumstances around the offense. However, on the other hand, I think what he did was uncalled for and wrong. And not the kind of conduct which should be encouraged, especially in an age of the internet where so many people get on the internet and have no idea who they are talking to. This kind of conduct does require a certain measure of general deterrence, as well as specific deterrence in his particular case. He probably has had some counseling and has made some efforts that he won't commit this offense again. But there are other people out there that do use the internet. I think an overly lenient sentence of this type would not be good for social policy. So, therefore, it is the judgment of this Court that you be sentenced to a term of imprisonment of three months.

A palpable shock rocked the courtroom. Three months. *Prison.* Bobby's robotic composure buckled. Quiet gasps were trailed by low whispers throughout the gallery. It was the last thing I had expected and I'm sure that I wasn't the only one. I looked over at Agent Waller and the prosecutor and they looked astonished. No one could believe it, least of all, Bobby.

> THE COURT: I will place you on supervised release for a period of three years. God save you if you get into trouble in the next three years, because you will be facing a much more substantial sentence than you are today. That will give you three years to straighten out your life and prove to me that your statements to the Court are true and accurate, that you won't get involved in this type of conduct again.
>
> They recommend a fine of $250,000. Frankly, I don't see that that serves any purpose. It doesn't. And that he has any assets –
>
> MR. KEY: -- he does not.

The judge had shown no sympathy and was not about to change his decision. Among other terms of his supervised probation after release from prison, the judge stated that Bobby shall not illegally possess a controlled substance, nor possess a firearm or destructive device and shall cooperate with the collection of DNA as directed by the probation officer. He went on to impose that Bobby shall submit his residence, vehicle, computer or any premises under his control to search on the basis the probation officer has reasonable belief that contraband may be found.

> MR. KEY: Yes, Your Honor. I would ask if the Court would consider, in lieu of three months in jail, three months of home confinement? Mr. Water, his partner, has just undergone double hip replacement.

THE COURT: No. He could voluntarily surrender.

MR. KEY: Thank you, Judge. If he wants to avoid the trip to the prison.

THE DEPUTY CLERK: Six weeks, Judge.

THE COURT: I guess they will take him at the local MCC for such a short sentence. It depends on them. I will let him voluntarily surrender to the marshal in six weeks.

THE DEPUTY CLERK: Friday, March 27, before 2:00 p.m.

MR. CAMP: I was going to ask one additional special condition, that the defendant refrain from conduct of any sort with the victim in this case.

THE COURT: I will impose that condition. He is not having contact with her anyway, but I will make that a special condition. Have a good day.

MR. CAMP: Thank you, Your Honor.

MR. KEY: Thank you, Judge.

And with that, it was done. The hammer had come down. We spilled out into the waiting area where I told Agent Waller and Marshall Camp how grateful I was for everything they did and how shocked I was at the sentence. They agreed. They weren't expecting prison either. Bobby's behavior before the judge was not well received and it probably had a lot to do with him receiving a prison sentence. Equally, Agent Waller and Marshall Camp also added that the MCC [Metropolitan Correctional Center] New York was considered a real hellhole as far as the Federal Bureau of Prisons went. It had a bad reputation and was known as something of a dungeon, a nasty place where bigger criminals like Mafia members and terrorists cooled their heels until they were shipped out to maximum security facilities across the country to serve long sentences. I could tell by their faces that they weren't kidding, the MCC was a pit. Bobby was not going to like it—at all.

As we waited for the elevator; everyone expressed their happy surprise that Bobby was actually going to serve time in prison. Suddenly, the courtroom doors flew open, Bobby in the lead, James limping behind with a cane, and their hired gun following alongside them. Bobby was in a visible rage. He was headed toward the elevator when he saw me. Locking his gaze on me, he swept over in my direction in a fury. He circled around the small group I was with and headed straight for me. He was white as a sheet, his eyes glaring and fixed with fury on me, he looked possessed. He wanted a confrontation and it appeared he was about to erupt all over me despite the judge's imposition that he stay away. Everyone in my group saw him coming and I was scared. As he reached within a foot of me, James came up behind him, grabbed his arm, and pulled him away. Bobby struggled a bit with his somewhat disabled lover, but after a moment relented and his lawyer led them off to the side. Agent Waller took me back into the side room to wait until they had all left.

Nolan, Bill, and I finally headed home to Brooklyn. It had been an incredible day. We bought a few beers and had a small celebration in my living room, toasting to justice. I was so relieved it was over, but Bobby's actions in court had left me wondering if it was really ever going to be over? Would I ever be able to safely stop looking over my shoulder?

EPILOGUE

*What the detective story is about is not
murder but the restoration of order.*
—P.D. James

Six weeks later, the prison doors closed on Bobby in a medium-security federal correction institution in Cumberland, Maryland. He managed to avoid serving his three-month sentence at the notorious MCC lockup in Manhattan, and I suspect that fancy legal footwork of his attorney enabled Bobby to evade the grim federal hellhole in New York. Agent Waller informed me that Bobby did his three months without incident. Upon his release he was placed under supervised probation for a period of three years, during which time he was subjected to unscheduled visits, as well as random examination of his computer activity. This was not ordinary probation that the general public might envision, perhaps correctly, of an overloaded, rubber-stamped system, a loosely-monitored revolving door. The probation was enforced to the letter. Any minor slip-ups or breaking of the rules on Bobby's part would likely have resulted in the full three-year prison term being reinstated, beginning at day one, no matter how far he had progressed in his probationary time period.

Meanwhile, my life went on as usual after the sentencing. Life's relentless pace, with jobs, deadlines, and bills, didn't allow me the luxury of sitting around licking my wounds. Justice had been meted out but recovering from my ordeal would prove to be a difficult and ongoing process.

Agent Waller and I stayed in touch, speaking occasionally, but less so as time rolled on. Peace of mind did not immediately accompany the last strike of the judge's gavel. Bobby may have been sentenced to three months, but ultimately, his assault took more than just two years of my psychological and emotional health. I found that I was unable to completely shake off the emotional aftermath as I tried to get on with my life. Perhaps I'll never fully shake it. It is difficult living with the fact that my best friend has done this to me. Smarting with the shame that I had been selected as an unwitting *roast du jour* for the insatiable delight of a sadistic voyeur, I felt like there was something wrong with *me*, that I myself was defective. Something obviously signaled to predators that I was easy prey. I had been chosen to be verbally and mentally abused and kept as an emotional and psychological prisoner—and that I had somehow deserved it. My friend of many years had enjoyed punishing me in the cruelest manner and seemed to believe that I never had enough of the abuse that, to him, was merely playful sport or a creative outlet.

A large part of recovering was overcoming this sickening feeling of being duped. It took quite a while to be able to forgive myself for being so gullible over such a lengthy period of time. How could I *not* have known? I knew that Bobby was unscrupulous, but I never thought he would be capable of displaying such vicious behavior and disdain toward me, his friend. It was not comprehensible to me, although friends had hinted that it might be him while the hoax was in progress. I staunchly defended what I believed to be the truth: that it was an unknown, or possibly a group of unknowns. I had come to grips with the undeniable fact that he really had not been my friend after all. In fact, I had come to realize that he was so angry that I had dumped him as a friend, again, that he responded with a systematic overtaking and commandeering of a human being's life. Mine. And my gravest mistake was in trusting him.

As I worked to process the whole ordeal, the ghosts of Bobby's actions continued to plague me until I read *Without Conscience: The Disturbing World of Psychopaths Among Us* by Robert D. Hare. It was only then that I was able to understand what—and who—I had been dealing with and was finally able to forgive myself. I learned that I shouldn't fault myself for Bobby's actions, and as much as he insisted that they were somehow my own doing, in reality, I hadn't done anything to cause his behavior, and therefore was not to blame.

I also had the matter of my own sense of personal safety to consider. Bobby had damaged my ability to feel safe, certainly to feel safe once I knew he was released. I wanted to disappear, to hide my existence since I knew he would always be watching. I was so determined to stay off the radar by avoiding leaving an online footprint that I went into a self-imposed version of the witness protection program, a state of hiding forged out of a sense of self-preservation. Over time, however, this survival instinct became yet another form of prison. One state of captivity had replaced another.

I had been living virtually incognito for so long that the thought of being on any form of social media made me worry that I might once again become human bait. I held out until the summer of 2013 and, after a decade, emerged and finally felt ready to trust again. Joining Facebook was like a fusing of my broken parts, as I reconnected with some of my old friends and made a lot of new and wonderful friends who I have grown to love. It inspired me to dig out my father's photographs of New York City, as well as my own, and share our work while seeing his pictures for the first time. Finally, I realized just how much of my life had been amputated by fear, which had literally truncated my life.

In the end, I discovered I haven't changed that much from my original self. I'm still the same person that I ever was, though somewhat flawed, I remain open, receptive, and curious about life. Only now, I have learned to look at things a lot more closely.

ACKNOWLEDGEMENTS

In gratitude for FBI Special Agent Brandon M. Waller for believing me.

Eternal thanks to William Hammett. Your keen writer's sense and natural talent for American noir helped me bring this complex story to paper. Special thanks to Harrison Muller, the love of my life, for being by my side throughout this long and circuitous creative process. Thank you to my agent Chip MacGregor and my partner in crime, Brian Whitney.

Last, but not least, this book is dedicated to my loyal friends throughout the trials and travails of the actual events and the writing of this book. Your friendship, generous critiques and encouragement kept me inspired, energized and buoyed, every difficult step of the way.

1.

July 25, 2003

The monster stirred inside him. Most times, he could tame it. Keep it hidden. Silence its screams. But tonight, the beast demanded release.

She lifted her head up. "You're taking too long. I'm done."

He pressed her head back down. "You're done when I say you're done ..."

She wriggled beneath the firmness of his grip. "No!" she protested, forcing herself up from his lap. She stared him straight in the eyes—defiant and unafraid. "That's all I'm doing for you, Devin."

His calloused fingertips nervously tapped the upholstered backbench and his spine tingled with an odd mixture of excitement and fear. The beast was rising. There was no going back. Not now. Not ever. "Rape her," the monster instructed. "Rape the whore!"

*

It had been a long night of hustling for Nilsa Arizmendi and Angel "Ace" Sanchez. Maybe it was the hot weather, but the regular johns were being especially cheap and irritable, and Nilsa was forced to negotiate smaller fees. Ordinarily, she charged $30 for a half hour, but tonight's tricks were turning a maximum of only $20 and some demanded blowjobs for a measly 10 bucks. Like shrewd customers at a turn-of-the-century street market, the johns knew that the vendor in question was desperate for cash.

Ace loitered around the corners of New Britain Avenue, where his girlfriend worked. He stared glumly at the filthy surroundings, trying not to think about Nilsa's activities. He did not like their lifestyle. In fact, he despised it. But how else could he and Nilsa score drugs? The couple's shared habit was not cheap. In July 2003, they were each smoking about 20 to 30 pieces of crack per day and shooting up a bundle-and-a-half of heroin, which translated to about 10 to 15 bags on the streets. Sometimes, Nilsa used up to three bundles of heroin a day, depending on the amount of crack she smoked. It was a nasty cycle. The crack got Nilsa and Ace ramped up and wired and the heroin brought them down. They needed both to survive.

Without the drugs, sickness set in. Being drug sick was terrible—worse than having the flu. In the darkness of their motel room, the childhood sweethearts huddled together in sweat-soaked sheets, shivering with nausea and chills. Every joint and bone ached as invisible bugs furiously crawled beneath the surface of their skin. In between fits of vomiting, their bowels loosened and the bed became soiled. Nilsa kept the curtains drawn and placed the Do Not Disturb sign on the outside door handle for days at a time. The room was a mess. Their lives were a mess. Besides the incessant and all-consuming craving for heroin, she felt shame.

"This shit has to stop," Ace thought as he watched Nilsa emerge from the back seat of an old man's car. She walked toward him, tucked her tie-dyed T-shirt into her dungaree shorts and offered a faint smile. Normally 140 pounds, the 5'2", dark-haired woman was now only skin and bones. "I'm tired," she said. "Let's go home."

On the walk back, Nilsa briefly disappeared and scored a blast of crack at Goodwin Park in Hartford. She returned to Ace and attempted to take his hand. He pulled away. "I'm done with this shit. You gotta go to rehab, Nilsa. We both gotta go."

She acted like she did not hear him. It was usually the best way to avoid a fight.

But tonight, Ace would not let up. "I'm done with the fucking drugs," he mumbled, running his hand through his greasy dark hair. Normally, he kept it long, but a few days before, he had cut it short. "Done with the hustling. Fuck. Fuck this shit."

Their shadowy figures forged into the night, softly illuminated by the neon lights of outdated motels. Rolling hills of forest stood far in the distance, strangely comforting and yet somehow sinister. When Nilsa's high wore down, they started to quarrel. This time, Ace would not take no for an answer. They both had to go to rehab in the morning.

Nilsa was reluctant. She had been in and out of rehab for years and it never did her any good. Still, she loved her four children and desperately wanted to be done with the drugs and get clean forever and for good. Overhead, the night sky opened and a warm drizzle began to fall. The blue rock watch on Nilsa's frail wrist ticked into the early morning hours. They walked southbound along the pike, past Cedar Hill Cemetery containing the corpses of Connecticut's affluent class, including legendary actress Katharine Hepburn, and then a smaller cemetery containing the remains of lesser-known citizens.

Ace gently elbowed Nilsa. "You gonna start singing?"

She sometimes sang Christian hymns that she learned in childhood as they walked along the pike. It passed the time and gave them both a sense of comfort in the midst of all the pain. She smiled beneath the foggy moonlight. "You want me to?"

"You know I like your voice," he replied.

Her smooth, clear voice chimed like a bell into the darkness of the night:

O Lord my God, When I in awesome wonder,
Consider all the worlds Thy Hands have made;
I see the stars, I hear the rolling thunder,
Thy power throughout the universe displayed.

By the time they reached the parking lot of the Stop & Shop in Wethersfield, Ace had persuaded Nilsa to agree to the plan. Nilsa was worthy of a long and healthy life. After all, Ace needed her. Her mother needed her. *Her children needed her.* She vowed to never turn another trick again or inject poison into her veins. The party was over and fuck her if it had not been the party from Hell.

Nilsa eyed a lone vehicle parked in the far corner of the store's lot. "That's Devin's van."

"Let's get back to the motel," Ace said.

"I'm just gonna say hi."

Nilsa walked across the lot to the beat-up blue van owned by their mutual acquaintance, Devin Howell. They had met Howell a few months before. At the time, he was pumping gas at the Exxon gas station on the corner of Broad Street and New Britain Avenue. The rain was heavy and Ace and Nilsa were soaking wet as they approached Howell's van and asked for a ride to their motel room on the Berlin Turnpike in Wethersfield. "We'll give you five bucks," Ace said.

Howell had to go to Lowe's to price out some supplies for an upcoming job. He was driving in that direction anyway, so it was not a problem to assist two near-strangers who appeared down on their luck. "Yeah, sure. The door's unlocked."

Nilsa and Ace squeezed into the bucket seat on the passenger side. Nilsa used her street name, Maria, when she introduced herself to Howell. As they drove to The Almar Motel, Howell told the couple in his mild Southern drawl that he had a lawn-care business. Ace glanced over his shoulder at the back of the van. The space was large, with a long bench sofa littered with lawn service tools and clothing. The stench of body odor pervaded the vehicle's interior.

When they arrived at the motel, Ace and Nilsa invited Howell into their room to hang out. Howell brought some beer and marijuana. Nilsa and Ace offered to share a little crack, but Howell refused. He was a weed and booze guy. Together, the three got high on their poisons of choice. Howell told them that he was living in his van and he often parked it at the Stop & Shop parking lot in Wethersfield. He left the motel less than an hour later. As he drove back to the Stop & Shop lot to bed down for the night, he glanced at the open ashtray and saw that a $20 bill rolled up inside of it was gone. "No fucking good deed goes unpunished," he cynically thought. Ace and Nilsa had ripped him off.

In the months that followed, the occasional contact with Howell proved beneficial to Nilsa and Ace. The couple had lived on the Berlin Turnpike for the last 18 months or so, first at The Elm Motel and then at The Almar. Their daily routine involved walking from the motel on the pike to the familiar section of New Britain Avenue in Hartford where Nilsa turned tricks, about 1½ miles from The Almar. Ace had not worked a job for seven or eight months and he no longer had a vehicle of his own. Especially in the cold weather, Nilsa and Ace relied on acquaintances to spot them walking along the busy roadway and offer a lift. Occasionally, they had money for a cab, but that meant less money for drugs.

Howell also proved useful in assisting Nilsa and Ace to cop drugs. He did not mind driving them to local dealers living 15 to 20 minutes away. He would not get high with them when they scored. He seemed content to do them a favor by giving them a ride in exchange for a few dollars. All told, Howell served as the couple's makeshift Uber driver on about five occasions over the course of one month.

At approximately 2:45 a.m. on July 25, 2003, Ace watched Nilsa's skeletal form traipse across the empty parking lot. It was hard for him to believe that this was the same woman whose weight had sky-rocketed to 180 pounds when she was last released from federal prison—all beefed up by the cheap, starchy food. Nilsa stopped at the van and appeared to talk to Howell, who sat in the driver's seat. Then she walked around the van and got into the passenger side. Howell turned on the engine and slowly drove away. It was the last time Ace would see Nilsa alive.

*

When Christ shall come, with shout of acclamation,
And take me home, what joy shall fill my heart.
Then I shall bow, in humble adoration,
And then proclaim: "My God, how great Thou art!"

Nilsa "Coco" Arizmendi, Jan. 29, 1970–July 25, 2003
Rest In Peace

http://wbp.bz/hisgardena

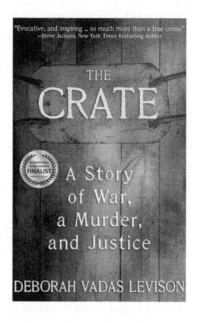
Chapter One

NATURALIZATION

Even in my darkest nightmares, I'd never imagined the words my brother would whisper in my ear.

My family and I had arrived at the hotel minutes earlier. Already the suite lay in a state of chaos, so that when my cell phone rang it took me a few moments to trace the sound and find the device, buried under boarding passes, sunglasses, and baseball hats on the kitchenette counter. I answered with one hand and loaded bottles of Gatorade into the refrigerator with the other.

The kids were arguing, staking their claims for pullout couches and cots in the spacious living area surrounding the kitchen, jostling for the best view of the TV.

"Hang on, I can't hear," I yelled into the phone, slamming the refrigerator door. "For God's sake, can someone turn the air conditioner down? It's like the Arctic in here." I turned around to see the boys poised for a pillow fight, and braced for the inevitable howls. Fourteen-year-old Jake would never allow himself to be bested by his eight-year-old brother, Coby.

Jordyn, our oldest, was seventeen. Coolly, she snatched the cushion out of Jake's hand before he could strike.

I turned my attention back to the phone. A familiar number shone on the screen. "Hey, Pete."

My brother Peter's voice came through muffled by the racket in the room. Still, he sounded strained, and a wisp of apprehension fluttered over me.

"Are Mum and Dad okay?" I shouted over the noise. My parents were eighty and eighty-four, increasingly frail, and with mounting health concerns. They lived in Toronto, hundreds of miles away, and I constantly imagined the worst.

"They're fine, Deb," my brother said, somber, with no hint of his usual chipper tone. I drew back a heavy curtain and unlatched the glass door, seeking the quiet of a balcony. In front of me lay a gorgeous screened lanai furnished with a large wooden dining table and chairs. Another world shimmered outside here on the deck in Florida: bright, mild, calm.

"Now I can hear you better," I said into the phone. "What's going on?"

"Everyone's okay," Peter repeated. He paused. "How about you guys? When do you leave for Florida?"

I glanced around. Beyond the table stood a row of recliners on an open-air balcony that wrapped around the lanai. I pulled a second door closed behind me and walked barefoot to the iron railing, gazing out on a magnificent, unobstructed view of blue Gulf waters.

"We're here! Just checked into the hotel. I'm looking at the ocean now, actually. Are you at work?" That might explain the tension in his voice, I thought; my brother's medical practice involved harried hours of examinations followed by long evenings of dictation, often leaving him stressed and exhausted. He still had a block of patients to see, he confirmed.

I continued, "I know you hate the heat, but it would be nice for you to get away from the hospital for a few days and relax. You sound like you're on edge. When did you last swim in the ocean?" I chattered on, my unease dissolving as I basked in the sunshine and told my brother about our trip.

My husband, Craig, our kids, and I had arrived in Fort Myers that afternoon with Jake's travel team, Xplosion, for an elite baseball tournament that would pit us against some of the best high school ballplayers in the country. Initially, I had not wanted to stray out from under the luxurious green and leafy canopy surrounding our New England home, where the woods near our house beckoned, shady and cool, just like those in which I'd spent my childhood in Canada.

I dreaded the prospect of Florida in July; "hot, thick, and humid" constituted my least favorite climate.

Peter paused again before answering my question. "The last time we were at the ocean? Probably when we came down to visit you last fall."

"Oh, that's just the Sound." I referred to Long Island Sound, the swirling gray bathtub of fresh and saltwater that rings the north shore of Long Island and the southern shores of Westchester and Connecticut. To my surprise and delight we'd found, though, an hour's drive from our home to the corner of Rhode Island, the open Atlantic rippling outwards in an endless spread of mint jelly, and dotted along the coast, quaint seafaring villages with weathered wooden piers like wrinkled fingers pointing out to sea. The discovery of this maritime scenery helped soften my docking in America.

I'd felt ambivalent about the whole move. Torontonians typically are not a migratory species. For the most part, those who hatch in Toronto nest there, attend college somewhere close, and settle in the suburbs for the long haul. That life, I had imagined for myself, too. When we moved away, I felt guilty, selfish for leaving my parents. They'd been immigrants themselves. Surely when they landed in Canada in 1956 they assumed that their family would huddle there together forever. When Craig and I left with two of their grandchildren, we effectively took away half of their family.

I'd cried when we all sat down at my parents' kitchen table to break the news. My mother had nodded slowly and said, "Anyvay. You have to do vhatever is best for your family." My father stood up quietly and walked out, but not before I saw that his eyes were wet.

But still, the company that Craig worked for, Trans-Lux, had offered him a good job and we were flattered that they seemed willing to go to great lengths to move us to the States. The tight economy in Toronto in the mid-nineties meant that another, equally good job might not be so easy to find. I'd left my own job in public relations to stay home full-time with Jordyn, a toddler then, and Jake, a baby. In the end, Craig and I agreed: We'd be a Swiss Family Robinson of sorts. We would embark on a year-long adventure, and after that we would come home. One year, we gave ourselves.

Trans-Lux sent a team of movers, and I watched as they packed our tidy little life into boxes and onto a moving van bound for the border.

Craig had wanted to live in or as close to New York City as possible since he would be working on Wall Street for three weeks out of each month, while the fourth week would be spent in Norwalk, Connecticut, the headquarters of Trans-Lux. To Craig, New York held all the allure of Oz: a furious pace, vast business opportunity, endless entertainment, and a spinning kaleidoscope of humanity that appealed to his adrenaline-junky personality.

I had no interest in living in Manhattan. Even though metropolitan Toronto bustled just as much, I perceived New York to be dirty and dangerous. I wanted more living space, not less. I hated traffic jams and parking hassles. And I wanted a stroller-friendly front porch, fresh air, and lots of green grass for our kids. We expanded the home search progressively north of New York City, moving along the Hutch to the scenic Merritt Parkway in Connecticut. As the numbers on the exit signs increased, the property prices decreased.

Eventually, our real estate agent brought us to Trumbull. Our agent had pegged Craig as a huge sports fan. When she pulled up in front of Unity Field, the town's main baseball complex, the sun appeared from behind the clouds and shone down, brilliantly illuminating a banner at the entrance. The sign read, *"Welcome to Trumbull, home of the 1989 Little League World Champions."* Craig practically drooled. I could almost hear a chorus of angels burst into song. *Well, that's that,* I thought. *Here's home.*

In 1996, when my husband and I and our young family first arrived in Connecticut, I'd heard some new friends say to their kids, "Let's have a catch." The phrase rolled around in my head. You "have" a headache or you "have" an appointment, I thought. My dad never said to me, "Let's have a slalom" when we went skiing. But having a catch seemed to be what people in Fairfield County, Connecticut, did on their wide, manicured lawns.

We found a sprawling, if dated, house on a flat acre of land with towering oaks and spacious rooms. Bigger than anything we could afford in Toronto, Craig said. Great bones, I said. Surely, with some modern finishes, we could turn a profit in the twelve months we planned to live there before flipping the house and returning home to Canada. It felt, as we say in Yiddish, *bashert:* fated, meant to be.

And it seemed safe, this little town. A keep-the-front-door-open, leave-your-car-unlocked, let-your-kids-play-outside kind of town. Where all sorts of townsfolk, Jewish or not, drove to the local temple every Monday night to play Bingo. We signed on the dotted line.

Somehow, as we settled into a warm and welcoming community, a wide circle of friends, and a comfortable routine of school, work, and family life, that one year stretched into two, then five, then ten. In 2010, we had been in the States for fourteen years.

In that time I had morphed into an all-around Trumbullite: Suburban mom, carpooling in a minivan and hosting cookie-baking play dates and sleepovers, birthday bashes and after-sports pool parties for the kids and their friends. And publicist, earning media for an eclectic clientele throughout the Northeast. And journalist, interviewing movers and shakers around the state for a local paper. And volunteer, member of this committee and that, fundraiser for this project and that, room mother for this class and that.

I transformed from *alien* to *citizen* on April 8, 2005, my husband by my side, both of us eager to obtain dual citizenship, to vote, to give our children opportunities that came with being American. I didn't want to be an alien. I wanted to belong. I pledged allegiance to the flag of the United States of America, learned the words to the Star Spangled Banner, and celebrated Thanksgiving with all its trimmings ... a holiday that in Canada, as Jews, we'd ignored.

Gradually, and without meaning to, I dropped my Canadian identifiers, shedding "*aboot*" for "about," "Mummy" for "Mommy," "pop" for "soda." I understood what the kids meant when they asked for my "pocketbook," not purse, so they could buy "cotton candy," not candy floss, or a "candy bar," not a chocolate bar. *Runners*? Sneakers. *Duotang*? Folder. *Eaves troughs*? Gutters. *Garburator*? Garbage disposal. I took care not to ask for homo milk, and soon I became accustomed to buying it in jugs rather than bags. I lost track of Canadian exchange rates and Members of Parliament and stopped loading up on Canadian-brand groceries during visits to the place I still called home. And I gave birth to a third child, an American.

I connected more to being Jewish than I had earlier in life, an aspect of my persona that I had minimized as my parents worked hard to assimilate. Perhaps my own marriage and motherhood had provided the impetus, or perhaps my yearning for a sense of community had propelled me along. Whatever the reason, trying on Judaism for size reminded me of standing in a dressing room surrounded by dozens of rejects, zipping the one thing that – at last! – fit perfectly.

And I embraced baseball.

After years spent on the bleachers at Unity, I'd finally figured out the game. I'd come a long way from the days of yelling "SLIDE!" to a runner headed for first, or referring to the dugout as a penalty box. I could recite the rules, use the lingo, follow the plays. I shouted "Give it a ride!" to the batter or "All right, one, two, three!" to the pitcher. I felt comfortable speaking *baseball;* it was yet another language I had learned.

Craig and the kids seemed thrilled to be here in Florida, and now, standing in the mild breeze on the terrace, I felt excited, too. During school vacations, three or four times a year, we invariably returned to Toronto to visit our families – a marked contrast to this rare junket due south. Here, we'd swim in the sea and bask on the beach. In downtown Fort Myers, we'd treat the kids to ice cream cones, browse the surf shops. Jordyn would try on straw hats. Jake and Coby would ask for necklaces with a shark's tooth. Something for everyone.

It would be a great vacation.

"You should come down for a few days," I urged my brother on the phone. "A change of scenery would do you good. It's a pretty hotel."

I leaned on the railing and gazed out at the tops of swaying palm fronds. The surf rippled, crystal clear and glistening in the late day sun. Gulls circled in the sky. Sailboats and ships floated across the horizon. Pastel colored umbrellas polka-dotted the coastline and little kids with plastic shovels dug for shells in the sand. I tilted my face upward to catch the sun's rays. *Ahhhh.*

Over the phone, my brother suggested I sit down. Slowly I lowered myself to the edge of a chaise lounge.

"Something's happened," Peter's voice dropped low.

The needles of anxiety returned to prick at me. "Peeps. For God's sake. What is it?"

"There's been a murder ... at the cottage."

http://wbp.bz/cratea

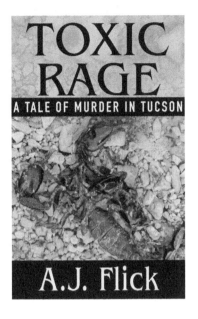
Chapter 1

On the morning of Oct. 6, 2004, in Tucson, Arizona, Lourdes Lopez was getting ready for work and listening to the news on the radio when she heard about a murder that occurred overnight. Her heart skipped a beat. Throughout her law career as a prosecutor and now criminal defense attorney, she wasn't unfamiliar with the situation of hearing about a heinous crime on the news and then having the case land in her lap. But this was different. What few details were being related over the radio concerned Lourdes. They, too, were all too familiar. A man was found dead in a medical complex at First Avenue and River Road the night before. His Lexus was missing. While the report didn't mention the victim's name, Lourdes knew in her now deeply troubled heart that she might have known him.

"Please God," she whispered to herself. "Don't let it be Brian. Just let it be some other poor person."

Lourdes's fears weren't just sympathy for someone who had just been killed, but terror that she knew the killer—a man she almost married. He had spoken often of wanting to have his rival killed … could he possibly have carried out his evil wish? Lourdes remembered countless times over the past two years that the threats had been made and the countless times that Lourdes dismissed them as ranting of a man pushed to his limits. Brad Schwartz, the man Lourdes had broken off her engagement to just months ago, couldn't have had Brian Stidham killed, she reasoned. But the more she told herself that, the more she remembered his lies, lies that led to the doom of their relationship and, perhaps, Brian Stidham's life.

Tucson, for all of its worldliness as a metropolitan center pushing a million residents, still thinks of itself as a small town. There may be drive-by shootings in certain parts of town that don't garner much attention, but this murder was different. It was at a midtown medical complex off a busy street where thousands drive each day. This murder topped all of the newscasts that day and was a front-page story in the afternoon daily, the *Tucson Citizen*. Lourdes couldn't shake the fear that she thought the murder victim was Brian and that Brad had ordered his death somehow. Lourdes tried to go about her normal business that day. She was working as a criminal defense attorney, but she'd spent years at the Pima County Attorney's Office as a criminal prosecutor. That's what she was doing when she met Brad Schwartz, who saved her foster daughter's eyesight, and began an on-and-off affair with him. Lourdes spent the morning of Oct. 6 in depositions downtown, but as she was heading back to her office that afternoon, she got the idea to call Brian's office. Maybe Brian wasn't killed, she thought. Maybe she's just overreacting. It was just an eerie coincidence that Brian had an office in that medical complex and drove a Lexus, right? Lourdes dialed Brian's office, pretending to be a parent who needed to make an appointment to see Dr. Stidham and hoping against all odds that the person who answered the phone would happily make that appointment. Instead, Lourdes heard a glum voice at the other end of the line.

"There's been a tragedy. Dr. Stidham has been killed."

Lourdes froze. This couldn't be happening. This doesn't happen in Tucson. To her. To people she knows. There have been many twisted turns in Lourdes's life, but this was just too bizarre to be true, right? How could someone she had loved so much that she wanted to convert to Judaism and marry have someone killed? If the victim had been anybody but Brian, Lourdes would never have thought Brad had anything to do with it. Her mind raced. If Brad did do it, and her gut told her he had, would he remember all the times he threatened to kill Brian in front of her?

"I'm gonna fucking get him," Brad had said to her earlier that year. "That fucking guy's gonna die. He's gonna fucking die."

Brad, a talented eye surgeon with a once-thriving practice, had brought Brian to Tucson from Texas to take over the children's eye surgery while Brad focused on the adults and other pursuits, such as plastic surgery. But the deal went bad when Brad was caught writing illegal prescriptions for Vicodin, a growing addiction to soothe his own shoulder injury (Lourdes had filled some of the prescriptions and was asked to leave the prosecutors' office when she was charged along with Brad in federal court). While Brad was in court-ordered rehab, he turned the entire practice over to Brian. Instead of maintaining Brad's lucrative practice, Brian decided to go off on his own. That infuriated Brad, and in the two years since, it had become his obsession to seek revenge. Sometimes, Brad had said he wanted Brian humiliated—perhaps by someone finding child pornography in his office. But other times, the threats were intimately sinister, including talk of having Brian killed at his new office and have it look like a break-in or fatal carjacking. By the time Lourdes and Brad broke up in May, his threats against Brian occurred almost nightly.

The more Lourdes thought about it, the more she convinced herself that Brad had somehow ordered Brian's death. She wondered if he was crazed enough to have Brian killed, would he want people eliminated who had heard him talk about it? Lourdes's name had to be on top of that list. Lourdes called her brother-in-law and asked him to stay at her house that night, just in case Brad came over and threatened her or the kids.

Lourdes, who knew Brad Schwartz better than anybody, knew it was just a matter of time before he made contact with her. The night after Brian Stidham's murder, he called and asked to come over.

"I need to show you something," Brad said. "I need to come over."

Despite her misgivings, Lourdes allowed him into her home, where he called up news reports about the murder on her computer.

"I didn't have anything to do with that, Lourdes," he said.

"I need you to leave my house," Lourdes said, trying to hold her ground.

"OK, OK," Brad said. "But please, Lourdes, come outside with me. Please."

Lourdes followed Brad out, but kept within eyeshot of her brother-in-law, in case she needed his help.

"Lourdes," Brad said. "I had nothing to do with it. Look me in the eyes. Lourdes, I didn't do anything."

"Please," Lourdes begged. "Please, Brad, just go."

Lourdes *knew* that Brad had Brian killed. She didn't know exactly how, but what really scared her was what she should do now. To have Brad hounding her for sympathy, for support, was only confusing her and adding to her agony. Typically for Brad, he called her constantly from that night on.

"I need a friend to talk to," he pleaded with her. "You are my friend. I need you. This is such a hard time for me."

Lourdes knew that she was Brad's only friend. He trusted her. But did she trust him? Their relationship began with a lie—Brad told her he was divorced, but he wasn't. Their affair—one of many Brad had throughout his marriage—led to his divorce. Lourdes knew that Brad wasn't faithful to her, too. So Brad lied to her. Brad dragged her down into the rapidly spinning decline of his personal and professional life, thus forever altering hers. Does this mean he's capable of having someone killed? As much as Lourdes didn't want to believe it, she was certain he did have Brian Stidham killed. But she also still loved Brad Schwartz. She couldn't trust him, and she wouldn't marry him, but could she hurt the man she loved by accusing him of cold-blooded murder? Brian Stidham, the talented eye surgeon and young husband and father of two, was dead and didn't deserve to die by someone else's hand. What would she do? What could she do? Lourdes just didn't want to believe that his threats were true—because had she taken them seriously, would Brian Stidham still be alive? Lourdes spent her days defending criminals accused of horrible crimes. Could she have let a killer get so close to her without knowing what his intentions were? Should she call the police? Brad denied anything having to do with Brian's death. But Lourdes knew he did. She just wasn't sure what she should do. So, for now, she did nothing.

http://wbp.bz/toxicragea

 WILDBLUE
P R E S S

See even more at:
http://wbp.bz/tc

More True Crime You'll Love From WildBlue Press

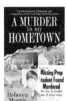

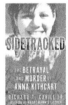

Made in the USA
Monee, IL
21 November 2020